ABOUT THE A

Born in 1937, Jonathan Hall grew up in an academic environment which was to shape his whole life. His parents owned and ran Arnold Lodge, a preparatory school in Leamington Spa. Despite his own largely unrewarding school days, a spell of teaching at Arnold Lodge made him realise that its future lay with him. Taking the reins at the age of only 25, he ran the school for almost thirty years, retiring early in 1991 when he was diagnosed with a brain turmour. Under his leadership, pupil numbers increased from 50 to 400, and on a visit to the school, the then Education Secretary Margaret Thatcher said: "I know that our inspectorate hold this school in very high regard and it is of a very high reputation."

In 2000 he published his autobiography *No End in Sight*, which topped the bestseller list at Waterstone's in his home town.

Jonathan Hall

SCHOOL TIES

AUSTIN MACAULEY PUBLISHERS™
LONDON • CAMBRIDGE • NEW YORK • SHARJAH

A CIP catalogue record for this title is available from the
British Library.

ISBN 9781398433359 (Paperback)
ISBN 9781398433366 (ePub e-book)

www.austinmacauley.com

First Published 2021
Austin Macauley Publishers Ltd
1 Canada Square
Canary Wharf
London
E14 5AA

— Prologue —

THE MOST VIVID memory of my earliest childhood is that we as a family led an isolated life. This was, I think, due to lack of money and wartime deprivations. Not having experienced the frills of luxury, I was in no position to miss what I never knew existed.

Awarded the Military Cross for gallantry as a young officer in the First World War, my father was incredibly determined. Having been wounded twice, it had taken him years to regain his fitness. He said regular exercise was the key to his success and he chose to walk everywhere rather than travel on a bus. A tax inspector by profession, wearing a suit and bowler hat, he was seen daily trudging the two-mile journey to his place of work, irrespective of the weather.

Mother worked part-time as assistant manager at the Red Lion Hotel in the centre of High Wycombe. Her hours of work were arranged to fit in with my father's own commitments, which enabled them to arrange my care without having to rely on outside help.

To make up for my being an only child, Father spent as much time with me as possible. He didn't spoil me with material possessions; instead, he fed my brain with knowledge and encouraged me to think. In precious moments together, we walked, played games, swam, had picnics, and explored woods, lakes, villages and towns. We watched old men bowling and younger ones playing tennis in the park. How I delighted in my father's grown-up tutoring!

Mother was always there to take control during the hours my father was at work. Her influence was strong and she had firm views on manners and politeness. Church attendance was a weekly ritual. Togged up in our Sunday best, we would sit in a pew at the front because father was a churchwarden and mother helped Mrs Trumpington, the vicar's wife, with a bible class after the morning service.

Father seldom spoke of his Christian beliefs, whereas Mother was more proactive. No matter how busy she was, she managed to visit the sick and support several worthy causes. She was the one who taught me how to read. Storytelling began in babyhood, followed by the regular handling of books. Our home must have contained enough literature to stock a library. Through Mother's patient guidance, I was quick to learn and was able to read quite fluently before I'd started school.

Secure in the knowledge my parents loved me very much, I revelled in my good fortune.

— One —

IT WAS A hot July day, two months after the Germans had surrendered to the Allies, marking an end of the war in Europe.

Not only was I to sing in the choir at the end of term concert, Miss Young had selected me to recite a poem. My parents arranged to take a day off work in order to support the occasion. In the morning they had planned to visit friends in Princes Risborough, after which they were going to attend the afternoon performance.

Visitors packed the school hall with smiling, happy faces. The front row was occupied by important-looking gentlemen in suits. The town's Mayor, wearing his impressive chain of office, was accompanied by an overweight lady whose entire face was hidden by her hat. The hubbub of high-spirited chatter had reached crescendo level. The anticipation was immense. After a call for order, there was silence throughout the room.

I looked for my parents among the audience. They were nowhere to be seen. I sang two items with the choir. My poem went well without prompting. Still there was no sign of them. The night before, father had helped me to rehearse my lines.

"You've no idea how proud of you we are," he said. "We can't wait until tomorrow!"

What could have happened to prevent them from being at the concert?

Mr Potts, the headmaster, thanked the staff for working hard, the pupils for their efforts. "Hip, hip, hooray," was shouted with traditional end-of-term gusto, signalling six fun-filled weeks away from the school routine.

I was alone in the changing room, scared and het up by then. My name was called. "Paul Elliott. Are you there, Paul Elliott?"

Miss Young clutched me firmly by the hand and led me to her classroom. No mention was made of my performance at the concert. Had I done something wrong? Why did she look so serious?

By the door stood Mr Potts and a uniformed policeman. Had I committed a crime? What possibly could have happened to bring a policeman to the school?

All three adults stared blankly into space, avoiding eye contact with me as if on purpose. The policeman cleared his throat, stuttering and stumbling as he issued his ice-cold statement.

"There's been a terrible accident," he said.

— Two —

NEWS OF THE death of my parents was broken to me with as much delicacy as Uncle Don and Aunt Olive could manage. Experienced as they were in dealing with large numbers of boys in a variety of situations, they were unused to consoling the victim of a tragedy. I could see my uncle was profoundly affected by what had happened. Despite his well-meaning intentions, he was unable to offer me any comfort.

"For you to be deprived of your father and mother must be the most dreadful shock imaginable," he said with down-to-earth directness. "From now on Aunt Olive and I are going to be your parent substitutes. We want you to look upon our home and Oxton House School as your permanent address."

Doing the best he could, Uncle Don's clumsy attempts to heal my fractured heart made not a scrap of difference to my jumbled thinking. Given the gruesome reasons for the move to Harrogate, it would have taken exceptional counselling skills to get me to look forward to the future. I needed time to come to terms with the dramatic changes in my life; time to weep; time to reflect without tiresome well-wishers intruding on my grief.

Adjustment to my new circumstances was made easier because the boys of Oxton House were on holiday. I had several weeks to prepare for the shock of attending a new school in an academic environment that was going to be much tougher than at my elementary school.

Cousin Giles was encouraged to be friendly. "Take Paul under your wing," advised his father. "In view of what he's suffered, make him a welcome member of the family."

Giles made begrudging efforts to be considerate for the first few days. Once the novelty wore off, his seeming loss of only-son status drove him to make spiteful remarks on the occasions we were alone together. Had I been in a more receptive frame of mind, I might have hated him. I was still too numb inside to feel anything at all.

I slept in what was referred to as the reserve dormitory, where there was plenty of space to house my personal belongings. "It's important for you to have your own room," said Uncle Don kindly, "but if we recruit more boarders, you may have to share with Giles."

I was aghast at the prospect of seeing more than was necessary of my antagonistic cousin. Sensing how much he had resented my arrival, it was essential for us to be separated whenever possible. For the two of us to be forced to share a bedroom was a thought too upsetting to imagine.

Occupying a two-acre site on the outskirts of Harrogate, Oxton House stood at the end of a badly potholed drive. The first impression was of a magnificent Victorian villa; on closer inspection, it was obvious the building was in a dilapidated state and money needed to be spent on the decaying fabric.

Two lawns at the front were bordered by flower beds filled with dozens of sweet-smelling roses. These were the creation of Aunt Olive, who tended the gardens lovingly during the rare moments she was not involved in directing domestic activities. Full of nervous energy, she was continually on the move, which was an explanation for her slimness. At the rear of the school, closed in by high walls and netting, was a large tarmac-covered playground. "This is where the boys play at breaktimes," explained Uncle Don. "Three times a week they go to the park for games. Cricket in the summer and football in winter."

Next to the playground were a number of outbuildings, one of which had been converted into a makeshift gymnasium. A high hedge separated the grounds from a paddock and market garden, areas of land that would in the years ahead prove vital in the programme of expansion.

Apart from the occasional day out with my uncle and aunt, I was left to my own devices. There was so much time in which to brood that I spent countless lonely hours agonizing over my bereavement. The joyfulness of childhood seemed a world away. No matter how much I prayed or tried to blot out the truth, the reality of my lot kept striking back with unrelenting harshness.

Deserted during the holidays, the school was a depressing place to be.

The empty rooms, long corridors and piled-up furniture gave the appearance more of purposeless neglect than of an educational establishment about to open up for business. "The school will come alive as soon as the boys are back," said Jennings, the caretaker, detecting my unease. "You'll be happy as a sandboy once you've made some friends."

Not knowing what a sandboy was, I found it hard to imagine what he meant. Happy was *not* a word that would ever describe my state of mind again.

"I want to assess your scholastic potential," declared Uncle Don mysteriously one morning. "The results will enable me to see which form to place you in." After being asked to write a short story, I read aloud a passage from a book that seemed familiar. After expressing mild approval, he went on to check my knowledge of tables, following which I was given a test to diagnose my mathematical attainment.

At supper that evening Uncle Don was in optimistic mood. "Your results were better than I expected," he said. "Not operating a streaming system here, promotion at Oxton House is based on ability rather than chronological criteria. You did so well I am going to place you in the third form." As an aside he added: "This means you will be making a start with French and Latin." Not understanding his cryptic jargon, I didn't know whether to be pleased or anxious. Giles, who was witness to all that had been said, looked resentful and ill-tempered.

Possessing a raucous voice, Uncle Don used it as a weapon to restrain the most unruly of his pupils. In consequence, remarks he made in private often became publicly known within the school community. One such conversation with Aunt Olive I could not help but overhear. "Paul's highly intelligent," he said. "He must have inherited my brother's genes. It makes a change from our dim-witted farmers' sons."

"They're not all like that," protested Aunt Olive. "Remember Perkins, who won a scholarship to Rossall two years ago? He was an asset from every point of view."

"That's as may be, but the fact is most of our boys have family businesses to inherit. They lack ambition because there's no need for them to bother."

11

"At least their parents pay the fees," Aunt Olive reasoned patiently. "Most of the farmers' sons are good at games and some make excellent prefects."

Unable to understand the pertinence of Uncle Don's remarks, it was not until later that I would begin to appreciate why he needed to attract more discerning parents to his school. Frustrated that most of the local intelligentsia chose to send their sons to a rival establishment in preference to his own, he was becoming worried and resentful. "If we catered more for sons of professional, educated people, our honours' board would soon be full," he complained repeatedly. "What we have here is a rump, consisting of dunces and problem rejects. The best schoolmaster on earth cannot make silk purses out of sows' ears. It simply can't be done."

Too young to understand the complexities of managing a school, I sensed nevertheless the tensions and stresses my uncle and aunt were having to contend with. The worry showed on their faces and they were frequently fatigued and overwrought. It would take years before I would grasp the nature of their burdens.

— Three —

A S THE START of term at Oxton House approached, activity began in earnest. Desks were moved, blackboards painted, windows cleaned, floors scrubbed and the heating boiler checked. The smell of polish and disinfectant everywhere reflected Aunt Olive's dedication to the welfare of the pupils. Obsessed with achieving the highest standards, she thought nothing of rolling up her sleeves to tackle a variety of domestic chores, no matter how menial they were. "On condition the boys are happy and well fed, a clean school is what the mothers of our boarders value most," she would say imperiously.

Uncle Don, who had been closeted for days in the confines of his study, finally emerged clutching timetables, lists and a number of typed announcements. These he posted on various noticeboards in and around the dowdy buildings. Bustling about with greater energy than hitherto exerted, Jennings cut the lawns, swept the playground, weeded the paths and mopped the changing room and lavatories. His ultimate task was to see to it that all the equipment, stationery and books were in the appropriate place in readiness for the boys' arrival.

Miss O'Sullivan, the resident matron, returned to the school three days before term was due to commence. Using hot water bottles for the airing of the beds, she took pains to pay attention to the minutest detail. Nothing annoyed her more than to witness slipshod efforts. An astringent manner enabled her to wipe the floor with anyone, including the headmaster, on the few occasions her authority was in doubt. Ruling her department with strict discipline, she was responsible for our clothes, upstairs behaviour and our health, which included a daily interest in the workings of our bowels. Aided by prunes at breakfast, most of us managed to pass her stringent test. On the occasions we were constipated, she forced down our throats a large spoonful of syrup of figs. How different this was from the easy life with my parents before the accident!

The boarders turned up on the evening before the start of term. Those who had travelled on the train from Leeds were collected by Jennings at Harrogate station. The majority arrived by car with their parents. After trunks and tuck boxes had been delivered to the boarders' day room, it was customary for the parents to call in at Uncle Don's study with the fees. Rumour had it that his favourites were rewarded for their loyalty with a glass or two of Scotch.

What had been a place of unnatural silence was suddenly enlivened by the jovial banter of the boys. Most were glad to be reunited with their chums, excited by the spirited companionship the environment provided. It fell upon matron to console the new boarders who, despite stiff upper lips, gave way to intermittent bouts of tearfulness.

Early next morning the day boys appeared in time for registration. Regarded as second-class citizens, it was not just in our imagination that they were physically less hardy than their boarder counterparts. I was unsure which category I came under, sleeping as I did in a room on my own. I would have done anything for my parents to be alive and be able to go home each day, even if it meant being branded a "stay-at-home wet" in common with the day-boy sissies.

In addition to Uncle Don, there were six assistant teachers. Apart from the married Major Gibson and Mrs Lloyd, an elderly widow, all resided in term time in spartan bed-sitting rooms on the attic floor above the dormitories. A miscellaneous bunch, the staff were either youngsters looking no older than the prefects or had been enticed from their retirements on account of wartime shortages.

Mr Palin was the oldest member of the staff. In mathematics lessons he tormented us with a rasping voice which croaked away menacingly as he fired instructions at us. To witness a man of such decrepitude refereeing a junior football game was an extraordinary sight. His distinguishing feature was the dewdrop that dangled perpetually from his nose. Viewing the ugly spectacle with fascination, we became more interested in when and where the drop would fall than in the content of his lessons. He called us "guttersnipes" and hated us as if we were his enemy. A year later he retired at the ripe old age of 82. All we ever missed about him was the unappealing dewdrop.

Invalided out of the army two years previously with shattered nerves, Major Gibson was a shadow of his former self. Regardless of his previous experience as a schoolmaster, he no longer had the knack of being able to control his classes. Merciless in our judgement of him, we led him a merry dance. There was pandemonium in every Latin lesson he presided over, at the end of which the soggy paper pellets on the floor offered proof of the acute disorder that carried on unchecked.

Mr Johnson was a sadist and a bully. Said to be a university reject, he was the youngest of the teachers. Capable of extreme brutality, in today's world he would have been locked up for his actions. Lacking qualifications, experience and teaching skills, he was the master whose job it was to introduce third formers to the subtleties of French. During the first lesson he wrote on the blackboard the present tense of the verb *être*, together with the meanings.

"Elliott minor," he boomed, "conjugate the present tense of *être*."

Not having heard mention of the word 'conjugate' before, I had no idea what I was supposed to do. "I'm very sorry, sir, but I don't know what you mean," I said, trying to conceal my state of agitation.

"I told you yesterday that I have effective ways of dealing with those who fail to cooperate," he roared. "The verb was written on the board for you to copy down and learn. I could not have made it easier than that. Conjugate it, boy!"

Tongue-tied and shaking with fear, I awaited the inevitable outcome in this no-win situation.

"I shall give you a choice," said Mr Johnson, rubbing his hands with unmistakable delight. "Either you write out the verb 250 times with meanings by tomorrow morning or I shall give you six with a slipper. Which would you prefer?"

I knew the trouble with writing the verb out again and again was that I would be no better able to pronounce the words than I had been that morning. A short, sharp punishment would be preferable to writing out hundreds of words to no useful purpose.

In common with the other boys, I suffered agonising tummy pains before every French lesson we attended. To escape attention was the key to survival, which meant avoiding eye contact with our tutor. My own strategy was to look keen and interested, answer

15

when spoken to, but otherwise disappear into a background of obscurity. Sometimes this policy worked. Often it did not. During the first few weeks of term, I must have been on the receiving end of at least half a dozen slaps on the head or beatings with a shoe. We all took our share of random punishments, except, that is, for Giles. As the headmaster's son, he had the good fortune to experience far less violent treatment than the rest.

I was only seven years old, yet I was being treated as an adult. Transfer from a happy home to this unfeeling new world was more than I could cope with. The one light in my mind was Miss Young, my favourite High Wycombe teacher. She was the only person who would have known how to assist me in my bleakest moments.

At half-term Aunt Olive arranged a birthday party for me. I was allowed to invite a number of school friends as my special guests. After tucking into jellies, trifles and blancmanges, Uncle Don organised some games in which the adults also took part. I remember laughing for the first time since my parents' death. I was reminded of the evening earlier in the year when they had taken me into High Wycombe after Victory of Europe had been declared. There had been singing and dancing in the streets, musicians playing, bonfires blazing, church bells ringing, and everyone was laughing. Thinking of that day made me miss them more than ever.

Uncle Don told me of the need to appropriate my bedroom. "Four new boarders will be joining us next week," he said. "Now you're settling in, it will be nice for you to have the company of Giles, He says he's happy for you to share with him in future. And by the way, the staff are delighted with the progress you are making with your work. Keep it up and we'll make a scholar of you yet!"

Giles had made it clear from the outset he objected to my presence. His resentment had grown much stronger since it became apparent I was outshining him in class. Once in a while he landed me a punch; more frequently he confined his hostility to making remarks that inflicted mental hurt. The thought of sharing a room with him had begun to fill me with the utmost dread. The move took place with the minimum of fuss. To begin with, Giles seemed friendly enough. It didn't take me long to discover he had been putting on an act.

I awoke one night to find a sock stuffed in my mouth. It must have been a very dirty sock because the smell was overpowering.

In my drowsy state I was unable to grasp what was causing the atrocious stench. Then out of the darkness came the sound of Giles' muffled voice. "I was hoping I'd have you to myself," he said, his tone malicious. "I don't want you here; nobody wants you here. Mum says we're not a charity. Your parents are dead. That's why we have to put up with you, you spineless brat." Pulling back the blankets, he hit me repeatedly on my arms and legs, "Don't you dare go telling tales," he threatened. "If you do, they won't believe you and I promise I'll biff you even harder."

I had disliked Giles from the start, but had not appreciated how horrible he could be. By carrying out his strong-arm tactics, he knew the only way he would be found out was by my splitting on him. A code of ethics existed among children in those times that regarded snitching as the lowest form of villainy. It was a matter of honour for me to endure the bashings without complaint.

A physically powerful boy, Giles became an expert at destroying what little was left of my morale. Night after night he walloped me with his fists, punches that hurt so much that I would lie awake for hours thinking that to live on the streets would be a better fate than this. My reserves of energy and hope used up, I was near to breaking point.

Aunt Olive had a thing about worms, the kind picked up by those of us who failed to wash our hands after opening our bowels. The boarders had a long walk from lavatory to wash basin, a fact which could explain the slackness in our habits. Linking threadworm infestation to the catering department for which my aunt was responsible, matron made it clear she would accept none of the blame. Matron one day detected a number of worms in my poo. Aunt Olive was summoned, following which Dr Taylor rushed to the scene of the emergency.

"If the pills don't work," he warned, "the only answer is an enema." Addressing me personally, he went on to say: "The little blighters come out at night, so if you scratch your bottom then bite your nails, you will eat the eggs and the worms will hatch and multiply. High standards of hygiene are essential. It's hardly surprising you have lost some weight." Made to feel I had behaved disgustingly, I was terrified I would end up looking as puny as a raw-boned skeleton. Revolting purple pills were taken with my food and I repeatedly washed my hands. No matter how hard I tried, I couldn't get rid of the worms.

A date was fixed for the enema procedure. I was taken to Giles' bedroom by matron and Aunt Olive. Dr Taylor was in attendance. After removing my trousers and pants, the three of them pushed me face down onto the bed. Without explaining what was about to happen, the two ladies grabbed my arms and legs. The doctor injected hot fluid into my bottom with agonising roughness. The more I wriggled, the more it hurt; the more it hurt, the more I screamed; and the more I screamed, the more brutal were my torturers. I was shaking like a leaf by the time the assault concluded.

The enema had been the final invasion on my sanity. All that was needed was for one person to understand the loneliness I felt, someone with the insight and influence to wave a magic wand and repair the scandals that had brought about my state of wretchedness. There was nobody, nobody at all, to whom I could relate.

The next time Giles thumped me in the middle of the night, I came to a decision. I didn't want to stick it out any longer. I planned to run away and seek refuge with Miss Young in far-away High Wycombe.

— Four —

I CHOSE TO run away on a Tuesday morning, the one day in the week we had to suffer a double period with the hated Mr Johnson. Grabbing my navy-blue raincoat, after eating a larger-than-usual breakfast to prepare me for the journey, I slipped through the domestic staff entrance next to the school kitchen. This led out onto a path with access to a tree-lined avenue and liberty.

My attempt to escape from the only security I knew was carried out on impulse. Too sick inside to consider the obstacles that lay ahead, I assumed all I had to do was to thumb a lift to High Wycombe and I would be transported in record time to the safety of Miss Young's doorstep. With the sum of five shillings and sixpence in my pocket, I thought I had more than enough money to be able to subsist until I reached my destination. Though sharp enough in the academic sense, it would have been hard to find a less streetwise eight-year-old than me.

I was quite familiar with the centre of Harrogate, having walked there with Aunt Olive on a number of occasions. I expected to see a signpost to London, showing the route I was to take. Looking about me in alarm, I was unable to find a single direction marking anywhere. Little did I know that signs throughout England had been removed during the war to hamper potential enemy invaders. It would take years for the signs to be reinstated. Panic-stricken, I decided to seek the help of a passer-by. I approached a white-haired lady with a stick who greeted me with a smile.

"Excuse me, can you please tell me the way to High Wycombe?"

"Surely you're not travelling all that way by yourself," she replied, a look of concern drawing my attention to her wrinkled face,

"I have to find Miss Young," I said simply.

"But where's your mummy and daddy?"

19

"They are dead. They were killed in an accident. Miss Young is going to look after me."

"High Wycombe is a very long way. Why are you on your own, my dear?"

"I won't be alone ever again when I'm back with Miss Young. *Please* tell me the way to High Wycombe."

"I don't like this at all," she said. "You need to make enquiries at the station. You may have to catch a train from York to London. I don't know whether it would stop at High Wycombe. Are you sure you have enough money, child?"

Fearing I had divulged too much, I told her I had lots of money and left her with a hurried thank you and goodbye.

At the railway ticket office I plucked up courage to ask how much it would cost to travel to High Wycombe. The attendant shocked me with his answer. I cannot recall the amount he quoted, but it was vastly more than I was able to afford. Like the old lady, he bore an expression of disbelief, making me anxious lest he might decide to hand me over to someone in authority. Determined to rid myself of his unwelcome scrutiny, I departed from the station as quickly as I could. York was the obvious place to make for. Once there, with any luck I would find a south-bound driver to assist me. Using a more devious tack, I stopped another passer-by, this time a uniformed soldier, whose perpetual grin gave the impression of laid-back affability.

"My father's car is parked round the corner," I lied. "Which road is the one for York?"

Without questioning the genuineness of my request, he informed me all we had to do was turn left at the first set of traffic lights and the journey would take less than an hour.

Spurred on by the faint warmth of the late October sun, I stood by the roadside, attempting to hitch a lift. Optimistic auguries made me confident that before the day was over, my dream of being with Miss Young would be fulfilled. I didn't have to wait long before a lorry drew up alongside. Beckoning me to join him, the burly driver helped me into his cabin and I was on my way to York. "I'm not supposed to take passengers," he said kindly, "but you look a good enough lad to me. By the way, call me Paddy if you like."

Treating the presence of a juvenile hitch-hiker as if it was an everyday event, Paddy kept me entertained with amusing tales about his wife and children of whom he was clearly proud.

"Where do you want me to drop you off?" he asked, as we approached the outskirts of York, the impressive minster visible in the distance.

"Please sir, will you take me to the best place for me to get to London?" I stammered nervously.

"You're a polite young man, to be sure. When I go home I'll tell Flo and the kids I've met Dick Whittington and helped him on his way to London to make his fortune. What you need is a mascot like a lucky cat to keep you company."

Halting the vehicle in a main road some way from the city centre, Paddy pointed to a bus stop in a lay-by. "You ought to get a lift from here," he said. "If I was going to London, I'd take you there myself. I wouldn't allow a son of mine to travel on his own. No doubt you have your reasons. We live in a dangerous world these days. You *must* take care."

Finding it difficult to assess what time it was, I became increasingly perturbed when none of the passing drivers were prepared to offer me a lift. Thirsty, hungry and getting very anxious, I remembered what Paddy had said about the dangers of my quest. It was bad enough in daylight hours; for me still to be on the road after nightfall would present enormous risks. Without proper shelter, where would I sleep and how would I survive? What if it rained?

Giving up hope, I reached a state of desperation. Nobody took any notice of the bewildered small boy who waited in vain for what seemed hours for his elusive rescuer. Unversed in the art of hitch-hiking, I followed the example of others I had seen. No matter how hard I tried or how flamboyant were my signals, countless cars and lorries rumbled by, impatient occupants continuing to ignore my frantic pleas for help.

Then a hand tapped me on the shoulder. I turned and found myself looking up at a man of indeterminate age, with greying hair, staring eyes and discoloured teeth. Bending down, he came so close that I began to back away, but not before I caught the foul odour of his breath, a smell that reminded me of someone with whom I was familiar.

"I've been watching you from over the road," said the stranger, his eyes focused on me in a disconcerting manner. "Where do you want to go?"

"I am travelling to High Wycombe to see Miss Young."

"Who is Miss Young?"

"She was my teacher until I went to live with my uncle and aunt in Harrogate."

"Do your uncle and aunt know where you are?"

"Please don't tell them I'm here," I begged him tearfully, terrified at the prospect of having to return to Oxton House.

"I take it that your journey to High Wycombe is to be carried out in secret. Mum's the word, I promise you. And talking of mums, where's your mum?"

"I haven't got a mum, she's dead."

"You poor little chap," said the stranger. "I lost my mother too. She was killed when a bomb dropped on the family home in Coventry soon after the start of the war. As you can see, we already have something in common. What's your name?"

"Paul," I said. "Paul Elliott."

"Well, Paul, I think I can help you find Miss Young. I can't drive you to her because I only have a motorbike, but I know someone who can. My friend has a car and he loves driving. It would be no trouble at all for him to take you to High Wycombe."

"Thank you very much, sir," I said excitedly, thrilled to think my troubles were almost at an end.

"Judging by the uniform and your gentlemanly accent, am I right in thinking you attend a private school?"

"Yes sir," I answered guardedly. "I hate it there and that's why I ran away."

"The jigsaw is fitting into place," he declared with an air of mystery. "I once taught at a private school. The masters were cruel and the headmaster was a thug. I was asked to leave when I was wrongly accused of being too friendly with one of the boarders. All I did was protect him from a brutal system. You wouldn't believe the awful things that happened there. Had I stayed, I would have reported the school to His Majesty's inspectors. I suggest you come with me and hop on the back of my motorbike. The sooner we leave, the sooner my friend will be able to drive you to High Wycombe,"

Donning a helmet, the stranger invited me to be his pillion passenger. Advising me to hold onto him tightly, he kick-started the engine and the machine began to chug away noisily in a southerly direction. Exhilarated by the wind blowing in my face and a new sense of freedom, I tried to imagine how surprised and delighted Miss Young would be to see me. A longer ride than I had expected, we finally stopped near a gated track in rugged countryside.

Separated by stone-built walls, undulating fields of various shapes and sizes spread out in all directions. Symbolizing the progress of civilization, the road carved a line through the barren landscape, linking the present to an area of scenic beauty that had remained unchanged for centuries.

Reading my thoughts with uncanny perception, the stranger produced a brown paper bag in which he said there was enough food to keep me going for the journey. "Nothing special," he warned. "Two fish paste sandwiches, a biscuit and some pop. I'm afraid it's all I've got. Why don't we walk over to that clump of trees? It's the ideal spot for you to have your picnic. My friend is going to join us in a moment. As soon as he arrives, he'll drive you to High Wycombe."

Seating ourselves on a smooth-faced boulder in a shady clearing well distanced from the road, I tucked into the sandwiches whilst my good Samaritan began drinking from a tiny silver flask. I had good cause to be very grateful to this man. A reflection of my naive and trusting nature, it never occurred to me that it was odd for him to have arranged the rendezvous with his friend at an obscure hiding place way off the beaten track with not a soul in sight.

What happened next left me dumbstruck with horror and disgust. Taking another swig from his flask, the man stood up, undid the buttons of his trousers and exposed his private parts, showing not the slightest qualms of conscience. "Don't expect you've ever seen a man's cock, have you, Paul?" he remarked proudly, stroking his penis in the casual way a more normal man might caress a cat. "What you need is an elementary lesson in biology; to discover about the birds and the bees; to be told of the things your mother would have taught you."

He went on to explain how the penis can grow larger in response to touch and when naughty thoughts arouse the sexual instincts. "As you get older," he informed me, "hairs will appear around your cock and a creamy white substance will flow out sometimes when you get excited. Like most boys of your age, I'm sure you are interested in magic. When I wave my magic wand, you will see all sorts of amazing things can happen. Shall I see if I can make your cock grow bigger?"

"No thank you, sir," I responded timorously, unable to conceal my acute dismay at the blatant crudeness of his words and actions. "When is your friend going to take me to Miss Young?"

23

Gripped by fear that disaster loomed, I sensed instinctively that my welfare was the least of his concerns. Before I had time to contemplate how best to deal with the horrendous situation, I felt myself being dragged towards him. He used force to place one of my hands on his penis.

"Watch it grow," he instructed. "Slide your fingers up and down with a rhythmic movement; you'll see my cock grow even bigger. Look, it's happening already!"

"Please don't make me do it anymore. You promised I would go to High Wycombe. When is your friend going to take me there?" I pleaded.

Ignoring my distress, he brushed my hand aside dismissively. He then started playing with himself, the movements getting faster and more violent, until the sensation must have been so painful that he groaned and spluttered like an animal about to choke to death.

Looking at me with glazed eyes in a way that could only be described as lecherous, he let out one final cry. Using me as his guileless pawn to gratify his lust, he had reached his climax. Energy depleted, the man closed his eyes and for a brief moment I thought he was asleep. When he came to, it was as if he was in a semi-conscious state, unaware of what was going on around him. No longer recognizing me, he genuinely appeared to have forgotten his attempts to indoctrinate me with his vile desires.

He asked me who I was and what was I doing on the Yorkshire Dales at approaching dusk? I recognised that this man was very sick as well as being dangerous. To get away from him unscathed, the best I could do was to have my wits about me and try to humour him.

— Five —

SLOWLY REMEMBERING WHO I was and the reason I was with him, the stranger apologised that his friend had failed to keep his promise. "He's normally very reliable," he said. "I'm afraid we shall have to leave your trip until tomorrow. If you come and stay with me, I shall give him a call to see what's happened. In any case, it would be more sensible to make an early start than depart as late as this."

Although his comments sounded plausible enough, there was no question of my trusting him. Aware that I needed his help, I decided I would not remain with him a moment longer than was necessary. Over-protective of me until the day they died, my parents had warned me to be cautious in my judgement of the people I met. "All that glitters is not gold," my mother used to say. As far as my abuser was concerned, her advice could not have been more apt. With my immature belief in the incredible, I was convinced that from her privileged place in heaven, mother had become my guardian angel. Comforted by her ethereal presence, I never doubted she would help me tackle the problems I had to face.

Trying to imagine what my mother would advise, I came to the conclusion it would be sensible to make myself scarce if the stranger lived in an out-of-the-way location. If, on the other hand, he was based in an urban setting where there was likely to be activity, noise and bustle, I would be wise to take a chance by remaining with him. The alternative was being left alone on the Yorkshire Dales at night.

On discovering he had rooms in York, I agreed once more to be his pillion passenger. In a built-up area I could much more easily escape from him, knowing his attempts to keep me captive would be impeded by my screams for help.

After what was a much colder ride this time, the motorbike at last came to a halt outside a large Victorian dwelling in a street not far from the city centre. I assumed it was here that I was expected to stay the night. Nothing would induce me to spend another second with this man. Running as fast as my legs would carry me, I made for a group of shops I had spotted round the corner.

A flustered voice was shouting: "Paul, come back! Come back this instant!" And then more faintly came the plaintive sound: "Paul, where are you? Where are you, Paul?"

Continuing to sprint along winding lanes, through alleyways and cobbled squares, past the minster into a particularly narrow street, I hurtled on, too afraid to look back in case my pursuer was behind me. At every dark corner I expected him suddenly to appear, his staring eyes compelling me to answer to his bidding. Entering a public park, breathless and fatigued, I sat down on a bench, my mind still exercising razor-sharp alertness.

It was starting to rain. As I sat shivering from the cold, the seriousness of the situation began to monopolize my thinking. My ambition to reach High Wycombe was obscured by the more immediate problem of where to shelter for the night. The horrifying sortie to the Yorkshire Dales had unnerved me so much that I knew I could never relax until I was far from York, way beyond the reaches of the stranger.

Hungry, footsore and with morale deflated, I prayed that by some magical process my mother would make a sign to show me how to act. An eerie silence was all my desperate exhortations could produce. Mother had always been a busy person. Perhaps Jesus had more important things for her to do. With not a ray of hope remaining, smothered by a cloud of total blackness, my tears flowed uncontrollably, a forlorn reminder of my inner emptiness. I was more relieved than anxious when I saw a policeman walking towards the bench. Taking a handkerchief from his pocket, he bent down and began wiping the tears from my face.

"Whatever is the matter?" he asked, showing genuine concern to find a doleful little boy alone in the park at night.

There was no logic behind my reasoning, yet instinct convinced me I could depend upon this man. I told him about my parents' accident; of my experiences at Oxton House; of my plan to run away; but I was too ashamed to speak of the encounter with the stranger. It helped me to talk about my troubles. For far too long I had kept my private thoughts all bottled up, unable to unburden the terrible imaginings with which I was afflicted.

"You *have* had it tough," the policeman remarked after I calmed sufficiently to catch my breath. "I'm sure something can be done to help. First of all we must get you in the warm and find you a bite to eat."

The officer in charge at the station welcomed me with a breezy benevolence I found surprising. "We've had half the Yorkshire force out looking for you," he said. "Our job is to catch thieves and criminals, not spend all our resources searching for a young truant absconding from his school." Hoping he was about to offer advice as to how I might get to High Wycombe and Miss Young, my heart sank when he declared: "A driver is going to take you back to school and one of my lady assistants will accompany you. Now don't you ever dream of going off on the razzle like that again!"

Earlier in the term another much older boy had run away. On his return he had been beaten by my uncle for the inconvenience he had caused. Uncle Don could beat me black and blue for all I cared. My ambition to escape remained unchanged, irrespective of the measures taken to deter me. Having learnt the hard way through my trial-run practice, it was patently clear that success next time would only be achieved with much more careful planning.

The extent of Uncle Don's wrath was yet to be revealed. I could hardly expect him to welcome me back with open arms, for my unpardonable sins to be forgiven without a massive fuss. The one redeeming feature of being back at Oxton House was that it wasn't to be for long.

Waiting for me at the school's main entrance was Uncle Don, purple-faced, cigarette in mouth, his scowling expression befitting the occasion. The boys often used to say they could judge his mood by the number of cigarettes he smoked. On a bad day his cough would reverberate around the building. He must have had a dreadful day because the cough was so pervasive that it took some while before he could clear his throat and was calm enough to speak.

"You and I need to have a little talk," he said, mouthing his words with clipped precision. "Your aunt is so upset she's taken to her bed. Without delay I want you in my study."

Uncle Don's study, known as the inner sanctum, was very much a man's room. The generous dimensions provided space for several leather-backed chairs. There was an antique table on which stood a pipe rack, two ash trays and an engraved cigarette case, offering

27

further proof of his addiction to tobacco. A fine feature was the enormous oak desk, positioned behind the French windows overlooking the front garden. Resembling a battlefield, the desk's top was littered with papers, letters, books; including a blackboard rubber and a dumb-bell from the gym, together with an assortment of confiscated objects belonging to his pupils. In contrast to the sense of chaos created by the desk, elsewhere the air of orderliness accentuated my uncle's dedication to high standards. Apart from a vacant area beside the door, where there was a painting of his Oxford college, the walls from floor to ceiling were filled with shelves containing hundreds of books, all beautifully bound, in the systematic manner of a public library.

The study was where Uncle Don administered his canings. Believing a punishment should fit the crime, he was of the view that for boys a good beating was by far the best deterrent. Rumour had it that he kept his weapons, three to be precise, in a cupboard beneath his desk. One was a bamboo stick; there was also a leather strap; and for the most serious offences, a cut-down walking stick. In no hurry to proceed with the inevitable, Uncle Don sat staring at me, his face so solemn that he had lost his usual eloquence. A bottle at his side, he was sipping from a tumbler. The sips became gulps and soon he was pouring himself a somewhat larger drink. I cannot be sure, but I thought his hands were trembling. When he finally opened his mouth, instead of the expected rollicking, he began slurring his words with inconsequential ramblings that could not have been more out of character.

A bigger coward than most, I wanted the beating to be over there and then. My brazen attitude of an hour ago was fast receding. I was so scared that I was beginning to wet myself. In the prep. school world, it was a matter of honour for a boy to take his punishment without complaint, not to be seen to cry or make a fuss.

Why was my uncle continuing to keep me in suspense?

— Six —

MINUTES PASSED AND still Uncle Don made no reference to a beating. For an offence such as mine, I'd be likely to receive six strokes on my rear quarters with the walking stick. The purpose of the correction, apart from strengthening my character, was to instil in me the knowledge that under no circumstances would disobedience be tolerated at Oxton House. The fact I was beside myself with unhappiness was immaterial. After all, I had caused disruption and inconvenience. I had no option other than to accept what was coming to me without complaint. By putting off the evil moment, my uncle was greatly adding to my torment. Please, please would he proceed without delaying the beating any longer?

Until then I had not sat physically close to Uncle Don for long enough to be able to study him in depth. For the first time I became aware how much he resembled my father, both with his mannerisms and the features of his face.

The thickness of the hair, the pale blue eyes and the aristocratic nose were a carbon copy of my father's. The main difference was my uncle's greater size and bulk and the undue redness of his face. The initial impression was that he possessed a dissipated look. A fairer estimate was that he bore the burdens of the world upon his shoulders, which gave him the appearance of being old before his time.

My father had often worried about his brother's health. On a number of occasions he had expressed concern that, having been an athlete in his youth, he had let himself go. "That school will be the death of him," he said repeatedly. "He works too hard, drinks and smokes too much and is grossly overweight. He's an obvious candidate for a heart attack. I keep telling him to get a grip, but he's as stubborn as a mule and will not heed my warnings." As I watched him, I could not help thinking he was ill. No matter how scared I was of him, he was still my uncle. The thought of Father's prediction coming true made me fearful that another tragedy was imminent.

Eyes watery and bloodshot, he coughed and coughed until tears were running down his cheeks. Could he have been crying or was it the cough that gave me that impression? Not having seen a grown-up lose emotional control, I might have been wrong with my conclusion. He looked tired and dejected, as if he wore a cloak of agony he could not shift. And then I knew. There was no doubt he was crying. My uncle, the stiff-upper-lip headmaster; the ruler of the roost; my father's younger brother.

"Are you alright, Uncle Don?"

"No, I'm not alright. Of course I'm not alright. I am angry, so angry it's as much as I can do to speak."

I must have been mistaken about the crying. He was behaving as I'd expected him to do. After a severe telling-off, six of the best would follow. Providing I braced myself for the assault and accepted my punishment with courage, I would suffer the minimum loss of face. Acceptance of pain was the inescapable reality. I fumbled for an apology.

"I'm sorry I was naughty. I didn't mean to upset Aunt Olive."

"You've done nothing wrong, my boy," he said. "We are the ones at fault. Why did you not tell us you were unhappy with us here? We have let you down and the best we can do is to try to make amends. To me your father was the most steadfast man I've ever known. His ghastly death left us with the responsibility of looking after you in the way your parents would have done. We've failed you, Paul. From now on everything will change. If it doesn't, I shall forever have it on my conscience."

Scarcely able to believe what I was hearing, I needed reassurance that I'd not misunderstood my uncle's apparent change of heart. His answer to my question would confirm whether or not I was mistaken.

"Are you going to cane me with the walking stick?"

"The cane? Why should I give you the cane? I don't even *have* a walking stick. I've already told you, you've done nothing wrong. I am the one at fault."

"Simpson was caned when he ran away," I pointed out. "The other boys won't think it fair if they see you've let me off."

"When Simpson ran away, he did it as a prank. He boasted to his friends that he was going to do it to make a nuisance of himself.

All he managed to achieve was to worry his parents and cause the police and me a lot of extra work. I was out for hours looking for him in my car, and after he was found he thought it was a joke. It was sheer naughtiness in his case; he *deserved* the beating. You ran away because you were unhappy. The situations cannot be compared."

He rose from his chair. Standing beside me, he placed his hands on my head as if he was delivering a blessing. There was a calm warmth about him now that I found relaxing, reminding me of the times the mere presence of my father had been enough to make me feel contented and secure. Judging by the intensity of his expression, I guessed he had something of significance to say.

"When I was younger than you are now," he said, "my mother, your grandmother, was taken ill. Our father deserted us soon after I was born, leaving Mother with the task of bringing up the two of us on her own. She was so weakened by the illness that she was confined to bed for months. Apart from one of my mother's friends who put in regular appearances, your father at the age of ten took charge of virtually everything. Not only did he nurse Mother, he looked after me by taking me to school and helping me with my work. Many a day I remember him doing the cleaning, the ironing and the cooking. His joy was to keep the household running smoothly and considering others before himself. Without your father's help and influence, I would have achieved nothing in my life."

"Daddy never spoke about his school or before he became a soldier in the war."

"I don't expect he did. Your father was a very modest man, an exceedingly good man, Paul. There is much more I think that you should know."

Covering old ground, he reminded me how my father had been unable to accept the place he had been offered at university. My mother always claimed this was because four years fighting for his country had prevented him from achieving his ambition.

"What you probably don't know," he continued, "is that after the war he still could have gone to Oxford. I was eighteen at the time and I, too, had been offered a place, though at a different college. One of us had to get a job and live at home, to keep an eye on your grandmother, who by then was very sick indeed. Your father refused to allow me to give up my Oxford place, saying that as the

31

senior male of the family it was his responsibility to take care of things at home. When you consider what he suffered during the war and how badly he was wounded, his was an example of greater unselfishness than I have known in any human being. Perhaps you can now understand why it is I owe him everything and of my need to repay that debt."

After his speech, Uncle Don bent down and patted me on the shoulder, a simple gesture conveying an affection of deep sincerity which made me feel safe for the first time in weeks. Strengthened by his words about my father, it was comforting to be reminded that the Elliotts had not been extinguished and forgotten, but rather the family still flourished within a new dimension in which I would one day play a part. A fierce pride burning inside me, I vowed there and then at the tender age of eight that I would strive to emulate my parents' selfless efforts and keep alive the sacred memories of the past.

Eager to know the root cause of my unhappiness, Uncle Don began to question me. "What is it you dislike most about Oxton House?"

Taken aback by his directness, I was too shy to come up with a coherent answer. "I don't hate everything," I said.

"Let's put it another way. If you had one wish, what would that wish be? Perhaps there is something we could alter to make life happier for you here?"

"I don't like Mr Johnson. I wish I could have someone else to teach me French."

"Why don't you like Mr Johnson?"

"Because he shouts and hits us when we make mistakes. I'm frightened of him."

"Mr Johnson's days are numbered. I've already given him notice to leave at Christmas. He's been told that if he so much as lays a finger on any of you again, he will be dismissed at once. His place is to be taken by a Miss Roberts, who I think you will find is very different from our Mr Johnson."

I tried to imagine what it would be like after the departure of the most feared master on the staff. At least I would no longer wake up with collywobbles, scared witless at the thought of the browbeating that invariably took place. Trustful of my uncle's good intentions, when asked if there was anything else he could do to help me settle down, I was bold enough to request a special favour.

"Please, Uncle Don, do I have to share a room with Giles?"

"If you want to sleep somewhere else, I'm sure this can be arranged. Giles can be bossy, but you must know he means no harm."

It would have served no purpose to have told him the truth about Giles' nocturnal bullying. Too young to indulge in politics, I settled for diplomacy instead. "I don't mind being in a dormitory with Smythe and Perkins," I volunteered.

"That's not a problem," said my uncle, "there's a spare bed in their dorm. So will that help to cheer you up?"

It was amazing how these two adjustments lifted my morale. Thanks to Uncle Don's scrupulous commitment to my welfare, the days of terror and confusion were coming to an end.

— Seven —

DESPITE NOT PUTTING out the flags to celebrate Mr Johnson's departure, all the Oxton House pupils were jubilant to see the back of him. My attempt to run away had rewarded me with far better treatment from my uncle and aunt than I could ever have expected. Uncle Don watched out for me at all times, adopting a protective attitude that smacked of favouritism. I expected Giles and the other boys to resent the privileged way I was being handled. Exercising my special care with subtlety, Uncle Don managed to avoid making me feel awkward in the presence of my peers. It became customary for my uncle to invite me to his study for a chat some evenings before I went to bed. On these much-valued occasions he quizzed me about my day, his prime aim being to reassure himself that I was beginning to come to terms with the disruptions in my life.

Aunt Olive was more circumspect in her dealings. A sincere and conscientious lady, she clearly wanted me to settle down. Her way of helping to achieve this was to support her husband in whatever he had in mind to do. They were a devoted couple, who took their responsibilities seriously. The worries of the school occupied their energy to such an extent that there was time for little else. It upset me to see them working in a constant state of stress. At the times Uncle Don's cough reached crescendo level, a nagging unease again caused me to think he was heading for an illness.

One evening Uncle Don was convinced I was holding something back in my answers to his questions. What he did not realise was that the smell of alcohol on his breath had revived memories of my miserable meeting with the stranger and of his revolting behaviour on the Yorkshire Dales. "You seem anxious about something," he said. "Are you sure there's nothing you want to tell me?"

Part of me wanted to offload my feelings of guilt by speaking about what had happened. I could not bring myself to do this, nor did I want to upset my uncle whose health might well have taken a turn for the worse had he listened to an account of my ordeal. He was a kind-hearted man and I felt protective towards him.

The Christmas period brought with it reminders of how much I missed my parents. Uncle Don and Aunt Olive could see I was distressed. Encouraging me as best they could, they were sensible enough to know it would have been pointless to steer me away from thinking about the past. I valued my memories, powerful reminiscences I wished never to remove altogether from my thoughts. For all the vacillation, I can now look back upon that particular Christmas with a modicum of joy, as by this time I was conscious of the love I was receiving. The only blot on the landscape was Giles. He lacked the tolerance needed to accept me as a member of the family; instead, his animosity now was expressed less openly than during the miserable weeks I had shared his room. Continuing to pound me with his fists, he was careful to ensure there was nobody about when he carried out his caddish antics.

I had made great strides since arriving at Oxton House in August. The traumatic events had toughened me in many ways, though there would have been time enough for this to have happened naturally under my parents' roof, had the hand of fate not intervened so cruelly. Uncle Don was well aware of the strength I was having to employ and the progress I was making. Bringing tears to my eyes, he said: "Your father would have been proud to see how well you are coping. I've told you he was a brave man; quite obviously you take after him. From now on it can only get easier."

The appointment of Miss Roberts to the staff marked the beginning of an era. Far from being the grumpy old biddy we had expected, she was young, humorous and possessed immense vitality. It was her ravishing appearance that caused me to fall in love with her the first day she appeared. Most of the other boys shared my sentiments. It is little wonder she soon had us bending over backwards to please her in any way we could. In addition to taking over junior French, she specialized in English and history, subjects she taught with such flair I can honestly say that throughout my entire schooling I never met a more compelling teacher. Mopping up every scrap of information like a sponge, I discovered that learning could be fun.

At half-term the Oxton House boarders returned to their homes for a weekend break. On the Saturday the Elliott family was treated to a special tea with cakes, following which Giles was asked to leave the room to enable my uncle and aunt to talk to me in private. "Do you still want to go and live with Miss Young?" ventured Uncle Don. Not having thought about Miss Young, I was taken aback by the very idea of leaving Harrogate.

"No, thank you, I'd rather stay here."

"Does that mean you are more at home than when you ran away last term?"

"Surely you can see he's much happier, Donald?" broke in Aunt Olive. "You *are* settled with us, aren't you, Paul?"

"Oh yes," I said. "I like it here now I'm getting used to everything. *And* I've made some friends."

"You seem to be popular with most of the boys," observed Aunt Olive. "Who are your best friends?"

"Smythe, Jones and Perkins. I also like Blenkinsop a lot."

"How are you hitting it off with Giles these days?" she persisted.

"He's not one of my best friends, but I do like him," I said, lying through my teeth. Once again I saw no point in making it known how unpleasant Giles could be when the spirit moved him.

Grinning from ear to ear, Uncle Don could not wait to explain the reason for the meeting. Content to leave most matters concerning my welfare in the capable hands of her husband, Aunt Olive smiled at us both benignly.

"I won't beat about the bush," he said. "Your aunt and I have decided we would like to adopt you. If this is to happen, it would mean you would become our son in the legal sense. At the moment we treat you as our own, but we are not technically your parents. You must know how much we love you and that our aim has always been to carry on the good work of your remarkable mummy and daddy. Of course, we can't live up to their standards, but you know you can rely on us to do our best. Well, Paul, how do you feel about being adopted?"

"It would be nice for you and Aunt Olive to be my parents. I'm not sure I would want to call you Mummy and Daddy. It would keep reminding me of my real mummy and daddy. Would it matter if I still called you Uncle Don and Aunt Olive?"

"You can call us what you like, my dear boy. What is important is for you to be happy with any arrangement that is made."

"Does Giles know you want to adopt me?"

"Yes, we have told him of our plans."

"Isn't he going to be angry?"

"It may take him a little while to adjust to what is only a minor change. Don't fret about it, Paul. I promise you Giles isn't going to be a problem. He's always wanted a brother, so what do you say?"

It would have been impossible to find two better substitute parents than my uncle and aunt. Regardless of my obvious delight, I could not help worrying whether Giles' behaviour towards me would become even more aggressive in the future. With or without the adoption, he would continue to be a thorn in my side.

— Eight —

I N VIEW OF the noticeable change for the better in Giles' attitude, it was clear Uncle Don was playing a significant part behind the scenes. In the presence of his parents, my cousin's behaviour came across as normal. Discerning the insincerity of his actions, I hoped others would see for themselves the potency of his hatred. Clever in the art of survival, he managed to disguise his venom with surprising skill. I was convinced that one day he'd be unable to keep up the pretence and would do me an injury. The fear never went away. So certain was I of the likelihood of this happening that I had frequent nightmares depicting the scenario. Avoiding Giles as best I could, my worries were largely misplaced, especially as his attempts to kick or punch me betrayed a reluctance on his part to risk being found out. Unwilling to express my anxieties to anyone, I hoped that in time the two of us would be sent to different schools.

Encouraged by the inspiration provided by Miss Roberts, I found most of the school work easy. By the end of her first term on the staff, I came top in every subject apart from mathematics. Infuriated that my success emphasised his academic deficiencies, Giles began spreading tales about me, saying I was a cheat. Aware of the tensions that existed between the two of us, Miss Roberts did her best to calm what was in danger of developing into an explosive situation. Expressing her concern to my uncle, it was not long before he raised the matter during one of my evening visits to his study.

"You must see it can't be easy for Giles," he said. "To be overtaken by his much younger cousin must at the least be very galling for him. I keep telling him he has gifts that differ from yours and you no doubt envy his athletic ability. A father could do with having the wisdom of Solomon in dealing with friction of this kind. There is, I think, a solution. Before I tell you what it is, I'm going to ask you a question. Are you prepared to work your socks off for the next five years?"

"Yes, Uncle Don. I enjoy the lessons and if it wasn't for Giles, I think I'd work even harder."

"That being the case," he said, "I want to promote you in the summer term to a more senior form. The gaps in your knowledge can easily be filled with private tuition. As you know, maths is my subject. In the holidays I shall try to cover most of the work you have missed. Do you think you are up to it?"

"Oh yes," I enthused. "Will Miss Roberts still be teaching me?"

"She will be your form mistress."

"Miss Roberts is the best teacher in the world. I've learnt more from her than with any of my other teachers."

"That's good to hear because we want to groom you for a scholarship."

Uncle Don went on to explain that most of the boys took the common entrance examination for their next school at the age of thirteen. To be a realistic scholarship candidate, it was going to be necessary for me to cover the basic prep. school syllabus by the age of eleven, leaving me two years in which to undergo intensive scholarship preparation.

"It's a tall order," said Uncle Don. "I can't pretend you will find it easy, but knowing you as I do, I suspect you will relish the challenge."

Under the watchful eye of Miss Roberts, transition to the 4th form could not have gone more smoothly. Competing with boys aged ten, it was up to me to prove myself. Fearful of being downgraded and having to rejoin my spiteful cousin, I worked as if my life depended on it. Regarded by the other boys as a one-off prodigy, some dubbed me "egghead"; others "the professor", but not with malice.

Getting to grips with my studies absorbed me to such an extent that much of my spare time was devoted to learning from scratch skills and topics my new classmates had mastered. Competing with the best, I was able to hold my own. Uncle Don and Miss Roberts were delighted, insisting my results had more than justified the decision to promote me.

The next few years saw many changes at Oxton House. Following the retirement of the nose-dribbling Mr Palin, his teaching duties were taken over by a number of masters, none of whom remained at the school for much longer than a term. Looking on me as a family insider, Uncle Don often aired his anxieties in my presence, knowing I was discreet enough never to betray his trust. It was during these private chats that I began to realise the huge part he had played in helping to rebuild my confidence.

On one occasion Uncle Don was in a particularly despondent frame of mind. "Giles shows no interest in the school," he said. "I don't doubt he'll forge a successful career for himself. He has no intention of becoming a schoolmaster like his father, not that I can blame him. When your aunt and I retire, we shall have to find a buyer for Oxton House. Schools are difficult to sell, in particular the ones which scarcely make a profit."

"Do you mind if I make a suggestion, Uncle Don?"

"I'm always open to ideas."

"Wouldn't the school be more successful if there were fewer changes on the staff? Since Mr Palin left, there's been four masters to replace him. As soon as we get used to a new master, he leaves and another takes his place."

"You're quite right, Paul. The trouble is I can only afford to pay the staff a pittance; in consequence, most of the best teachers go to schools where the salaries are higher and where staff accommodation is better. It boils down to a matter of pounds, shillings and pence."

"Miss Roberts is a brilliant teacher. If you had more like her, Oxton House would be the best school in England."

"We all know she's one in a million. Teaching is her mission. She's not ruled by money. The reason she stays is because she's happy here and is treated as a member of the family."

It was at this point Uncle Don began to cough. A longer and more husky coughing fit than usual, his face became puffed up, the strain showing in his eyes. The breathlessness was getting worse. Alarm bells in my imagination continued to warn me of impending doom. The love I had received from this man had helped to provide the security needed for me to be able to start afresh. Having lost both my parents, the thought of my uncle being struck down by illness was a consequence too awful to imagine.

My father had spoken to me about his ambition for me to go to grammar school. As most of the Oxton House boys were destined at the age of thirteen for boarding public schools or fee-paying day schools, it didn't matter whether we passed the eleven plus or not. Uncle Don still made us take the exam.

"The only reason I am putting you in for it is as an insurance step," he told us. "A place at grammar school would only be of benefit if for some reason you need to transfer to a state school."

On account of his birthday falling in June, Giles sat for his eleven plus two years before I did. In common with most of the other boys of his age, he did not perform well enough to pass. The result caused no eyebrows to be raised and life carried on as normal.

One of the few times Uncle Don made an error of judgement was when he announced at morning assembly that I had been offered a grammar school place, saying pointedly that no other boy in the school that year had achieved the distinction. Giles, who was upset by the tactless way the matter had been handled, began bullying me again after a lull of several months. I could appreciate his frustration, knowing as we all did that it was going to be a struggle for him to pass the common entrance later in the year.

Achieving the entry requirements for Shrewsbury School by the narrowest of margins, Giles saw himself as an academic failure. His perception of himself might have been less negative had his father taken the trouble to highlight his strengths rather than denigrate his weaknesses. Schoolmasters rarely get the balance right when it comes to the education of their own children.

What little sympathy I felt for Giles evaporated as soon as the dirty tricks began. My exercise books were damaged; pages were torn out; essays and project work went missing; ink-stained blots appeared on some of my most prized efforts. Once Giles was away boarding at Shrewsbury, I was free at last to be able to develop my potential without occasioning his wrath. Already way ahead of him scholastically, it had been an uncomfortable situation for the two of us, a state of affairs that had prevented me from pulling out the stops.

"You've two years in which to prepare for the Shrewsbury scholarship," encouraged my uncle. "You're likely to be the strongest candidate we've ever had."

Horrified at the thought of having to join Giles at Shrewsbury, the time had come for me to make known my feelings before it was too late.

"I would rather go to grammar school. Please don't make me go to Shrewsbury."

It was Aunt Olive who came to my rescue. More intuitive than her husband, she had detected at once the reason for my reticence.

"Sedbergh is another first-rate school," she said. "It's not too far from Harrogate and is set in some of the most breath-taking scenery in Cumbria. My brother was there and was very happy. The poet William Wordsworth also chose it for his sons. How does the idea appeal?"

Coming to a decision in a flash, I settled for Sedbergh. Anything was better than having to suffer once more the humiliation of my cousin's spiteful influence.

The school's abysmal results in Latin were a reflection of the bedlam in Major Gibson's lessons. The ravages of war had knocked his self-esteem so badly that he had become a nervous wreck. His teaching career in tatters, he decided to do the honourable thing by resigning from his post.

An Oxford scholar by the name of Hewitt took his place. Unlike the unfortunate Major Gibson, he had no difficulty in maintaining order.

Systematic with the preparation of his lessons, he demanded nothing but the best and generally he got it. Progressing with great rapidity, Latin for me became a pleasure. To keep boredom at bay, Mr Hewitt set tasks that stretched me to my limits. Tutoring me privately, he made a start in teaching me some Greek.

Knowing how important it was to Uncle Don for my name to appear on the honours' board, I worked as never before, determined to bring much needed credit to the school. Having been appointed captain of cricket and a prefect in my final year, winning a scholarship to Sedbergh would prove to be the icing on the cake.

In the May prior to my fourteenth birthday, Uncle Don drove me to Sedbergh for the scholarship examination. Staying in one of the boarding houses, for three exhausting days I joined up with some thirty other boys to take papers in a variety of subjects. Although the last few terms in the protected world of Oxton House had taught me what to expect, no amount of preparation could have helped me overcome the nervousness. Morale plummeted when I convinced myself all the other candidates were brighter, more sophisticated and more smartly dressed than me. Anticipating disastrous results, without even the offer of a place, my greatest fear was what to say to alleviate my uncle's disappointment.

On the homeward journey, I was disconsolate and morose. Attempts to cheer me up were fruitless. "It was only an exam," said Uncle Don. "There's no disgrace if you don't get an award. To be selected as a candidate is an achievement in itself."

A week later, as I was about to go to sleep, Uncle Don rushed into my dormitory. "I have some news for you, Paul," he called me urgently. "Aunt Olive is waiting for you in the lounge. Get up and join us as quickly as you can!"

Overcome with emotion, he had difficulty in assembling his words.

"You are a genius, Paul, do you know that? I've just received a telephone call from the headmaster of Sedbergh. Not only were you the strongest candidate, you came first on the list by far. You've been awarded the top scholarship. I can't tell you how thrilled we are."

Tears of relief fell like a waterfall. Through misty eyes I noticed that my uncle and aunt were crying through sheer joy as well. The kindest people on earth, they had shared in my triumphs and supported me when times were bad. By empathizing with my mood at this rapturous moment, they exhibited a love that was unique.

The following weekend, the teaching staff and prefects were invited to what was referred to as a special jamboree in the school garden to honour my success. In an atmosphere of hilarity and warmth, I was offered my first-ever taste of beer. Behaving like an indulgent emperor, Uncle Don made a speech, proclaiming an extra day's holiday for the school, which made me hero of the hour.

I vowed I would one day repay my uncle and aunt for providing me with such a privileged start. Considering the misadventure I'd encountered earlier, the turnaround could not have been more blessed.

— Nine —

DURING MY FIRST term at Sedbergh, at the end of one of his fortnightly letters, Uncle Don penned an unexpected postscript.

You will doubtless be surprised and delighted to learn that Aunt Olive is expecting a baby. We have, as you know, always wanted a daughter. Dr Taylor tells us that the birth will take place, all being well, at the end of January. We know you will wish to pray for a happy outcome.

To say I was surprised would be an understatement. Aunt Olive did not enjoy a robust constitution, added to which she was about to celebrate her forty-fifth birthday. The part she played in the running of the school was so vital that I wondered how she would manage to look after the baby as well as attend to her professional duties.

Emma's birth was a hazardous one. Born prematurely on Christmas Day, she weighed four pounds exactly. Instead of the usual jollifications associated with a baby's birth, we anxiously awaited news from the nursing home, where Uncle Don maintained a constant vigil. On the few occasions he returned home, he smoked with the fury of a haunted man, spluttering great coughs, his inflated face a hideous purple colour.

It was touch and go whether Emma would survive. It might have been better had she been spared setting out on life's journey that would forever be a puzzle to her. She was mentally and physically retarded. In no human being can there have been greater sweetness or more natural goodness. At the age of fourteen I was chosen to be one of Emma's godfathers. To have achieved this dizzy height was an honour I treated with the utmost seriousness.

Aunt Olive returned home bruised and thoroughly dejected. It was as if the flame that kept her lively personality alight had been extinguished. Her eyes expressionless, the pinched features of an emaciated face gave her the appearance of a much older woman, aged overnight by life's cruel buffeting. At her wits' end, she appointed a full-time nanny by the name of Elsie Chapman, a spinster in her thirties.

When Uncle Don first told me of the impending birth of Emma, I should have been delighted. Whether through instinct or a paranormal insight, I feared there was trouble brewing. Long before the birth took place, with the vivid certainty of words written on a page, I could foresee the practical complications that would follow. Despite the tragedy of her impairment, nothing will ever destroy for me the good derived from Emma's sweet-natured disposition or the pride I felt in being able to love her as a brother.

* * * * * * * * * *

Sedbergh was not a school for lily-livered wimps. Taking a while to settle in, I slowly adapted to what by today's standards would be regarded as a tough regime. With cold showers before breakfast and an emphasis on physical toughness, I bore an initial unhappiness from which it was difficult to escape.

It was not until I took part in the ten-mile Wilson Run, the hardest school run in existence, that I was finally accepted. Scrambling through streams, up and down ghylls and valley sides, across moors, negotiating fences and stiles, I completed the course with a smile of jubilation on my mud-splattered face.

Sensitive boys fared less well than did the macho rugby-playing types. A limited number left with a chip on their shoulders, thinking that the school had let them down. For the most part we were treated fairly. Considering my fragile nature, it is surprising that I flourished as well as I did in a philistine environment. We had heard tales of some of the bookish pupils being made fun of in the past, but there was no evidence of negative pressures of this kind in the 1950s. In consequence, I was able to make use of any abilities I possessed without having to keep untapped talents out of sight.

Founded in 1525, Sedbergh enjoyed a fine reputation in the north of England. Receiving spectacular support from former pupils, large numbers chose for their sons to follow in their footsteps.

An atmosphere of self-satisfaction dominated, whilst few had the temerity to criticize a proven system.

It didn't take me long to realize it was the staff who made the school. In contrast to the struggling Oxton House, Sedbergh ran smoothly like a well-oiled machine. Most of the masters were committed and effective. Because they were recipients of generous perks, few were in a hurry to uproot themselves. This in turn added to the feeling of stability, an asset which strengthened the entire establishment. Until my uncle could match the conditions of better paid staff in the most sought-after schools, he would be unable to attract a dynamic team of teachers.

Homesickness is a strange condition. I think I must have suffered from it, though it was never severe enough to prevent me from involving myself with the activities on offer. The House matron, Mrs Turrell, was a compassionate and kindly soul. Her bosom was large and her heart even bigger. She could see I was finding it hard to adapt to boarding away from home. She must have known I had lost my real parents because she occasionally made reference to Uncle Don and Aunt Olive as my stepparents. She took special care to check I was alright and during the first few weeks she gave me several reassuring hugs.

What also helped me to settle was my friendship with Clive Starkey, a music scholar in my House. The son of an army surgeon stationed abroad, he was forced to spend most of the holidays with grandparents in Carlisle. He often confided in me and I was able to discuss with him some of my own concerns. A naturally gifted pianist, Clive devoted most of his leisure time to boogie-woogie, syncopation and to developing a style of jazz playing that was unique.

Encouraged by his enterprise and skill, I decided to take up an instrument. Uncle Don bought me a tenor saxophone and I practised and practised until I could play a number of melodies faultlessly in different keys. As my ambition increased, I was determined to play well enough to become a member of a band. A year later the Sedbergh jazz quintet was formed, consisting of Clive on piano, a drummer, a bass player, a trumpeter and myself on sax. We gave concerts to raise money for charity. This was the only way we were able to get the school authorities to allow us to participate in an otherwise unsanctioned activity. The director of music was furious that one of his ablest musicians had discarded classical music in favour of what he described as "that sickening tin-pan-alley nonsense!"

It was a tradition for each House to put on a variety show after the final supper of the term. As a special privilege the prefects were permitted a glass of cider. The fags and more junior members were restricted to lemonade or water. I well remember the time when Clive and I rehearsed two jazz numbers for the presentation. Before our performance we had helped ourselves to some cider from the larder. At the end of the evening in merry mood we escaped to the back yard by the dustbins and took it in turns to kiss one of the young kitchen assistants, an eager but rather plain girl from the village. Tommy Price, the housemaster, appeared suddenly out of the shadows and castigated us roundly. "I always thought jazz was a corruptive influence. If, as it seems, music of the decadent variety leads you astray, I would suggest you take up the viola!"

An inveterate letter writer, Uncle Don kept me regularly in touch with developments back home. Much as I looked forward to receiving any news, the gloomy content of some of his epistles had the effect of worrying me unduly. Powerless at a distance to be of help, I bit my nails in silent agony, convincing myself with an uncanny sense that had I been there with him I might have been instrumental in averting some of the disasters.

As a result of one of the letters, a disordered plan I had kept hidden at the back of my mind for years developed into a burning ambition. I have kept the frayed piece of paper to this day to remind me of what he wrote.

Oxton House School,
Harrogate,
Yorkshire.
15th May, 1953

My dear Paul,
Knowing how fond you are of cricket, Aunt Olive and I hope your dream to play for the Colts' XI will not be affected by your General Certificate examinations. Giles now opens the bowling for the Shrewsbury 2nd XI and last week he scored 50 in the match against Malvern.
I had been planning to watch a Yorkshire county cricket match. There appears to be no chance of my doing this before August, in which case perhaps we can go together. My desk is piled so high with letters

that need answering and problems to be solved that my usual bedtime has had to be extended. If only I could afford to pay a secretary!

The Oxton House cricket team is doing well and has not lost a match. I regard this as the one redeeming feature of the term, because there are no scholarship candidates and the CE results are unlikely to be impressive. As I keep on saying: "You cannot come up with the goods without the right material."

Staff headaches continue. Last week Mr Hewitt told me he has been offered a job at the Dragon School for January. It is not that he is unhappy here. If I could pay him what he is entitled, he would not dream of moving. It is a bitter blow. He has done so much to improve the Latin after the unfortunate Major Gibson. As you know, Mr Hewitt contributed more than any other master to your scholarship success. He has served me loyally for the last four years, so I cannot but be grateful to him.

Miss Roberts is as keen as ever and a tower of strength. I marvel at the way she continues to support us when we all know any prep. school would consider itself lucky to employ her. She often asks after you and sends her best wishes.

Numbers for next term are worryingly low. Unless we can recruit at least another dozen, half of whom need to be boarders, we shall be in trouble. I should hate nothing more than having to cut the staff still further.

Our accountant is advising us to sell up before numbers drift downwards yet again. I keep telling him that we have had these problems in the past and that before September there are bound to be more entries.

Giles would never want to burden himself with the running of Oxton House. He has aspirations of a different kind and is determined to make some money. Should the idea of one day taking over from us appeal to you, we would endeavour to hang on in order to make this possible. I feel you have the potential to make a splendid headmaster and would gain pleasure from following on the family tradition in the school we love so much. Whilst there is no question of exerting any pressure, it would be helpful to know if you consider the idea to be preposterous.

You will no doubt be pleased to hear that Emma has shaken off her cold and is her cheery self once more. Elsie Chapman is so very patient with her. If Emma could verbalize her thoughts, she would be sending you her love and kisses.

We all miss you and greatly look forward to coming up to Cumbria for the Sedbergh Speech Day.

Ever your loving

Uncle Don

P.S. I am glad you enjoy playing in the school jazz band. Have you ever thought of trying the clarinet as well? This would enable you to be a member of the school orchestra and widen your musical experience.

I realized with unwavering conviction that the future of Oxton House would one day depend on my abilities. Either it would sink, or like the phoenix born again from the ashes, would develop, flourish and excel. Positive thinking convinced me that failure could never be an option.

Uncle Don looked so ill sometimes that I suspected it would not be long before the strain of running the family business would prove too much. Dr Taylor had warned him about the smoking and drinking, telling him in no uncertain fashion that if stubbornness persisted he could do nothing more to help.

"What John Taylor will not get into his thick skull," grumbled my uncle, "is that if I didn't do the things he wants me to avoid, I'd go round the bloody bend. How would *he* cope were he to be asked to teach a group of dunces?"

Severely depressed following Emma's birth, Aunt Olive was much altered from the zestful lady I remembered from the past. The migraines from which she suffered made her nauseous. Hardly a day went by that she did not suffer from some debilitating ailment. More noticeable still was the change in her attitude to the people with whom she worked. Known for her diplomacy, the fractiousness she had developed frightened and confused those who chose to tussle with her. It was clear for all to see she was heading for a breakdown.

For Uncle Don and Aunt Olive to sell up and retire would have made a lot of sense. Rational thinkers would have considered this preferable to having to bear the strains of Oxton House and the destruction of their health. But to watch their life's work peter out, with nothing to show after twenty years of selfless energies expended, would have left them with a worthless epitaph.

A signal of my intent was what my uncle wanted. To be given the strength to carry on, he needed a successor, someone with fire in his belly and whose revolutionary ideas would enable the school to forge ahead and modernise its outlook. Replying to his letter, I confessed it had for a long time been my desire to assist him with the school. Promising to always do my best, I reminded him it would be years before I qualified and be equipped to face the test.

Had I been less strung up about the problems at Oxton House, I might have benefited more from the amenities of Sedbergh. For an inward-looking teenager, it is surprising I had so many friends, especially as what the other boys saw was merely a façade that masked my true identity. My hail-fellow-well-met jollity was the act I put on to avoid having to share the private nightmares I was facing.

Tommy Price, a receptive man, must have tumbled to the fact I was a deeply anxious boy. He questioned me repeatedly, asking me what, if anything, was wrong. "I feel there is some sort of impediment holding you back," he said. "Part of you is miles away and this unknown burden is stopping you from producing your very best. Are you quite sure there is nothing going on at home you want to talk about?"

In spite of not understanding what he meant by an impediment, I could see he was getting frighteningly near the truth. A fierce pride prevented me from divulging the foundation for my woes. His remarks brought me to my senses, leading me to think the best I could do was to concentrate on my work rather than waste time on matters I could not alter.

To show appreciation for the sacrifices made on my behalf, I just *had* to pass for Cambridge. Apart from the jazz band and the cricket, I distanced myself from the more boisterous of my peers and worked with dedication, leaving not a stone unturned in a desire to make the grade. The school library became my sanctuary. It was here that I researched my essays and where I prepared myself for the much more liberated life to be found at university.

Returning from Cambridge after a gruelling interview, I feared the worst. Having disagreed strongly with one of the senior Trinity fellows about the Reformation and its effects on the Church of England, I expected outright rejection. When a telegram arrived, advising me I had been awarded a scholarship, I was flabbergasted and elated. My uncle telephoned to say Aunt Olive was so gladdened by the news that it was helping to lift her from the doldrums.

On my final night at Sedbergh, the headmaster invited me to a dinner to celebrate the successes of the term. Attended by school governors, staff and a number of other leavers, I found myself sitting next to a silver-haired gentleman, who was known to be chairman of a well-known tobacco company. Having done his research, he was curious to hear what career I intended to pursue.

"Elliott, my dear chap, the world of commerce is crying out for young men with your ability. Have you ever thought of the advantages to be had by working in industry? With a brain like yours, the sky's the limit."

"No sir, that particular idea does not appeal. I already know what I want to do."

"Something high-flying, no doubt. Let me take a guess. Is it to be the diplomatic service, or are you to become a lawyer, a barrister perhaps?"

"I want to teach," I said simply.

"A noble profession indeed," he observed. "Does that mean we may have the pleasure of seeing you back here on the staff one day?"

"I'm afraid not, sir. I've decided to help my uncle with the running of the prep. school he owns in Harrogate."

"Which school are we talking about, Elliott?"

"Oxton House," I said.

"The name doesn't ring a bell."

"I hope one day it will, sir. I hope one day it will."

— Ten —

HAVING INSTALLED MYSELF in my rooms at Trinity, the first person I met was a bespectacled young man, whose tousled red hair covered most of his boyish face. He was carrying two suitcases up the stairs as I was about to descend. Greeting each other with the diffidence of freshers, we exchanged names and were delighted to discover we were both history undergraduates.

"I'm Stuart Pennington," he said perkily. On hearing my name, he told me that one of his heads of house at Shrewsbury had been an Elliott. "A smug bugger if ever there was one," he remarked jovially.

"This is an incredible coincidence," I said, "because if it's the same Giles Elliott I think it is, he happens to be my cousin."

"I don't know where to put myself," he stammered with embarrassment.

"No apology needed. He and I don't get on and never have. Did you know he is doing his national service and is serving in Malaysia? Since he became an officer in the 11th Hussars, he's far too full of himself to want to mix with we lesser mortals and that includes his own parents."

Stuart and I repaired to the Eagle for a beer that evening. He was typical of many of the people I was about to get to know. Intellectually brilliant, his probing mind dissected every issue we discussed with a clarity and speed that was amazing. A ready wit softened the harshness of his arguments, making him a natural entertainer and invigorating confidant.

When he learnt of my modest plan to become a schoolmaster, he surprised me with his views.

"Teachers more than any other professionals are equipped to help change the inequalities in our society," he declared. "They have the ability to make the children of future generations aware they have a choice; that inertia and conforming to the status quo will only hamper progress."

"What do you propose doing with your life?" I asked.

"To be part of a Labour government, preferably a member of the cabinet. For example, the public school system, as I see it, is about to undergo a transformation. If it does not, it's bound to fail. If you decide to teach, you will have it in your power to assist with this reshaping process. Without your influence, the politicians can do nothing."

"And what if I don't agree with the changes you want to implement? Teachers never were transformers," I contended. "It's their job to encourage the young how to think, so that they have the wisdom to make informed decisions. Your cut-and-dried approach is a form of indoctrination which is not what education is about."

Stifling a yawn, he smiled. "Once you've seen the light, I'm sure I can persuade you to become a member of the Labour Party."

Cambridge was a joy to me. Recognising I was one of the most privileged people on earth, I took to university life from the start. Away from the petty rules of Sedbergh, I was at last treated as an adult, debating every issue imaginable with like-minded souls, all with opinions and ideas worth listening to. In common with several of my fellow undergraduates, I came to the conclusion that the cerebral banter with which we were so often engaged was equal in benefit to the more formal elements of our course.

Of the friends I made in the first few weeks, Stuart was the one I valued most, Standing by me in every crisis situation that came along, he offered solutions to some of the emergencies I faced. Years later when he had transferred his allegiance to the Conservative party and was a charismatic MP with a controversial reputation, we remained in touch.

Then there was Millicent, the classicist from Newnham, a product of a co-educational boarding school in the south of England, A bundle of fun, she impressed us with her enlightened attitude to sex. Famed for her shapely legs and enormous breasts, we menfolk felt a stirring in our loins at the very sight of her desirable credentials.

Another friend I thought I could rely on was Horace Bletchford. To make up for early loss of hair, he had allowed greying sideburns to grow bushily above his cheeks. Disagreeing with everyone else's point of view, he argued with the tenacity of a limpet. Not once did he have the humility to admit defeat. In spite of the ruthlessness he revealed at times of disputation, he endeared himself to all the members of our clique.

The most unlikely inclusion in our circle was Harrow-educated Aubrey Duncan-Jones, whose tailored suits and jackets depicted him as an aristocrat of breeding. Tall, dark and handsome, with a smile that revealed the whitest teeth I'd ever seen, he was like a magnet as far as women were concerned. Attracted to him in the way bees surround a honeypot, they did their best to vie for his attention. The more they pursued him, the more frightened he became. Thinking at first he was a woman hater, we soon became aware it was lack of confidence that held him back. A man of great wealth, Aubrey was reluctant to talk about his background. We fancied that a childhood in which he had been deprived of the things that mattered most was what had brought about the shyness. Be that as it may, he was a compassionate and agreeable individual who was glad of our support.

Some of my fellow undergraduates grumbled about the quality of the teaching. I was fortunate enough to get on well with my tutor, Dr Maurice Denman, an erudite eccentric, who was renowned for his writings of ecclesiastical biography. Kind enough to compliment me on my essays, towards the end of my second term he gave me encouraging advice. "I am pleased to predict you are heading for a first," he said. "Don't let anything or anyone deflect you from this goal. The temptations are legion: girls, drink, gambling. Keep your eye on the ball and you'll be a winner."

In line with Dr Denman's expectations, all my grades were alphas in the June examinations. "Good man," he vocalized with genuine satisfaction. "If you continue to work with flair and dynamism, in your finals you will be rewarded with a first."

Stuart Pennington was the only other member of our group to achieve results on a par with mine. To mark our success, Aubrey was generous enough to organise a champagne party for a dozen of us in his rooms at Magdalene. I had felt guilty accepting hand-outs from Aubrey, despite knowing it gave him enormous pleasure to spend money on his cronies. Relying on a modest grant, I was conscious I was associating with students who were much better off than me. Uncle Don's financial position had worsened in the five years I had been at Sedbergh. The week before I started at university, I was upset to be told he had been forced to take out a second mortgage to help pay the school fees and enable Giles to maintain an extravagant lifestyle in his snobby army regiment.

Keen to keep up my jazz playing, I had managed to join a modern jazz group early in my first term. The leader, Eddie, an accomplished drummer and vocalist, was a surveyor by day, but he hankered after a career in music. A stickler for precision, at the regular practice sessions he insisted on disciplined intros and crisp endings. Each tune was rehearsed over and over again until perfection was achieved.

Competition for gigs in and around Cambridge was fierce, as there must have been at least a dozen jazz bands jockeying for work. Eddie was a master at securing engagements for his band. The extra money I earned made it a lot easier to hold my own financially with the more affluent of my peers.

I had been saving up all year to attend the Trinity May Ball. Uncle Don lent me his white tie and tails which was so large that Stuart Pennington got a fit of the giggles the night before when I tried it on and said it made me look more like a scarecrow than a dancer. "It's too late to have it taken in," he declared, bellowing with laughter. "Don't worry! After a few drinks, it won't matter how any of us look."

I shuffled about the floor with a selection of pretty young ladies throughout what turned out to be a rip-roaring evening. I'm quite certain the more I drank, the better I danced. By the time of the survivors' breakfast at 4.00 a.m., I was ready for anything. Leading me astray, Stuart and several others inveigled me to help them borrow a College boat to go punting along the River Cam to Grantchester. I cannot remember how or why the punt capsized, but I do vaguely recall scrambling up a muddy bank, still in my uncle's tails, which despite two visits to the cleaners were unfit for use again.

During vacations it was essential for me to get a job. As well as planning to help out that summer at Oxton House for the last few weeks of term, I had arranged to work as a barman at a hotel in Exeter for the months of August and September. Prepared to do anything to earn some cash, I was determined to stand on my own feet to avoid having to depend on my hard-pressed uncle for my keep.

I had looked forward to practising my teaching skills and being with the family again. Sad to say, my arrival in Harrogate couldn't have witnessed a more horrifying upset. Uncle Don, who unknown to me had suffered a heart attack, was seriously ill in hospital. Aged overnight, he had lost all drive and optimism.

After visiting him in his ward, I tore into my aunt with a rage that conveyed the hurt I felt.

"Why didn't you to tell me Uncle Don was ill? He's as much to me a father as any man could ever be. I can't forgive you for keeping me in the dark."

"We agonised over what to do," she said. "We didn't want to unsettle you in the midst of your exams. We've had to contend with the most awful problems here. To have told you of all the complications, you would have worried yourself to death."

"I'm nearly twenty, Aunt Olive, I know exactly where my loyalties lie. How dare you deprive me of the chance to make decisions for myself!"

Dissolving into tears, my aunt was incapable of coherent speech until after a pause she rounded on me fiercely, her eyes ablaze with indignation,

"Why is it young people can *never* understand? I'm going to tell you exactly what made your uncle ill. Half the staff are leaving, school numbers are badly down, *I've* been off the map again and if that wasn't enough, Emma nearly died six weeks ago."

"I knew nothing of this," I muttered sheepishly.

"Of course you didn't. What earthly good would it have done to have burdened you with every disaster that came our way? It's only because of you that your uncle refused to sell the school. If I'd had my way, we would have got out long ago."

I said "I apologise for reacting in the thoughtless way I did. There must be something we can do. Give me twenty-four hours to come up with a plan."

Because of her overbearing manner, Aunt Olive had upset two members of the teaching staff. Both had handed in their notice, with others threatening to follow suit. Spending time finding fault rather than attempting to improve relations with her fretful colleagues, she had become a source of aggravation. Worse still, a mutiny in the kitchen endangered the provision of meals and basic services.

News of my uncle's ailing health and the low state of staff morale had leaked out to the paying public. In anticipation of the likely closure of the school, pupils were being withdrawn and registrations cancelled. Numbers for the following term were down to fifty-six, way below what was needed to cover the running costs. The situation could not have been more serious.

To fulfil my mission, it was vital for me to carry out discreet enquiries without delay. Speaking individually to all the school's employees, I was heartened to discover that most were as committed as they had ever been. Job security and Aunt Olive's weird behaviour were the most serious stumbling blocks. I was convinced a vigorous strategy with well thought-out solutions would receive unqualified support. With the welfare of the Elliott family the essence of my concerns, I drew up a suggested action plan.

Inside an envelope marked "Private & Confidential" I placed a letter to my uncle. Delivering it to him at the hospital, I had no idea how he was going to react. It was a now-or-never opportunity to avert disaster.

Dear Uncle Don

Knowing that family health issues are of prime importance, you may consider it inappropriate for me to choose this time to list my ideas for the school's development. All I can hope is that you will read what I have written and treat the contents with an open mind.

1. You need a competent deputy, someone you can trust. The drawback is that you will have to pay a realistic salary to attract the ideal person. Might it be worth contacting Mr Hewitt to see if he is interested? As a stop gap why not choose Miss Roberts? What matters most is for you to have time to make a full recovery and be freed from stress.

2. Constant worries have made Aunt Olive ill. She badly needs a rest. A term off staying with her sister would do her the world of good. She says she wants to get away.

3. I have spoken to Miss O'Sullivan, who would be willing to take charge of all the domestic arrangements until Aunt Olive is strong enough to pick up the reins again. You could not find a safer pair of hands.

4. I am concerned about Emma. She lacks contact with children of her age and now she is six ought to be attending school. Have you considered opening a junior section for boys aged 5-7? It would not matter having one girl in the group. Emma could well blossom, given this opportunity.

5. I understand Elsie Chapman used to be a secretary and has retained her typing skills. With Emma at school, she would have time at her disposal to assist with the paperwork. Nothing would please her more than to be able to help you in this way.

6. It makes sense not to replace Mr Jones or Miss Simmons until numbers pick up. There are other ways, too, of cutting costs. As the saying goes, "If you look after the pennies, the pounds will look after themselves!"

7. I have a number of ideas on the subject of publicity. I know you do not believe in advertising, but there are subtle ways in which to promote the school. It is vital to get a positive message through to parents about the future of Oxton House. Many are convinced it will close. We must dispel this myth.

When you are well enough, I can elaborate on my views.

All at Oxton House are lost without their leader at the helm. We pray for your recovery.

Your devoted nephew
Paul

Concerned lest my actions had upset my uncle, I visited him at the hospital a second time that day. Before giving him the chance to tear my arguments to shreds, I began with an apology, "It was stupid of me to bombard you with ideas whilst you are ill," I said, "Forget what I wrote. I have something better to suggest."

"And pray what might that be?" he asked, a trace of irritation in his voice.

"I don't want to remain at university, knowing the mess you're in. I would prefer to come back home to help you out."

"To leave Cambridge would be an act of madness. I thought you had more sense. Don't you realise you would have to do your national service? How could that be of help to us in Harrogate?"

"You sound angry, Uncle Don. All I'm trying to do is to support you in your hour of need."

"I could never be angry with you, Paul. I'm just grateful for the trouble you've taken to address the concerns we have."

"Does that mean you approve of some of my suggestions?"

"How could I not? All have merit and in a day or two I hope to be well enough to discuss them with you fully."

— Eleven —

A S SOON AS he was back from hospital in the familiar surroundings of home, Uncle Don was much more like his old self. What bothered me was that he had developed the strange habit of tapping his fingers nervously on any object he could find.

"Not to be able to smoke is driving me up the wall," he complained. "I'm determined to stick to my promise, but it's going to be a bloody nightmare. When I tried giving it up before, it made me impossible to live with. Your aunt can vouch for that. And by the way, I've spoken to her about a change of scene."

"How did she react?" I asked.

"Positively, I'm pleased to say. She wants to stay with Aunt Maude in Felixstowe. As you know, Maude lost her husband a year ago and because she and Olive get on so well, it will be a tonic for them both to be together for a while."

"How are you going to manage without her?"

"I shall be alright. Thanks to your painstaking research, it appears that her duties can be covered. Miss O'Sullivan always did like a challenge. We are lucky to have such loyal retainers. What matters is for Olive to stay away long enough to recover completely and be able to look upon life more optimistically."

When I raised the subject of my recommendations, he was more circumspect.

"I'd rather not discuss them today, old chap," he said. "I've got dozens of things to deal with, what with the post and countless messages. Let's leave it until Monday, by which time I hope to be a lot fresher."

"Don't go like a bull at a gate, Uncle Don, or you'll crock yourself up again. I'm willing to be your personal dogsbody for as long as it takes. *I* can help you with the post.

Monday's mail brought with it a letter that contained distressing news. As he read the contents, my uncle's face turned deathly pale and his hands began to shake. "This is the final straw," he murmured plaintively. "The school will *have* to close."

"What on earth has happened?" I asked.

"Brigadier Dunn is removing his two sons at the end of term. He's the most influential parent we've had in years. The result will be a vast exodus of pupils with nobody left to teach."

"I can't believe other parents would follow him like sheep."

"You don't know the brigadier. He's a man with strong opinions. I thought he was a friend. It's unlike him not to have the guts to come and tell me face to face."

After this fresh disaster, it was an uphill struggle to dissuade Uncle Don from throwing in the towel. Reminding him of the sacrifices made by my father in the past, I urged him at the least to give consideration to my suggestions.

"You would never forgive yourself were you to allow a temporary setback to destroy everything you've ever worked for," I exhorted.

"I suppose no harm can come by giving it one last try," he said wearily. "But don't forget that to sell up whilst there are still some assets is preferable to going bust. I'm prepared to let you experiment with your ideas because I believe you have a gift. If you don't succeed, we lack the resources to carry on beyond next term."

The first priority was the appointment of my uncle's deputy. It was decided to offer the successful applicant a salary of six hundred pounds per annum. The assistant teachers were paid the niggardly sum of only one hundred pounds a term, with no increments, which is why few could be encouraged to remain at Oxton House for long.

"I cannot agree with your thoughts on Mr Hewitt," reflected my uncle. "Good though he was in the classroom, he was sometimes disruptive as a colleague and could be very moody. He wouldn't make a leader. I suggest we telephone Philip Betts at Gabbitas and Thring to see who they have on their books. The best of the bunch are bound to have been snapped up already, so don't set your hopes too high."

The first person to present himself for interview was Rodney Berrington, a fair-haired man in his mid-thirties. Walking with a limp, his distorted face gave the impression he had been injured in an accident. The fact one eye would not close gave him a shifty look, a disfigurement that would not have endeared him to the parents.

Despite his somewhat menacing appearance, glowing references made him a strong contender for the post. Speaking up well when questioned, he seemed to know his stuff. Uncle Don was all for offering him the job.

"I have a nagging doubt," I said. "Didn't you think he has a funny smell? It's as if his clothes are musty and unclean. I'm sure something's not quite right. How much do we really know about him?"

A telephone call to a school in Kent provided us with the answers. Not only was Mr Berrington an alcoholic, in less coherent moments he had behaved violently towards his pupils. A more unsuitable applicant would have been hard to find.

As my uncle had predicted, the best candidates had long since been appointed. The ones still searching were from a motley list of rejects: at best they were inept; at worst they came from the ranks of sexual deviants, with the potential to bring shame on the schools at which they taught.

Attempting to steer clear of schoolmasters with a seedy past, two more gentlemen were called for interview. The first was cultured and refined, with a respectable degree from Bristol University. His failing was that he lacked the ability to keep the boys in order.

"Nice though he is," said Uncle Don, "he could never command respect, let alone run things in my absence."

Next there was an overweight man of fifty, who suffered from an inflated opinion of his value to society. A loud voice resounded pompously as he reeled off the attributes he thought were required of the ideal deputy headmaster.

"What posts of this kind have you held in the recent past?" we probed him carefully.

"I've managed a shop, a zoo and, believe it or not, I've nursed in a mental institution."

"But have you ever taught?" we asked.

"Not yet," he said. "I imagine it's a piece of cake. All I have to do is model myself on the best practices from my days at school. At Blundells old Monty Paxman made us do twenty press-ups every time we got an answer wrong. I can't think of a more effective way of encouraging high standards!"

Aware of our predicament, Gabbitas and Thring recommended a divorcé by the name of Duncan Knott. With a track record of success at a large grammar school in his native Australia, he had come to England to recover from a broken marriage. So highly thought of was he that his position of assistant head was to be kept open until he felt ready to resume his duties.

On meeting Mr Knott, we found him personable and impressive. Unlike the other candidates, he possessed all the attributes we needed. If only he could be persuaded to become my uncle's right-hand man, there was every chance he would help to restore stability within the school. The crucial question was whether he would be satisfied with the salary on offer.

"Money is the least of my concerns," he said. "I want a challenge, to be able to help to make things work. I like the emphasis you place on family values here. I'm sure I would fit in."

Engaging the services of this experienced Aussie teacher was a red-letter day in the life of Oxton House. After months of negativity, the sun had at last begun to shine.

In preparation for the new school year, it was essential to increase the numbers. Recruitment of five and six-year-olds would be a start in the right direction.

A barn next to the gymnasium provided the space for a conversion. Assuring my uncle that Mike Jennings and I were capable of carrying out the work, he gave the go-ahead for the ordering of materials.

A builder in his younger days, Mike knew exactly what to do. Following his directions, I soon became proficient with a paintbrush and a drill. Working at weekends and late into the night, in less than a month the project was completed.

"All we need is some tables and chairs," I informed my uncle.

"What's the point if there aren't any pupils?" he responded cynically.

I urged him to relax and leave it to me to make things happen. Telephoning the editor of the *Harrogate Advertiser*, I told him I had an important story to relate. On the dot of nine next day, I sat facing him in his office.

With careful manipulation of the truth, I knew the school could be portrayed as a thriving institution. The brazen confidence I was forced to display was as unreal as was the upbeat version of events to be presented. In modern parlance, marketing is the word. In those more basic times, I had to use gut instinct. Impressed with our expansion plans, the editor agreed to include an article featuring the school in the next edition.

The newspaper boy was late with the delivery that Friday morning. Thumbing through the pages of the *Advertiser*, I could not find the article. The editor had clearly failed to keep his word. Then, much to my surprise, I spotted on the centre page a photograph of the Oxton House building, a picture that made Aunt Olive's rose garden look like an oasis of tranquillity. Next to the photograph was an article entitled: "Demand for places strong at Private School."

This is what appeared:

The town of Harrogate has many family-run concerns. Oxton House preparatory school in Berwick Drive is one such enterprise. Purchasing the school in 1931, the owners, Donald and Olive Elliott, have for twenty-five years successfully prepared boys for the leading public schools. Surviving the difficult war years, the school has continued to go from strength to strength. Established by the Rev. J. Scott in 1883, a spokesman for the school informed us that events are being planned to mark the seventy-fifth anniversary in two years' time.

A huge demand for places has necessitated the provision of a new extension. From September, places are to be offered for boys aged five and six, whereas in previous years the starting age was seven. Applications for entry to the new junior department will be treated on a first-come-first-served basis.

The school is pleased to announce the appointment next term of Mr Duncan Knott as deputy headmaster. For the last eight years Mr Knott has been assistant head at Pultney Grammar School in Adelaide, Australia. A graduate of Sydney, he says he looks forward to taking up the post and joining a well-respected team of teachers.

It had never occurred to me that Uncle Don would be angered by the article in the paper. What I had forgotten was how sensitive he was about publicity. His thunderous expression warned me I was in for a telling-off.

"If you *must* inform the general public of the school's achievements, it doesn't have to be a pack of lies. To blow our own trumpet in this manner makes us sound more like a Butlin's holiday camp than the respectable school we've always tried to be."

"It may be gilding the lily a bit," I said defensively, "but if you read each sentence, it's all quite credible; a little exaggeration perhaps. All I'm trying to do is to change in people's minds their perception of what we are and what we have to offer."

"It will always be my view that discerning parents are not taken in by commercial gimmicks. I shall eat my hat if we gain a single entry," griped my disillusioned uncle.

To supplement the newspaper coverage, at my own expense I inserted a small advertisement for the next few weeks announcing the opening of the junior department. I was determined not to ask Uncle Don to help me out financially. Able to live at home for next to nothing, it was fortuitous I was too tired each night to want to seek the bright lights of pleasure and adventure.

Willing a miracle to happen, never in my wildest dreams had I expected so many enquiries to result from the promotion. Requests for prospectuses came flooding in. Summer holiday appointments were usually unheard of. This year a record-breaking number of parents wanted to pay a visit to the school. By the end of August, eleven boys had been recruited for the new department and there were three more registrations for the upper age groups.

"Forgive an old stick-in-the-mud for being suspicious of your tactics," apologized my uncle. "Olive will be overjoyed to hear the latest news."

Throughout July and August I spent as much time as possible with my goddaughter. Unsettled by her recent illness, little Emma had become disorientated and lethargic. Elsie Chapman agreed it was desirable for her to make a start at school. By mixing with other children, it was felt she would gain confidence and improve her social skills. To help prepare Emma for the new experience, I showed her how to count to ten, pointing out the numbers as we went. Using the phonetic method, the recognition of the sounds of letters was, as yet, too advanced for her to master. Slow reactions made it difficult for her to concentrate, but when she did succeed her eyes shone brightly and she gleamed the sweetest smile imaginable. I loved her for her trusting nature, her modest innocence; above all, I wanted her to lead a normal childhood like others of her age. Having had the opportunity to give Emma modest preparation for the next hurdle in her life, I prayed for her protection during the periods of my absence.

Much as I wanted to remain in Harrogate a little longer, I needed to go to Exeter, a month later than planned, to earn some money before the start of the Cambridge term.

— Twelve —

THE OPPORTUNITY FOR me to earn money in Exeter had come about as a direct result of my friendship with Stuart Pennington. Living in a large manor house seven miles from the city, the Penningtons were well known and respected throughout Devon. Stuart's father, Adrian, reputed to have inherited a fortune from an industrialist uncle, was chairman of the county council, as well as being on the board of several companies. If strings needed to be pulled, he knew who to contact in order to make things happen.

Working as a barman at the Royal Clarence Hotel had the advantage of providing me with food and accommodation, which meant outgoings were negligible. With only one month left in which to generate savings before returning to university, I wanted to supplement my earnings through some additional activity. Free time during mornings and afternoons provided spaces that could be filled with further paid employment, but I had no idea how this could be achieved.

Soon after my arrival in Exeter, I was introduced to Adrian Pennington by his son. A grey-haired gentleman of unclear age, he was wearing an impeccably cut pinstripe suit. I noticed, in particular, the brilliant shine on his shoes and piercing blue eyes that were sizing me up shrewdly behind pince-nez spectacles.

"I've heard a lot about you, Elliott," he declared. "Stuart tells me you've had a rough time back home and are eager to make some extra cash."

"That just about sums the position up, sir," I replied.

"I happen to know that Sir John Hutchins, a business colleague of mine, has a son he's hoping to get into Sherborne," he said. "He's taken him away from a boarding prep. school in Tavistock where he was making no progress. How would you like to tutor the boy for the next four weeks? He is due to start at a crammer's in October;

some intensive work meanwhile could prove invaluable. Sir John's a wealthy man who can afford to pay you handsomely."

Visiting the boy's home twice daily, I tested him in the basic subjects to see where his weaknesses lay. Discovering he was lazy rather than stupid, I concentrated on stimulating his interest, with astonishing results. So delighted was Sir John with his son's progress that when I submitted my bill, he doubled the amount I was due to receive.

"You have the makings of a fine schoolmaster," eulogized Sir John. "If you continue in the sphere of education, I can see you running your own show one day."

This stroke of good fortune confirmed the notion that success in life can be greatly enhanced through making the right contacts. Thanks to Mr Pennington's introduction, I was able to look forward to the forthcoming term in the knowledge that I would not have to call upon my undergraduate friends to bail me out financially.

For the remainder of my time at Cambridge, I became adept at securing lucrative work during vacations. I wanted to be self-sufficient, able to prove to Uncle Don that I had the ability and character to stand on my own feet. He had enough money problems of his own without taking on other burdens.

Stopping off in Harrogate to collect essential items before returning to college, I was amazed at the air of vitality and purpose in evidence within the school. Tensions from the recent past had vanished; staff and boys were going about their activities with such energy and keenness that it was as if the place had been uplifted by a massive transformation.

Uncle Don was delighted with my observations. "I'm glad you've noticed the more positive atmosphere," he said. "I can't take any of the credit. It's all down to Duncan Knott. Not only a brilliant organiser, he is skilful in dealing with the staff and is a highly competent teacher. To have a deputy of his calibre is making my work a pleasure. Were I to put Duncan in charge, I could go away for a month and nobody would notice."

It was a great relief to witness Uncle Don's renewed optimism. Having made a startling recovery from his heart attack, the perkiness with which he used always to be associated was visible again. Little Emma was feeling grown-up now she was mixing and working with other children. Despite the risks involved, she was noticeably benefiting from the experience. Duncan Knott, who took a keen interest in her welfare, was doing his best to help build up her fragile confidence.

News from Felixstowe was also encouraging. Aunt Olive's despondency was beginning to recede for the first time in months. She talked about the future and in one letter stated she hoped to be well enough to be home in time for Christmas. I wrote saying I would visit her one weekend when back in Cambridge.

Having been preoccupied for years over matters I could not control, Duncan Knott's appointment had come as a heaven-sent miracle, indicating the rebirth of a period of stability at Oxton House. In July I had been convinced the school would have to close. A different picture was emerging. Now I could visualise a flourishing establishment, its success based on the sound foundations promoted by my dedicated uncle.

With the home front more on an even keel, I could think about my career and the commitments I'd eventually have to face. The respite from family health concerns was only temporary. It would have been delusional to pretend the problems would go away. Little imagination was required to see that illness lurked, hiding in dark corners, and would strike again when least expected.

Mr Knott's arrival on the scene heralded a period of hope. His stay in Harrogate was unlikely to be permanent in view of his plan to return to his post in Australia. Whether his departure in due course would lead to disastrous consequences for the Elliotts was a question I was in no position to answer.

Aware of the responsibilities that lay ahead, I came to a decision, one that was not in keeping with my cautious nature. Before long I knew I would be devoting all my energy and abilities, such as they were, to the family school. Apart from my determination to gain a respectable degree, the last two years at Cambridge offered me a one-and-only chance to let off steam in an atmosphere far removed from the serious world of adulthood. For the first time ever I had the freedom to kick over the traces and was hell-bent on enjoying myself.

Most men if they speak the truth will admit that transition from the innocence of teenage years to the maturity of manhood is a painful process. Women, on the other hand, have tended to find the adjustment less traumatic. Had I been plunged into the workplace at the age of fifteen, many of the rough edges that highlighted my naivety might well have been eradicated sooner.

The fact was I knew nothing about girls or how to handle them. Garbled explanations of the birds and the bees from fellow students mystified rather than enlightened me. My housemaster at Sedbergh had given inexpert advice on the subject, whilst Uncle Don had once begun his own appraisal that did not progress beyond a jumbled sentence,

Girls intrigued me. A mere glimpse of some of these fascinating creatures was enough to cause an urgent throbbing in my groin. To me girls were as dangerous as the most ferocious animals on earth.

— Thirteen —

BUT BACK AT Cambridge, much as I hankered after female company, I was far too diffident when it came to taking the initiative. Impressed that Aubrey Duncan-Jones had overcome his inhibitions and was going steady with a gorgeous mathematician, I felt the time had come for me to follow his example. After unsuccessful attempts to impress any of the girls I met, I tried to discover what was wrong with my approach. It took forthright Lisa, a buxom bank clerk with no university connections, to volunteer an answer.

"You're a likeable bloke," she said, "but because you are too scared to open up, you contribute nothing in a conversation. All you have to do is relax and be yourself. Why not have a couple of drinks before you take someone out?"

Noting her advice, I invited Kate, a fellow historian, to accompany me to a popular film at the cinema. By the time we met at the appointed rendezvous, I had consumed three pints of beer. A modest drinker up until then, I had not expected the change in my personality to be so sudden or dramatic. Ushering the unfortunate Kate to a seat at the back, I began fondling her with such forwardness that a less tolerant companion would have called for my arrest.

Out in the street afterwards, an irate Kate gave me the bollocking I deserved.

"What gives you the right to think you can use my body as a piece of meat, you self-opinionated maniac? Not in a million years could you add me to your list of conquests. If our paths ever cross again, I promise I shall kick you where it hurts."

Preferring to be regarded as a Don Juan than a timorous no-hoper, I adopted the policy of always drinking alcohol prior to socializing with a female. Thinking the loquaciousness I had suddenly acquired made me entertaining and appealing, the reality couldn't have been further from the truth. Sidestepped by every girl I targeted, some said it was a tragedy that a young man with potential was ruining his life through drink.

Looking back I don't honestly think I was in danger of the ultimate self-annihilation. What puzzles me now is the conflicting ambivalence that drove me to distraction at the time. Part of me was rational, conscientious to a fault and utterly predictable; yet on an emotional level I was still a child.

A psychiatrist would have deduced that the insecurity stemmed from the loss of my parents at an early age. I would dispute this argument because my uncle and aunt had always treated me as their own, doing everything possible to ensure my childhood was a normal and happy one.

We all grow up differently. My weak spot happened to be a lack of confidence with women. No amount of expert nurturing would have reduced my suffering from this mortifying hang-up. Stuart Pennington was smart enough to suggest a remedy. "To become emotionally resilient, resistant to the devious inconsistencies of totty, you must first fall in love with someone who will break your heart. Only then will you be cured," he advised.

Taking what Stuart said with a pinch of salt, little did I know that Lorenza Bono, a first-year student, had taken a shine to me. A stunning six-footer with jet-black hair, expressive brown eyes, her slim figure sculptured to perfection, she was endowed with the most exquisitely shaped breasts I'd ever seen. Added to these attributes, she possessed a lively sense of humour that made her the life and soul of any party.

Content to study this delectable goddess from afar, I was paralysed with shock when she stopped me in the street to ask a favour. Speaking with a sultry sweetness, she opened the conversation by asking whether I was attending a play reading that evening in Horace Bletchford's rooms.

"Yes, I am," I said. "Do you want to come along? There's always space for an extra reader."

"I would like that very much," she cooed, breathing her words coquettishly.

It astonished me that Lorenza was even aware of my existence. On the few occasions our paths had crossed, I remembered hiding in a corner, too over-awed by her sexual magnetism to dare risk a face-to-face encounter. Flattered to be of help, the mere thought of winning her approval made my whole being glow with pride and satisfaction.

Lorenza performed well at the play reading, demonstrating exceptional diction and expression. Had she been an actress, she would have lit up an entire theatre, hypnotizing the audience with her vibrant personality. A talented musician, she excelled as a concert pianist and had written the words and music for a comic opera. Her standard of tennis was equal to that of the best women players at the university and if that wasn't enough, she was one of the most gifted scientists in her year. No wonder she made me feel out of my depth, inadequate and unworthy of her friendship!

The following day Horace took me to one side, whispering in my ear that Lorenza was dying to get to know me better.

"You're pulling my leg," I protested, blushing nervously. "Give me one good reason why she would be interested in a social misfit with not a penny to his name."

"Because she happens to find you attractive, that's why. She likes your slim build, thick fair hair and thinks you're very sweet. I made a pass at her myself, but she didn't want to know. Why don't you ask her out, you jammy bugger?"

I arranged to meet Lorenza at the Eagle. Unable to believe the reality of my good fortune, I kept pinching myself to confirm I was wide awake and not experiencing another of those erotic dreams that had begun to excite and trouble me. Braced for the inevitable, I knew I was playing with fire. In next to no time Lorenza would expose my emotional frailty and consign me to the bin.

We sat in the quietest corner of the bar. Smiling eyes scrutinized me with such warmth that I was beginning to think she genuinely liked me. She showed an interest in my past, I told her of the years spent in High Wycombe; and when I explained my parents had been killed in an accident, she had the sensitivity to relate to the hurt in a way that helped to bring us closer.

I told her how Uncle Don and Aunt Olive had adopted me, of the love they had invested in my upbringing, the sacrifices made in order to send me to Sedbergh; and of the debt I owed them. After I touched on the problems of managing the family school, Lorenza said it was absurd for me to consider it my duty to have to take on the burdens of the business when I graduated.

"Of course you are grateful to your uncle," she argued. "That doesn't mean you have to devote your life to paying him back. Your brain is too sharp for you to vegetate in a backwater. You could do so much better than waste your time teaching a bunch of lazy brats in a sleepy Yorkshire town nobody's ever heard of."

"I'm sorry you should see it like that, Lorenza. The development of Oxton House offers me an enormous challenge. Nothing is going to alter the plans I'm making. No matter how difficult the task, I intend to put the school well and truly on the map."

Having made my stubborn point, it was time for me to find out more about Lorenza.

"Your skills are self-evident," I said. "Did you inherit them or have you gained them through years of work and effort?"

"I don't know what you mean by skills. My father's mad about tennis, whereas Mother hates sport of any kind. She prefers cultural pursuits and is a keen musician. It would be hard to find a less compatible couple than my parents, which is why they divorced some years ago."

"That must have come as an awful shock," I said.

"My world turned upside down. Mother, who is English, insisted on bringing me to London and father fought hard to keep me in Milan."

"Do you have any siblings?"

"No, I'm an only. Because it was felt I needed to mix with young ladies of a similar background to my own, I ended up at Roedean, which is as strait-laced as you can get."

"Boarding school doesn't appear to have done you any harm," I observed. "Nothing fazes you and you exude confidence and sophistication and can mix with anyone. These are qualities I envy."

"I find your vulnerability appealing," she whispered softly. "If you'll let me, I think I can be of help."

Too bashful to get her to divulge the nature of her therapy, I hoped in time she would teach me what I had to do to become an enlightened man. By now it was unheard of for me not to rely on Dutch courage every time I met a female. The thought of alcohol hardly crossed my mind, so at ease had I been in Lorenza's company.

At the end of a magical evening, I accompanied her on the reluctant meander back to Newnham. A full moon surrounded by awesome flickering sentinels beamed out its spotlight glare, illuminating the paths on which we trod. The prospect of romance induced palpitations of my heart equal in intensity to the pain of physical hurt. Enlightened undergraduates boasted that making love was commonplace at Cambridge. I don't know how this could be true because the opportunity for men and women to be alone together were limited. Regulations were strict and the law-abiding majority accepted a lack of freedom as the norm. Thanks to Lorenza's ingenuity, she came up with a plan.

"I think I've found somewhere we can be alone," she informed me cheerfully. "A friend living in digs is going to be away at the weekend and she's promised to let me have her keys. Males aren't normally allowed to visit, but as the landlord's absent until Monday, I'll take you Saturday and we can have the place to ourselves."

"It all sounds very Machiavellian," I said, doubting the wisdom of the arrangement. "What if one of the neighbours sees us?"

"Sometimes you have to take a risk. Either you want us to make love or you don't. The decision is yours".

Shocked and surprised by her offer of sex, I stuttered a disconcerted answer. "Of course I want to, but never having done it before I'm frightened you will despise me afterwards".

"Stuff and nonsense," she said roaring with laughter. "Comfort and privacy are vital first time round. After that it doesn't matter where you do it; in a country barn, a wood or in a more public place, where danger adds to the excitement. Like it or not, I'm going to seduce you."

Whist longing for Saturday, I was sickened with apprehension, convinced I would fail to live up to Lorenza's expectations. Creeping furtively into the empty house shortly after dusk, my seductress escorted me to a spacious first-floor bedroom, which much to my surprise was furnished with a double bed.

"I told you comfort matters," she enthused, psyching herself up for the challenge. "I want you to think of a romantic setting and imagine we are there together: Venice, Paris, Honolulu even. Dismiss all thoughts of Cambridge. You lie down on the bed. I'm going to get you to relax. There's no need for us to rush. No one will disturb us."

From a leather shoulder bag she removed a bottle of whisky and two glasses. "One drink is all we need to get you in the mood," she said. "Spirits are known to enhance performance. Too much can dull the sexual instincts. As a scientist I know the exact prescription to work the magic." Having dispensed two good measures, she lit a candle which she placed on the bedside table. "It helps lovemaking to take place in a darkened room," she warned. "Not total blackness though, because to be able to see a little strengthens the sexual urges. Have you ever seen a naked woman, Paul?"

Overcome by a fearfulness that caused me to tremble like a terror-stricken child, I admitted I had yet to enjoy that pleasure. Holding me firmly, she pressed her lips to mine, the voluptuous mouth thirsting for more and more of me as it opened wider. Not wanting the kissing to stop, I was awakened from my trancelike state by a seductive invitation.

"You have permission to feel my body and touch me anywhere you like. Stroke my breasts, my fanny, all the forbidden areas that make a woman desirable to a sexy, eager stud. Do it gently, caress every part of me. Explore, savour and enjoy. Take your time and then I want you to undress me."

Shaken to the core, I began the complex process of unbuttoning her blouse. As I fumbled with the ineptitude of a beginner, she giggled good-heartedly at my nervous reticence. To support me in the anxious moments that ensued, she uttered encouraging noises of approval, high-pitched sounds that signalled her arousal.

"Unhook my bra," she ordered. "Kiss my nipples and watch them harden."

Enraptured by the sight of her perfect nakedness, I gasped for breath, eager to satisfy my petrifying urges.

With the delicate touch of an expert, she massaged my lengthened penis, increasing my desire so savagely that I feared I would ejaculate at once. "The thrill is in the waiting," she cautioned. "If you prolong the pleasure, we can come together."

Clutching my hand, she made me place a finger on what I'd considered her sacred areas. "The key to a woman's pleasure lies with the clitoris," she said. "Here's the spot, stroke it gently and soon I'll be screaming for you to enter."

Penetrating with a final thrust, I blubbered like a baby, having discovered at last the meaning of Utopia.

With Lorenza at my side, there could be no obstacles. Inspired by her devotion, I was capable of conquering phobias, developing unseen talents, emulating the confident man about town I'd always envied. To achieve the impossible was now within my grasp. Instead of giving up before the start, I was inspired to have a go. Poisonous snakes; a fear of heights; the brutish sport of rugby; these and other pet hates I could tolerate, on condition my angelic tutor was there to spur me on.

I was head over heels in love with a passion so powerful that all my cherished values had been superseded by an overwhelming force that was fanatical and intense.

Lorenza had it in her power to make or break me. Without the reciprocation of my feelings, I would lack the will to carry on.

— Fourteen —

MY MIND NO longer on my studies, all I could think of was Lorenza. Instinct told me she was a little in love with me already. Her shrieks of delight on the amazing night she climaxed provided ample evidence of that. I had to compose myself, so as not to put her off by being overeager. Providing I played my cards intelligently, I would have an engagement ring on her finger in time for the summer vacation.

Following our tryst, I had expected to see a great deal of my sweetheart. For two weeks I tried to contact her. Telephone calls to her college met with no success. "She's out. I'll pass on your message and ask her to call you," was the standard answer.

Remaining elusive, she failed to return my calls. Imagining she was playing hard to get, I convinced myself nothing could destroy the strength of our feelings for each other. That scientists were said to work longer hours than some of the other undergraduates provided an explanation for the silence. Impatient but still basking in the certain knowledge that my eagerness would be repaid, I continued to play a waiting game,

I spotted her one afternoon emerging from a café. Scarcely acknowledging me, she began walking briskly in the direction of Newnham. The snub was so obvious I had to confront her to find out how I'd upset her. Catching her up, I placed an arm around her waist, with the intention of giving her a kiss. Etched on her face was the weirdest of expressions. Far from the affectionate response I had expected, she was looking at me with a mixture of pity and disgust. "I thought we were supposed to be friends," I said, whimpering like an abandoned animal.

"Of course we are friends, but remember it's nothing more than that. I've fulfilled my promise. The future is up to you."

"What do you mean by a promise? What promise?"

"You wanted to be taught some adult things and I've done that for you. One day you will meet a lucky girl and will make her very happy. That person isn't me. I'm far too independent to want to commit myself to any one man just yet. *Au revoir*, Paul. Perhaps one evening before the end of term we can have another drink."

Deprived of Lorenza's approval and support, I plummeted into a terrible depression, seeing myself as a failure with no redeeming features to compensate for my sense of worthlessness. When I lost my parents, I had been left shell-shocked, devoid of any sense of purpose, the home base shattered and extinct. Yet the tragedy had not reflected defects on my part. The love I had received from them was a reality that could never be deleted. Lorenza, on the other hand, had judged me as a man and judged me harshly. Removing the love I had assumed was genuine destroyed at once all the emotional energy I possessed.

What saved me from going off my head was the knowledge that, no matter what, I could trust in the loyalty of my friends. Stuart, Horace and Aubrey made up a powerful team and with Millicent providing a woman's point of view, I hoped between them they would help guide me through the crisis.

Horace was the first to muscle in. "What's the state of play with Lorenza?" he enquired facetiously.

"Bloody awful. She's given me the boot."

"That's not what I heard," laughed Horace. "I gather you scored a bullseye and managed to achieve your goal."

"How are you privy to such personal information? What happened is private and nothing to do with you. Your attitude stinks," I shouted angrily.

Too upset to pursue the conversation, I left his rooms in tears, slamming the door behind me.

I found it incomprehensible that Lorenza could have stooped so low as to discuss our personal business with my friends. Assuming she was discreet, I had kept the memories and my secret plans well hidden, preferring not to admit how much I loved her. Horace's flippancy was outrageous. How dare he make knowing references to our liaison!

Stuart was the one person capable of offering fair and rational advice in this emotive situation. Confident of his honesty, I could rely on him to tell me what he knew. When I asked to speak with him, I detected an awkwardness in his manner, not in keeping with his customary openness. Admitting my heart had been broken in the way he expected it would, I explained that, contrary to his view, in no way would my state of desperation ever go away.

"Worse than that," I said, "Horace gave the impression he's in league with Lorenza and is treating the matter as a joke. For Christ's sake, Stuart, what the hell is going on?"

"I'm sorry it's all got out of hand," he said, his face reddening. "I was against the idea all along."

"I haven't a clue what you're talking about. If you're half the friend I thought you were, tell me everything."

"Since last term we've all been worried about you," he confessed. "Your paranoid interest in females has done you no favours. It began as a mild fixation, but when you took to the bottle you changed overnight from a mature, pragmatic guy to a raving lunatic."

"That's a gross distortion of the facts."

"No, it's not. Your character *has* changed. We can't all have been wrong with our opinions. That's why I said your heart needed to be broken to help you escape from your affliction."

"You couldn't be more wrong," I said. "Where does Horace fit into the equation? How has he acquired such intimate details of my life?"

"Believe me, Paul, what Horace and Millicent arranged was done with the best of motives. I didn't support the plan, but I could well understand what they were trying to achieve."

I told him he was talking in riddles and pissing me off.

"This may come as a shock," he said. "Because you were making such a fool of yourself with every woman who came your way, Horace thought once you'd poked a floozie you'd rid yourself of being always on heat and find yourself again."

"As simple as that? I can *never* be myself after what you've done. You could flog me till I bled and that would have been a far better fate than the harm done by your meddling."

"It wasn't meddling, nor was it my invention."

"You're just as much to blame," I said. "I feel betrayed, battered and appalled. How was Millicent involved?"

"She encouraged Lorenza to make a play for you, knowing she was attracted to your looks. It began harmlessly enough. Millicent thought she was doing you a favour."

"A favour, my eye," I said. "If we're talking of an act of friendship, please God protect me from my enemies. What you forget is I *love* Lorenza. What's happened is a barbaric act of treachery. Bugger the lot of you!"

Alcohol was bound to lift my spirits. Convinced there was a bottle of whisky stored in a drawer next to my desk, my sole ambition was to find it and consume the lot. Once I had done so, problems would melt away, resulting in temporary liberation from my ills.

At first I could not trace the crucial alcohol. Flinging books and ornaments about the room, smashing a vase of sentimental value, the bottle was finally located. Grabbing it greedily like a man possessed, I drank and drank until I collapsed in a stupor, an incoherent, whimpering wreck.

Waking up late next morning surrounded by vomit, and with a splitting headache, I was laid so low with self-pity and exhaustion I decided to stay put rather than attempt to stir myself. Ignoring the mess, I got up from the floor and made for the comfort of my bed.

For two days I remained there drowsy and dejected, not caring whether I lived or died. Thoughts oscillating between anger and despair, I was inclined in the blackest of moments to kill myself. Were it not for Uncle Don's faith in me and the hallowed memories of my father, I would have taken the coward's way out.

It hurt me to the core to have been tricked into thinking Lorenza's affections had been spontaneously expressed. Her loss was enough of a catastrophe, but to have been betrayed by my so-called friends was the bitterest of pills to swallow. Feeling as I did, I would never forgive any of them for their conniving actions.

Stuart's attempt to make amends stiffened my resolve to banish him from my life. Visiting me one afternoon, he mumbled an apology. "Believe me, Paul, we thought we were acting in your interests. It never occurred to us you would take it so badly."

"Don't patronise me, you bastard," I stormed. "Next time you decide to take on the role of do-gooder, first boil yourself in oil, then chop off your tongue. Only by doing that could you understand the pain I'm in."

Immersed in a stultifying blackness, for days I lay moribund, unshaven and unwashed, lacking the will and energy to drag myself from the brink. Not until I developed the desire to resume the drinking did I creep out after dark to purchase more alcohol and a bite to eat. Money was running out. To replenish my diminishing resources, I did the unthinkable of applying to work as a barman in a seedy backstreet pub.

Having sunk to my lowest depths, I aggravated the situation further by my negative responses. Not bothering to hand in essays or read any of the recommended books, I absconded from lectures and committed the cardinal sin of failing to attend a seminar with my tutor. To all intents and purposes, I had absolved myself of all my university commitments.

I received a terse note from Dr Denman, demanding to see me at once. He reminded me of the cautionary advice he had prescribed during my first year as an undergraduate. Throughout the admonishment, however, I was impressed by the genuineness of his concern.

"As a young man," he admitted, "I could either seek a wife and settle down to the tedium of domesticity or I could paddle my own canoe and maintain my sanity. My single status suits me admirably and I make no bones about it that I admit to being selfish."

"What would have happened had you fallen in love?" I was brazen enough to ask.

"Not having experienced that particular dilemma, it's a question I cannot answer. But let's consider your predicament from a different angle. In less than a year, probably much sooner, you will have recovered from the trauma. When we elected you a scholar, we recognised your potential. Why waste it? *No* woman is worth the ruination of your prospects."

Unprepared to give consideration to my tutor's point of view, I argued that I didn't care a tinker's curse about my future.

"A very short-sighted attitude," he said. "If that's the case, it would be better for you to leave Cambridge for a while. Until you pull yourself together and begin to face your problems, we can do nothing for you here."

Dr Denman had in effect given me my marching orders. The shock treatment struck home with such force that it went a long way to bringing me to my senses.

Like the prodigal son, my unexpected return to Harrogate was met with much rejoicing. Had there been a fatted calf to rustle up, I have no doubt it would have been provided.

"It's obvious something's sadly wrong," said Uncle Don. "I do not wish to pry, but should you want to talk about it, you know I'm here to help."

Emma's stoic determination to cope light-heartedly with the obstacles she faced played a large part in helping me see my own problems in perspective. I was humbled by her unselfishness and pluck, which emphasized the futility of my self-absorption.

Aunt Olive had been to hell and back. By dint of sheer will power, she had fought her way back and was once more playing an active part at Oxton House. If Emma and Aunt Olive had the strength to defeat their own enormous problems, surely I could do the same.

I dreaded having to relate my sorry tale to Uncle Don, knowing how much the news of my debauched behaviour would upset him. Instead of castigating me in the manner I was expecting, he blamed himself.

"How stupid I've been not to have alerted you in advance of some of the dangers," he lamented. "Women are capable of being so much more artful than we menfolk." He went on to describe how he had fallen in love at Oxford, and having been rebuffed, went to pieces during the critical final year. "I nearly failed to graduate. The wretched girl led me such a merry dance that it was driving me crazy."

"Lorenza is different," I asserted. "Not only is she the most remarkable person I've ever met, I can't get her out of my mind for a single second."

"She may be special, but she's not for you. Two people have to love each other for a relationship to work. Much as it grieves me to have to say it, Paul, the sooner you can cast her from your thoughts the better."

Crestfallen by uncle's plain-spoken words, I was nevertheless surprised he was astute enough to identify the root cause of my hurt. "I think you are more upset by the actions of your friends," he said. "I genuinely believe they were trying to be of help. Their plan backfired and they must be feeling wretched. If you can find it in your heart to forgive them, and put the unsavoury incident behind you, I'm certain it will help you recover your self-esteem."

Uncle Don was the wisest man alive. His reassuring words acted as a tonic, reminding me of his quiet strength and common sense.

Not once had he criticized my stupid antics, though his message was plain enough.

To rehabilitate myself, I needed to focus on my desire to change before tackling the serious problem of the drinking. Failure to succeed would lead to the ultimate disaster. Only by using my new-found qualities would I once again be master of my destiny.

Keeping a low profile for the remainder of my time at Cambridge, I knew that work had to be the top priority. Dispensing with the reckless conduct which had so nearly caused my self-destruction, with hypocritical smugness I spared little sympathy for those who strayed from the paths of righteousness in the way that I had done. All work and no play was making this particular Jack into a dull and bigoted young man.

It wasn't easy to forgive my friends. Because Horace's arrogance continued to annoy, I found it hard to forget the part he had played in the Lorenza ploy. The others were glad of the chance to declare a suspension of hostilities. Delighted by my call for conciliation, Stuart, the most steadfast of them all, was unstinting with his loyalty.

Determined to remain on the straight and narrow, I tried to banish all thoughts of totty from my head. Seeing them as the cause of past mistakes, I decided to avoid them like the plague. I undertook first to graduate before succumbing to temptation again.

During an uneventful final year, I kept my nose to the grindstone, my ambitions focused on gaining a first. Dr Denman advised me the goal was still attainable, warning me that my second-year glitch meant there was much catching up to do. When the results were finally announced, I was devastated to learn I had been awarded an upper second, missing the target by the narrowest of margins.

"It was touch and go," remarked my tutor. "You have the insight of a scholar, yet the intellectual rigour you displayed two years ago was somehow missing."

"Poppycock," commiserated Stuart, who was one of only two Trinity historians to gain a first that year. "By pulling yourself from the mire, you demonstrated exceptional self-control and strength of character. You're brighter than me by far and the reason you weren't marked alpha plus points to prejudice on someone's part. Why don't you challenge the result?" By continuing to extend the hand of friendship, Stuart was trying to be kind. He knew as well as I did it was the shenanigans of the previous year that had scuppered my chance to achieve the ultimate distinction.

My lack of success was bad enough. What worried me most was the thought of uncle's acute disappointment on hearing I had failed to gain a first. Since his illness he had developed the ability to treat most things phlegmatically, making it hard for others to discern what he was thinking. The burden of guilt lay heavily on my shoulders when I apprised him of my news.

— Fifteen —

ON HEARING MY university results, Uncle Don's face was a picture. Unable to contain his pleasure, a toothy grin stretched from ear to ear, his flushed cheeks making him look more like a jovial clown than a schoolmaster. He congratulated me warmly.

"I don't deserve to be congratulated. I'm ashamed of my performance."

"A Cambridge upper second is a splendid achievement," he declared. "Considering how close you were to packing it in, you have reason to be very proud of yourself." No matter how hard I tried, I was unable to disabuse my uncle of his moment of elation.

I had expected to start work at Oxton House almost at once. When Uncle Don told me it was essential for me first to qualify as a teacher, I was angry and resentful.

"I've waited years for the opportunity to assist you," I complained. "You haven't got a Dip. Ed., nor have most of the masters at Sedbergh, so why is it important for me?"

"Two reasons," he said. "First, if you join me now, you will be forced to do eighteen months' national service, which would be a waste of time. And second, I'm certain it will help your career to have the diploma as well as a degree."

And so it was that I spent a year at York University's Institute of Education, learning how to teach. Reading masses of books on a wide range of topics, I concluded that good teachers were born rather than made. Some students showed natural flair; the majority developed passable techniques through diligence and dedication; a small number, it seemed, would never be capable of inspiring the interest and attention of their pupils. I can't say which category I came under. What I do know is that by standing in front of a class of lively teenagers, I found the experience less of an ordeal as each day passed.

Uncle's high opinion of Duncan Knott was well deserved. Keen to observe Duncan's dynamic influence in action, I marvelled at the way he had helped restore stability to our frangible community. Respected by all, he possessed that rare gift of being able to solve problems by some uncanny form of magic. Pupils and staff were putty in his hands on account of his mesmerizing influence. Not once did he need to raise his voice as everyone knew that slipshod standards of any kind were banished from the school.

Nothing was left to chance at events arranged by Duncan. A wet weather schedule was planned for sports days, which provided alternative indoor entertainment for the participants and their parents. All such arrangements were carefully documented so that future organizers would find it easy to follow the directions.

Among Duncan's admirers was the capable Miss Roberts, who would hang on his every word with child-like devotion. What made me aware she was possessive of him was the occasion she flounced out of the building after she'd seen him having an intense discussion with the pretty mother of a boarder. In spite of his popularity with the ladies, Duncan knew exactly where to draw the line, always managing to maintain his professional decorum. Parents were attracted in record numbers to the school, impressed by his charm and personality.

The year living at home enabled me to follow the progress of my goddaughter. Eager to keep up with her peers, Emma had made great strides and was now able to read basic words and sentences. What endeared everyone to her was her cheery and self-denying nature, characteristics which made her a likeable companion. Making light of her disabilities, she recognised the qualities in others, none of whom made fun of her impairment. Despite her struggle to compete, as the only girl pupil she was adored by the boys who looked upon her as their mascot.

Fooled by Emma's courageous character, I had forgotten how frail and vulnerable she was. As she was walking up the stairs one evening, I noticed she was badly out of breath, scarcely able to continue. So shocked was I by this change in her that I alerted Aunt Olive.

"Emma's health has been declining for a long time now," she said. "Twice we've nearly lost her and it's only a matter of time before we face another crisis. The trouble with treating her like

86

a normal child is we are imposing expectations on her that are beyond her limits. I think she'd be far happier in a special school."

"She seems to me to be coping brilliantly," I contended.

"What you forget, Paul, is that I see much more of her than you. When she stumbles, coughs or flounders in some way, I suffer with her. The torment, the frustrations, the unfairness of her lot bring home to me all the more my powerlessness to help. Sometimes I think my heart will break with sadness."

Seeing the pained look on Aunt Olive's face, I realized how deeply she cared for Emma. She was more sensitive than appearances suggested, blaming herself for bringing into the world a fragile living entity whose survival prospects at best were limited. The appointment of Elsie Chapman as the nanny had been an act of self-preservation rather than callous abandonment by a mother. I could well understand what had caused aunt's mental agonies and the breakdown in her health.

Once I had acquired the diploma, I could no longer avoid being called for national service. Let off the hook for four years to complete my education, my days of freedom alas were numbered. Aware how heavily Uncle Don relied on Duncan, I shuddered to think what would happen were his deputy to leave. As Duncan's contract was open-ended, we all knew it was only a matter of time before he returned to his post in Australia.

When it was announced that national service was to be abolished, I was overjoyed at this unexpected stroke of luck. There was nothing now to prevent me from working for my uncle, whose exhausted demeanour confirmed he had more than had enough. I saw it as my role to help relieve him of the stress, whilst devoting all the energy I could summon to the school he loved so much.

I could not believe my ears when Uncle Don again told me he was still not ready to employ me. Did he no longer think me worthy to succeed him? I was sure he was going to offer the flawless Duncan Knott a partnership.

Pessimistic imaginings led me to believe it was the unsavoury Cambridge happenings which had brought about his change of heart. The more I thought about it, the more my imagination ran riot. Working myself up into a panic, I felt mortified to have been passed over in such a shabby fashion. What I wanted to know was why my uncle kept stringing me along?

I decided to have it out with him. Striding into his study, perspiration dripping down my cheeks, I began to unburden my complaint.

"For years I've backed you to the hilt," I said. "At Cambridge I let you down, but as you said yourself, I pulled myself together when it mattered. I thought the plan was for me to take over from you when the time was ripe. Why have you changed your mind?"

Following Uncle's promise to give up smoking, he had mostly managed to desist. On occasions of strain he would light up again and this was one such moment. Using a cigarette as an essential crutch had the immediate effect of lessening his tension.

"Calm down," he advised. "Surely you trust me well enough to know my word's my bond. Of course you are going to succeed me."

"I'm not asking to take your place," I said. "All I want is the chance to gain experience and prove my worth."

"So we think alike," agreed my uncle. "Rather than vegetate here for the next three years, it would be better for you to gain experience somewhere else."

"By remaining here, you can teach me all you know," I reasoned.

"Remember you are not yet twenty-three. To come straight here would be a huge mistake. First you need to widen your horizons in an environment as far away as possible. It's important, too, to be absolutely sure it is still your wish to settle here in Harrogate. Assuming you do not change your mind, nothing will give me greater pleasure than to see you take my place."

Scanning the *Times Educational Supplement* for a suitable post, a vacancy at a school in Eastbourne caught my eye. Travelling to Sussex for interview, I was met at the station by the headmaster, Mr James McNee, who drove me to the school in a rickety shooting brake that strongly smelt of dog. Greying sideburns and an untidy black beard made Mr McNee look fierce and unapproachable. His genial manner was in marked contrast to the dourness conveyed by his appearance. Heartened by his ready wit and affability, I took to him from the start.

Situated two miles from the seaside town of Eastbourne, the school building, an eighteenth-century Palladian mansion, was surrounded by open parkland stretching as far as the eye could see. Alighting from his car, Mr McNee began walking briskly in the direction of a walled garden about which he waxed lyrical with the zeal of a fanatic.

"We grow all our own vegetables here," he said. "Nothing but the best will do for the boys of Taunton Hall. That's always been my maxim. And now I'm going to show you the tennis courts, cricket square and adventure playground. There's a squash court and rifle range beyond the spinney over there."

Displaying the stamina of an athlete, a faithful dachshund yapping at his heels, he marched me round the premises at such speed that I had difficulty in keeping up. Chronologically he must have been more than thirty years my senior. His energy was prodigious. Having invested years of hard work and effort to his mission, he had transformed a deficient school into a haven of excellence, acclaimed throughout the south of England. I could well understand why Taunton Hall was full to overflowing, with vacancies at a premium.

After the exhaustive tour was over, Mr McNee led me into his spacious lounge. On the dot of four, as if good timekeeping was of the essence, synonymous with the metallic chiming of a clock, there was a knock at the door. In came two smartly uniformed maids bearing trays, one of whom carried a silver teapot. The other held a selection of sandwiches and cakes.

"Food is a male weakness," my host declared. "As educators we fail to recognise this at our peril. Believe you me, a badly fed boy is a recalcitrant one. The masters are no better. The boys' high tea is at six o'clock. Staff supper, a three-course meal, is served at half past seven in the refectory annexe."

Before setting about the serious task of eating, he removed his jacket, which revealed a yellow food-stained waistcoat underneath. After demolishing three cakes and most of the sandwiches in Billy Bunter fashion, he began my interview. An unconventional eccentric, Mr McNee was not one to follow accepted guidelines or procedures. Moving about the room like an unruly jack-in-the-box, he conducted our meeting in a state of manic frenzy. Living on his nerves, he was incapable of sitting still.

Bursting with enthusiasm, he expounded his views on education, labouring the point that schoolmasters owed it to the next generation to seek the highest goals. "If we don't, the already crumbling empire will cease to have a place," he warned. "Among our old boys are two members of parliament, an admiral and a bishop, all of whom began their leadership training here at Taunton Hall. And by the way, Elliott, I've decided to offer you the job."

Amazed at the bizarre way in which the deal was being struck, I wondered whether there was something fishy going on. Because it was August, the only people in evidence had been two gardeners and the maids who brought the tea. Preferring to have seen the school in action, I was nonetheless taken with the up-to-date facilities, which created the impression of a progressive, well-run institution. Saying he found references a waste of time, Mr McNee claimed he based staff appointments solely on his judgement.

"Very rarely do I get it wrong," he boasted airily. "Should my intuition let me down, no contract is irrevocable. I pay Burnham rates, which is more than can be said of some of our competitors. You will have a bed sitting room in the lodge, with no deductions for your keep. A half day in the week will compensate for the occasional Sunday duty. What have you decided, Elliott? Do I hear a yes?"

— Sixteen —

THE LETTER OUTLINING my job offer gave cause for a celebration. On top of the basic salary, I was to be paid a responsibility allowance, which perked me up no end. Having already passed my driving test, I decided to buy a car in keeping with my status. Visiting most of the dealers in and around Harrogate, I opted for a bright red second-hand Mini. Two days later, the paperwork complete, I drove the sparkling treasure back to Oxton House, believing the world was my oyster.

Motoring down to Sussex for the beginning-of-term staff meeting, I was excited at the prospect of my new adventure and of earning money for a change. Relieved to discover I was to share the lodge with two of the youngest masters, I was first introduced to Douglas Peers, who told me with pride he had been appointed head of French.

"I served for two years under Smoky Symonds, a man old enough to be my grandfather," he disclosed. "He was a brilliant linguist, but hadn't a clue how to teach. We shall miss his sarcasm in the common room, but not his death-rattle cough."

"I take it he was a smoker," I ventured.

"Got it in one! He smoked more than sixty a day and rumour has it he smoked in class whenever the little villains played him up."

I questioned Douglas about the third person to be sharing the lodge with us.

"A reclusive Welshman, Gavin Jones by name," he said. "He's into poetry and wants to write a book. When he isn't marking essays, he sends daily missives to his mum in Swansea. In view of his uneventful life, I wonder what electrifying things he finds to say."

The advantage of dealing with an indiscreet workmate is that he can invariably be pumped for information. Realising that Douglas was not backward in expressing an opinion, I thought he might enjoy talking about his boss. "What sort of a man *is* Mr McNee?" I asked.

"A mad genius, with an obsession for food," he declared. "With his appetite, God knows how he manages not to put on weight. But I must warn you never to question his policies, because he doesn't take kindly to criticism. Last year he sacked a master for being subversive when all he did was to make a mischievous suggestion."

"Sounds as if I shall have to tread carefully," I said. "Does he have a wife?"

"She died five years ago after a long illness. Since then he has plunged himself even more deeply into his work. His passion for the school and all it stands for is quite unnerving. As you can see from his dishevelled appearance, he needs a good woman to sew on his buttons and take him in hand."

Addressing the staff with exuberance and style, Mr McNee began the meeting with a bullish reference to the food. "Last term's survey afforded every boy the chance to comment on the quality of our meals," he said. "Eighty-one per cent were very satisfied, leaving a small minority who put forward certain ideas of their own. Having consulted matron and the staff, the following changes are to be adopted: rice pudding is to be dropped from the menu in favour of an extra serving of ice cream on Wednesdays. I am pleased also to announce that cook now has the facilities with which to provide toast at breakfast and chips on Fridays, when non-Catholics will be offered sausages as an alternative to fish. The selection of fresh fruit has proved so popular that the scheme will be extended to introduce a wider choice. Does anybody have a view to express on the subject of diet?"

"Yes, indeed, headmaster," volunteered a giant of a man, whose inflated cheeks and jowly chins indicated he was a hearty eater, "I think I speak for the entire staff when we applaud your efforts and those of the catering department for the high standards achieved. The glass of sherry before staff suppers is a particularly welcome innovation."

For two hours, Mr McNee lectured us, leaving no stone unturned in his attempts to ensure the term began without a hitch. Taken up with detail, the topics he covered included boys' allergies, common entrance candidates, potential scholars, requests from matron, parental complaints, pocket money, tuck shop arrangements, visiting lecturers, lost property, an outing to the zoo, the school magazine, plans to produce *The Tempest,* matters relating to sport, the renewal of gymnasium equipment, building projects, fire drills, supervisory duties and the need for staff to know how to act in an emergency, including first aid.

He did not ask for offers when a job needed to be done. His method was to state the task, then name the person he'd selected, I almost fell from my chair when he announced: "You, Elliott, will edit the *Tauntonian* and will stage-manage all drama productions from now on."

As we left the meeting, we were each handed an envelope containing our timetables. Scrutinizing my programme, I was horrified to learn that I had been given very little history; instead I had been assigned to teach a variety of subjects to a class of nine-year-olds. Mr McNee had promised me some senior history and had gone back on his word. Douglas calmed me down by explaining that new masters were always treated in this manner.

"Maccy's philosophy is that you must start at the bottom in order first to prove yourself," he said. "I guarantee it won't be long before he lets you loose with a common entrance set and, if you're honoured, some coaching of the scholars."

Enquiring about syllabuses and schemes of work, I became even more perturbed. "There aren't any," added Douglas simply. "You have to compile your own. Providing you get results, Maccy isn't bothered about the content of your lessons. His view is that too much red tape inhibits good practices in the classroom."

Having committed myself to buying a car on the never-never, there was no question of my walking out, disgruntled though I was. Rather than allow frustration to influence my judgement, I began slowly to appreciate the redeeming features of the post.

Charging high fees, Taunton Hall catered for a wealthy clientele. Coming from upper-class backgrounds, most of the boys were confident and robust, aware of their privileged position in society. One had inherited an earldom; three more were titled. The father of a pupil in my class was a multimillionaire shipping magnate with homes in Athens, London and New York. Apart from their plum-in-the-mouth accents, I was heartened to find the boys were little different in character from the ones I'd encountered in the remoter areas of Yorkshire.

Quickly acclimatizing to the routine, I gained much satisfaction from the teaching. Boys who attempted to disrupt my lessons discovered I would accept from them nothing but their best. Once I had achieved the respect and co-operation of my charges, the daunting responsibilities over which I had agonized so much, became a pleasure.

The night before the half-term break, Maccy called me in to review my progress. "So far so good," he said. "Not only do the boys like you, you appear to know your stuff. I always thought you would make a go of it."

Handing me some past scholarship papers, he delighted me with a further compliment. "Lennox-Browne and Pilkington major are to be candidates for the Eton scholarship in May. I want you to take over their history preparation. I've asked Major Peacock to amend your timetable with this in mind, from next week onwards." Knowing the headmaster was difficult to please, it boosted my morale no end to have been chosen to perform a task of such importance. Puffed up with pride, I wrote a letter to Uncle Don, relating the news of my good fortune.

The lack of female influence was a major drawback at the school. The only lady teacher was the formidable Miss Harvey. With short-cropped hair, she could have been born of either sex. Whenever she wore a shirt and tie, the deception was complete. Scaring the living daylights out of the youngest pre-prep entrants, she was the most feared of all the teachers on the staff.

Most of the masters were bachelors, whose lives they devoted to the school. Housed in a purpose-built block in which they were provided luxury and peace, they were too comfortable to risk the upheaval of a move. Resisting any form of change, these ancient pedagogues strove to maintain old-fashioned standards and traditions.

The presence of three married masters helped link our isolated circle to the outside world. Like a breath of fresh air, acting as ambassadors, they helped bring to Taunton Hall the balance of normality. Major Peacock, the second master, a town councillor in Eastbourne, tried without success to persuade tired colleagues to broaden their activities beyond the horizons of the school.

The male emphasis was moderated by the presence of four assistant matrons, whose job it was to help matron Kelly, a state-registered nurse, administer to the needs of the one hundred boarders.

Treating her hard-pressed juniors like slaves, with never a please or thank you, Miss Kelly had everyone dancing to her tune.

"Turvey," she screamed. "Go to sickbay and take Schofield minor's temperature. Benson, get more syrup of figs and bromide from the store. And Edwards, put out the clean underwear and socks, and don't you dally, either."

Controlling her assistants with the severity of a jailer, matron Kelly had introduced some stringent rules. During their time off, she allowed them to visit Eastbourne on the clear understanding they had to be back no later than nine o'clock. Forbidden from mixing with the masters, they were banished from staff suppers and were made to share the boys' high teas instead.

The one exception was nurse Parker, a grey-haired lady of shapeless build, who was as ugly as a frog. Desperate for a lover, she made not the slightest impression even on the randiest of the males. Taking charge when matron was off duty, she was allowed the doubtful privilege of dining with the staff.

"Why doesn't Maccy let the assistant matrons attend staff suppers?" I asked the genned-up Douglas.

"It wasn't his decision. You have droopy-drawers Kelly to thank for that. Surely you've noticed she does everything she can to make the girls' lives a misery."

"It's a wonder they stay," I remarked.

"They don't. Apart from the poisonous Miss Parker, none of them stick it out for longer than a year."

"I'm only interested because I should like to get to know Miss Benson."

"You mean the delectable Catriona. If you try so much as to speak to her you will be committing a sin of astronomical proportions. Droopy-drawers won't permit the girls to converse with any of the masters. If they do, they are likely to be flung out on their ears."

"Bloody hell," I said, unable to believe the insanity of the situation. "I wouldn't want to get Catriona into trouble, but were I to meet her outside school on one of her evenings off, what harm could come of that?"

"My advice is to forget the whole idea," he cautioned. "You'd be mad to risk the security of your job."

Even though Catriona and I had never spoken, my body froze each time she passed me by. Did I perceive a probing stare, a plaintive glance, a teasing beckoning? Or was it mere wishful thinking on my part that her seductive lips were yearning for a kiss? The vibes were strong enough to entice me beyond the bounds of normal reasoning.

Like it or not, I was falling for Catriona. Having made a fool of myself at Cambridge with Lorenza, I was ashamed to think I was in danger of giving way once more to an intrinsic weakness in my character. It must have been Catriona's unattainability that spurred me on, adding to the impression of her worth. So much did the obsession occupy my thoughts that I knew I would not rest until I came up with a plan.

Deciding not to tell Douglas what I was thinking, I began to keep track of Catriona's movements. On Thursday afternoons she was often to be seen walking past the lodge on her way to catch a bus. This couldn't have been better, as my own half day was also on a Thursday. The first time I watched out for her, she did not leave the school. The following Thursday when the sky was as black as soot and it was bucketing with rain, I saw her running in the direction of the lodge. With no witnesses to view my risky conduct, I went out to meet her in order to perform the gentlemanly act of offering her a lift.

"We'd better be careful," she said. "I'll get it in the neck if we're seen here talking."

"Surely it's not a crime to help a damsel in distress, especially when it's raining. Where do you want to go?"

"Can you drop me off in Eastbourne?"

Sitting beside me in the car, moist from the rain, her face as smooth as silk, she had no need of make-up. Alluring blue eyes stared out like sapphires conveying an enigmatic brand of brightness I found intriguing. Wearing a gabardine raincoat that matched her flaxen hair, she looked more sophisticated than the girl in overalls I'd seen at breakfast that same morning. Little did she know how much I admired her graceful movements, the texture of her skin or that I lay awake at night imagining the thrill of making love when I could apply some of the things I'd learnt from Lorenza's rigorous instruction. Conscious that the opportunity might not arise again, I had to take swift action. When I suggested we had tea in a sea-front café, Catriona was elated.

"For two months I've seen you eye me up and down," she said. "I thought you were too shy to make a move. That's why I changed my half day to a Thursday."

A girl of mystery was Catriona, much more brazenly persuasive than I thought. It always turned me on to meet a self-assertive female. The moment of truth was fast approaching. Once I had crossed the line that directed my emotions, there would be no turning back.

— Seventeen —

SPEAKING FRANKLY ABOUT her past, Catriona explained how she had attended ballet school from the age of eleven, but that weak ankles had prevented her from becoming a professional dancer.

"I can't pretend I'm not bitter when I think of the countless hours I wasted slogging away with nothing to show for it," she said. "Two years ago I was toned and muscular with the body of an athlete. Now look at me! Since giving up dancing, I've put on more than a stone in weight."

Preferring women to be cuddly and voluptuous, I was not at all sure I would have found her so appealing had she been as skinny as a rake. "I like you exactly as you are," I grinned, eyeing her with approval.

She went on to tell me that after ballet school she had taken a secretarial course in order to qualify her for a job. "Before settling for a sedentary existence in an office, I first wanted to consider a career in nursing, which is why I came to Taunton Hall."

Giving a graphic description of the coercive tactics adopted by matron Kelly, Catriona confessed she had reached the end of her tether and would be handing in her notice after Christmas. Expressing my anger that the assistant matrons and masters were not allowed to mix, she gave me the official explanation. "Soon after the war, one of the girls is said to have caught syphilis from the master in charge of games," she revealed. "As a result, Kelly introduced the ludicrous policy of forbidding her assistants from associating with any of the males. Poor Maccy hasn't the spunk to override the decision as he's scared stiff of her."

For the remainder of the term, Catriona and I met secretly each Thursday. Wearing our winter coats, we escaped to nearby coastal towns, whose desolate emptiness gave us the chance to carry out our covert activities unheeded. Like solitary refugees, we wandered along soulless streets, seeking to preserve our anonymity. In a Hastings cinema we thought we saw a familiar face as we sat close together in the stalls. Nowhere on earth, it seemed, was it safe for us to be together.

When I raised the subject of Christmas, hoping the two of us might meet, Catriona was evasive. "I'm committed to seeing my parents," she said. "Since the divorce, Daddy has been living on his own in Brighton. After marrying her lover, Mother and I lost touch until out of the blue she invited me to stay with them for Christmas. The remainder of the time I *must* be with Daddy. He says I'm the only person who can help cheer him up."

Catriona had never spoken of her mother, which is why I had assumed her father was a widower. Discovering she was the product of a broken home put me on my guard. Lorenza had been badly damaged by the domestic turmoil in her life and I well remember Uncle Don saying that children of divorced parents rarely make good partners. Dr Phillips, an education lecturer in my postgraduate year, cemented this belief by stating categorically: "A natural consequence of divorce is that in nine cases out of ten, the children suffer the equivalent to a nervous breakdown and become psychotic."

The most level-headed girl I'd ever known, Catriona was not psychotic. Lacking confidence in my ability to retain her interest and keep the flame alive during periods we were apart, I convinced myself that every man she met would be trying to seduce her. Telephoning her every day throughout the Christmas holiday, I became insanely jealous when she was not available to speak, wondering who she was with, what she was doing and how I was going to survive the next few weeks without her. I had learnt nothing.

Behaving like an infatuated teenager, I snapped at my uncle and aunt, whose attempts to get me to take part in the festivities were met with indifference on my part. No matter how hard they tried, they were unable to lift my mood to one of optimism. Aware of the inner turmoil that burdened me, Uncle Don had the good sense not to denounce my thoughtless conduct. Instead he involved me with a number of practical tasks to help focus my mind on something other than Catriona. "I can see that coming home has been an anticlimax," he said. "You are bored and need a purpose. Emma has been talking non-stop about you for the last few weeks. She would be tickled pink to have a ride in your car. Why don't you take her on an outing?"

His suggestion highlighted how selfish I had been. To have neglected my goddaughter was indefensible. To make amends, I arranged to take Emma on a guided tour of York. She always blossomed when people made a fuss of her and it humbled me to see the pleasure she gained from being in my company. Back in Harrogate, her eyes sparkling like diamonds, she described to everyone she met the excitements of the day.

Spending time with Emma was richly therapeutic. Fulfilled by taking an active interest in her needs, I found Catriona's magic spell somehow less intrusive. In telephone calls I began to convey the impression I was cooling off and was engrossed in a busy round of parties. The result was immediate. She sent me an illuminating letter.

Brighton
5th January, 1961

Dearest Paul

I suspect you sense I have not been entirely open with you. For a long time I have been trying to end a previous relationship and the reason I did not tell you about it was because I was frightened of losing you. I needed time over Christmas to sort matters out and this has now been done.

You already know that our friendship means everything to me and you said yourself we have the ability to make each other very happy. I promise to make it up to you. My aim next term is to look for a job in Eastbourne so that I can continue to be near you when I leave Taunton Hall at Easter. At least we shall not have to worry about Kelly spying on us after that.

Christmas with mother was a nightmare. I do not like my stepfather, Max, and never have. He is a narrow-minded bully, who went out of his way to antagonize me and make me feel unwelcome. I cannot understand what Mother sees in him.

Days spent with Daddy have been more productive. He had flu rather badly and I was glad to be of help. I think I have been successful in cheering him up a little.

Am longing to see you, darling.

Till next week. All my love,

The letter proved my instinct had been right. Rather than question Catriona about her past, I accepted what she had to say, seeing myself as the winner in the end. What mattered was that she had chosen me above all others, and by so doing had replaced my gloomy thoughts with confidence at last.

The thrill of seeing Catriona again was dampened somewhat by our need to keep the friendship under wraps. If word got out we were involved in a clandestine affair, Maccy would be forced to sack us on the spot. To succeed in the deception, I needed an ally on the staff, someone I could trust.

Most of the masters were too loyal to the regime for me to dare to entrust them with a confidence. Much as I liked Douglas Peers, past experience had shown he was incapable of keeping private information to himself. My choice of Gavin Jones was absolutely right because discretion was an essential feature of his character.

Gavin's quiet assurance led me to think he would lend me his support. Alone in the lodge one evening, he sat huddled beside the fire, marking essays with the care of a professional. Interrupting his endeavours, I proceeded to tell him about my feelings for Catriona, of how I believed they were reciprocated, and of the dangers we were facing.

My career under threat, Gavin was well aware of the seriousness of the situation. Placing an unlit pipe in his mouth, he sucked at it earnestly as if the pointless motion was going to inspire him in some way. For what seemed an age, his eyes shut, he remained deep in thought, with nothing but the ticking of a clock to break the silence.

A short-term commission in the army had endowed Gavin with problem-solving skills. Trained to use his initiative, he had the ability to eradicate irrelevant issues from his mind. As soon as he had conjured up a plan, he told me what he considered I should do. Warning me I would be foolish to be seen driving Catriona in my car or to invite her to the lodge, he thought it safer to confine our meetings to a Thursday. Describing Douglas as the biggest gossip in the school, he said under no circumstances should I risk confiding in him.

I found his advice reassuring, especially as it coincided closely with my own appraisal of the facts. There were worse fates than having to restrict my meetings with Catriona to once a week. By the end of March she would have left Taunton Hall. Then we would be able to meet as often as we wished.

As time went by, it appeared that nobody on the staff was aware of what the two of us were up to. Thankfully there had been no need to use Gavin as an alibi. To show our appreciation for the part he had played in keeping up the pretence, two weeks before the end of term we asked him to dine with us in a country pub we occasionally frequented.

Far from being a feeble mummy's boy, Gavin was a fine specimen of manhood, tall and athletic looking, with rugged features. A dark horse, he had kept it quiet that he was engaged to a girl back home in Swansea and was planning to marry as soon as he had saved enough for a deposit on a house.

I yearned for physical contact with Catriona. A hurried embrace in the car or in a darkened corner was not how either of us wanted the friendship to develop.

"You know I'm committed to you," she said. "Please don't spoil what we've got by rushing things before I'm ready."

Understandably she had in mind a more romantic setting in which to indulge her sexual instincts. In contrast with Lorenza, Catriona's unattainability offered a prize worth waiting for, one that I knew would belong exclusively to me. To earn that valuable reward, my self-control and patience were essential.

After weeks of searching for a job, Catriona had become despondent. Not wanting to spend a large proportion of her wages on basic living costs, she had applied for posts in Eastbourne that provided food and lodging as a perk. On our final Thursday get-together of the term, she arrived brandishing an official-looking letter, unable to contain her glee. She had been offered the position of secretary to the manager of the Grand Hotel, with double the salary she was getting at the school.

"I can't believe it!" she exclaimed, clapping her hands with delight.

"This is fantastic news. When do you start?"

"Two weeks after Easter."

"Why don't you spend part of the holiday in Harrogate and meet my family?" I suggested. "We might even snatch a few days on our own."

Much as the idea seemed to appeal to Catriona, she said taking such a step would impose on her an obligation that would put her under pressure. Embedded in her brain was a reticence I simply could not shift. Each time I attempted to move the relationship forward, she cautioned me to wait rather than let impulsiveness take over.

I was beginning to wonder how long I could endure the pain of holding back before lustful urges reached bursting point, unloosening an animal aggression that would ruin everything.

I pined for Catriona throughout the Easter break, willing for spontaneous action on her part. Concerned at my state of mind, Uncle Don worked hard to lift my spirits by proffering advice.

"Has it not occurred to you she's playing hard to get? The fact she's left the school will put the friendship on a much more normal footing."

At the start of the summer term, I divided my life into two compartments: time for work and time for Catriona. Free of her distracting influence at school, I was able to pay more attention to the teaching. On our evenings off, at last we could experience the luxury of being seen in public without fear of repercussions.

The scene was now set for a mutually agreeable arrangement. In actual fact, it turned out not at all as I expected. Imagining Catriona's hotel room was the perfect spot to commence our amorous adventures, my optimism was dented by a shock.

"We aren't allowed to have visitors in our rooms," she stated flippantly.

Something in her manner indicated she had been pleased to make that statement. For months she had kept me at arm's length, unwilling to agree to anything more sensual than a kiss.

Yet despite keeping me at a distance, she never used harsh language, confiding in me sweetly that she respected my ability to exercise control. Showing consideration, equability of temperament, a generous heart and supreme good humour, to me she was a woman of perfection. Even her coy aloofness could be regarded as a strength. On the occasions we were together, she was admired by every passer-by. To be seen as her companion made me the proudest man alive.

Every gesture she made led me to believe she felt affectionate towards me, but for a male with normal inclinations, I craved for a great deal more than that. Resorting to masturbation, I tried to imagine what it would be like to awaken her by my touch and transport her to unrivalled realms of ecstasy. This was wishful thinking seeing that virginity was a treasure she was determined not to lose. In my love-sick condition, I was in no position to question her intentions.

After weeks of patient waiting, I became bad-tempered and morose, concluding the deadlocked situation would not alter. It was obvious that any response to my attempts to arouse her was as unlikely as a visit to the moon. Having kept my despair well hidden, following a taxing day at school, my temper finally erupted.

"Why won't you let me near you?" I exploded. "Is it that I've got smelly breath or do you imagine I'm suffering from some contagious illness? Whenever I try to touch you, up come the barriers and you shy away from me. I put in ninety per cent of the effort and your only response is to freeze me out."

"You're being silly, Paul. You know perfectly well I think the world of you. I've loved you since the day I first set eyes on you. Surely you know that."

"You have a funny way of showing it. I feel shut out, unwanted, superfluous to your needs. I don't think I can carry on like this much longer."

"If it's sex you're after, pure, undiluted sex, I'm not the girl for you. Not yet, at any rate," she said. "Of course, I want us to be lovers, but I've always believed sexual intimacy should be reserved for marriage. I don't want my future husband to be short-changed with tarnished goods."

My depression evaporated in an instant. From Catriona's short speech, I had learnt more than in a hundred conversations. It was proof she loved me and wanted us to marry. That was all that mattered. Her attitude to sex was entirely consistent with the strict code by which she lived her life, staunchly upholding moral values. To prove myself worthy, it was vital for me to employ restraint. If Catholic priests were capable of abstinence, I would have to do the same.

I had always romanticized the idea of marriage. It now dawned on me that such a commitment would involve practical responsibilities on my part. It wasn't fair to expect Catriona to marry a man in no position to keep her in the manner to which she was entitled. Despite not having met me, her mother had made a callous judgement, stating that she expected more than a prep. school teacher for her accomplished daughter. Given the third degree, I could not guarantee my prospects would improve, nor could I raise the money for a place to live.

To remain close to Catriona during the summer holidays, I obtained some private tuition work in Eastbourne. I met her one evening outside the Grand, having arranged to take her out to dinner. She had rightly guessed I had planned to use the occasion to talk about the future. Relaxing in the cosy atmosphere of the restaurant's dimly-lit interior, the wine inflating my confidence, I urged her to give serious consideration to what I had to say.

"I promise this isn't a proposal," I warned her solemnly. "Is there a gesture I can make, some guarantee of my intentions? One day I want us to get married. I've never tried to hide that fact."

"Do you mean an engagement?" She spoke these words tentatively, trying hard to mask her apprehension.

"That would be presumptuous of me. I wouldn't dream of asking you until I can provide you with comfort and security."

"You know I love you," she confided. "We get on like a house on fire, but after my parents' divorce, I can't take any risks. If by Christmas we are still compatible, you have my permission to pop the question and my answer will probably be yes."

In view of Catriona's unforeseen disclosure, I decided to write an urgent letter to my uncle. As a young man hopelessly in love, out of his depth, who else could I turn to?

— Eighteen —

EXPECTING A QUICK reply to my letter, I was troubled by the lack of a response. Three weeks passed and still no answer. Conscientious to a fault, Uncle Don was incapable of resting until his desk was clear of correspondence. It was unheard of for him to ignore a single letter, let alone one with important contents such as mine. Assuming it had gone astray, I telephoned him late one Sunday evening. Distant and restrained, he was not at all his usual bullish self. Before cutting the conversation short, he said he was experiencing problems but he would write to explain.

This was the first time I had been fobbed off by my uncle. Something was wrong at home. It worried me beyond measure to have been silenced in this mystifying fashion. Remaining out of touch, he failed to keep his promise. Driven by a desire to discover the reason for his inertia, I decided to pay a surprise visit to Yorkshire to see for myself exactly what was going on.

As soon as I was back in the Oxton House building, I was struck by a sense of doom that permeated the entire establishment. During school holidays the place had always been quiet. On this occasion it was like visiting a mausoleum. Making for my uncle's study, I encountered Duncan Knott standing in the hallway. He looked embarrassed and subdued, indicating my arrival had taken him aback.

"If you're looking for your uncle, you'll find him at the hospital," he said. My forebodings had been right. Indignant and upset that Aunt Olive had failed to contact me, I urged Duncan to tell me what had happened. The story began to unfold when he explained my uncle had suffered a cerebral haemorrhage and that Aunt Olive was staying with her sister, having been ordered a complete rest by Dr Taylor.

"What brought all this on?" I asked, stunned by the news. "I thought everything was going swimmingly."

"It was until after I'd handed in my notice."

"I don't understand. You'd better start from the beginning."

"What caused the upset was my decision to return to Australia," he said. "Your uncle complained I was leaving him in the lurch, but when he heard I had got engaged to Jean Roberts and that she would be coming to Adelaide with me, he went berserk, accusing me of treachery."

Now I could see why my uncle had been reluctant to respond to my letter. His own pressures were such that my love antics must have seemed inconsequential. I needed to visit the hospital as a matter of urgency.

On my arrival at the ward, the Sister in charge explained that my uncle was partially paralysed. "He is having physiotherapy to help restore his mobility," she said.

"I knew nothing of this," I complained. "Why did nobody send for me?"

"We tried to contact Mrs Elliott but were told she was ill and not well enough to visit."

"All the more reason for me to take her place. It's bloody ridiculous nobody bothered to get in touch with me."

"Mr Elliott expressly said he didn't want to worry you."

"That's absurd. I want to see him NOW."

I had focused my attention exclusively on Catriona, showing scant regard for my responsibilities back home. The feeling of shame increased the moment I saw my uncle. His face contorted by the stroke, a raised eyebrow had given him a detached, uneven look. Worse still was the glumness of his expression. It was as if a veil of gloom enclosed him, its clutches so strong that not even a miracle could break the lethal influence.

He had difficulty in speaking but managed to string together two short sentences. "Glad you've come. This illness is a bugger, not like the other time."

I phrased my questions carefully. Slowly it emerged that a succession of disasters had finally proved too much.

His words hard to decipher, I was only able to catch a fraction of what he said. Emma had been taken ill in July. Aunt Olive then accused Elsie Chapman of negligence and threatened to sack her. Other ugly incidents had taken place involving members of the staff. Injured parties were more forgiving when it emerged that Aunt Olive was experiencing another nervous breakdown, but the harm done had been far-reaching. Feathers had been ruffled, morale damaged, on top of which considerable strain had been inflicted on my uncle.

News of Duncan's resignation was the final blow. Miss Roberts' resolution to leave as well compounded the shock. She was the rock who had helped to keep things going in leaner times, an innovative teacher with superhuman qualities. I had always regarded her as irreplaceable, fearing her departure would be cataclysmic for the school.

It was little wonder Uncle Don gave the impression of not wanting to recover from his illness. His world collapsing around him, there were no optimistic features. I saw it as my duty to help restore his will to live. So valuable was he as a friend and stabilising influence that the possibility of his demise haunted me with persistent eeriness.

I was relieved to discover Duncan and Miss Roberts would not be leaving until the following August. By allowing one year in which important decisions could be made, they had not behaved dishonourably. Counting on their co-operation, I was hopeful we would come up with some answers.

Professing the constancy of her love, Catriona was understanding when I chose to stay in Harrogate for the remainder of the holiday. During telephone conversations, she repeated her desire for us to marry and said she would be prepared to move to Yorkshire if that was what I wanted.

Were I to return to Oxton House, I would inevitably suffer a drop in salary. There was no accommodation for a married couple; it concerned me, too, that Catriona might feel isolated in an environment that would present enormous challenges. Despite these obstacles, it was unthinkable to imagine life without her, irrespective of the practical considerations.

Duncan paid me a surprising compliment, "I'm sure you have the ability to take over the school in a year from now," he said. "I've seen how you operate. You're keen and efficient, a talented teacher, a quick learner. Your uncle has always thought of you as his successor. There can be no better substitute."

The prospect of having to take the helm at such a young age filled me with alarm. How would my older colleagues react? What would the fee-paying parents think? Two years' experience working for Maccy at Taunton Hall was nowhere near enough to prepare me for the task.

I thanked Duncan for his words of encouragement, which had given a boost to my morale. "I wish I could share your confidence," I said. "I can't see myself making any kind of a mark here, not until I'm a great deal older."

"It sometimes takes a disaster to force unpalatable decisions to be made," he said. "You've got the backbone to enable it to work. I know you have."

In what was left of the holiday, there was much for me to do. To succeed in bolstering my uncle's spirits was the prime consideration. Unwilling to trust my good intentions, he remained stubbornly withdrawn, wallowing in self-pity, testing my patience to the full.

"You are wrong to be so hard on Duncan and Miss Roberts," I accused him angrily.

"They stabbed me in the back," he retorted. "I thought I could bank on their loyalty. How wrong I was!"

Surprisingly there was no slur or faltering, nor was there any trace of defect in the words he had uttered faultlessly. I wondered whether the bitter outburst had helped to clear the air, displacing muddled incoherence with more commonsensical normality. I prayed a desperate prayer for this to be the case.

"You once lectured me that forgiveness is central to recovery," I said. "Duncan and Miss Roberts think the world of you and have given years of dedicated service. There is a whole year in which to find replacements. They couldn't have been fairer than that."

From that day on, my uncle showed signs of wanting to get better. A flicker of a smile touched his lips as his disordered mind began to regain its sharpness. Learning how to walk again sapped his energy so much that he cursed crude obscenities whenever he failed to meet the targets of his therapist. No matter how many times he fell, he would rise from the floor, determined to triumph in the end. A fortnight later he was hobbling with a frame. Through doggedness and pluck, he had turned a crucial corner.

Since my Easter visit, there had been a sharp decline in Emma's health. Laid low by two epileptic fits, my goddaughter had become frightened and subdued. On both occasions Elsie Chapman had acted promptly, providing the best care possible. Jealous of her steadfast influence, Aunt Olive had criticized her efforts, saying the fits would never have occurred had she spotted the symptoms sooner. An almighty row ensued, nearly resulting in Elsie's departure, which would have been catastrophic for both Emma and the school.

Despite Emma's pleasure at seeing me, her glazed eyes disclosed a tired resignation that worried me immensely. Elsie tearfully recounted the neurologist's conclusion at a recent consultation. Predicting the attacks would increase in frequency, he said she had little resistance to infection and that we must brace ourselves for the inevitable. I was gutted by the starkness of this statement. To have two members of the family with major health problems was bad enough. With Emma added to the list, it was hard to decide what action I should take.

I was convinced the key to bringing about a change in fortunes lay with Aunt Olive. By reacting aggressively to setbacks, she was highlighting the loss of confidence that had played havoc with her sanity. Those who knew her well remembered the dedicated part she had played in days gone by. She had been the buttress, the dominant personality, whose influence was even greater than my uncle's. Capable in an emergency of doing the impossible and performing three tasks at once, she had set high standards that characterized the ethos of the school. If only she could win back her self-assurance, she had the ability again to perform a vital role.

Not knowing what reception I would get, I drove to her sister's house in Felixstowe. At work in the front garden, looking happy and relaxed, my aunt was following her favourite pastime of tending to the roses. On seeing me, for a split second she appeared defensive and upset. The angry grimace softening, she said she was about to have a cup of tea and invited me to join her.

I began with the positive news of Uncle Don's determination to recover from his illness. "Nobody could try harder," I said. "His efforts are inspirational. The fact he's swearing like a trooper must prove he's on the mend. But one thing's missing, Aunt Olive. We all need you back home. Don, Emma, the staff, the boys, all of us. Particularly Emma, who is now a very sickly child."

She breathed great sighs of anguish. There was a pause of several long minutes before she was calm enough to speak. "I feel so guilty," she sobbed. "I want to go back, but I can't. I know I've failed you all. You are better off without me."

The crying intensified. Never before had I witnessed a human being overwhelmed by depression of this magnitude. I willed for an act of providence that would give me the power and wisdom to provide succour to her fractured reasoning. Realizing she was too distraught to take a positive view, there was a faint hope she would react differently if the burden of having to cope was removed from the agenda.

Christmas was going to be the crucial time. By then Uncle Don would mercifully be fitter and Emma's health might have benefited from an alternative form of treatment. Decisions of my own would also have to be made: my relationship with Catriona, settling back in Yorkshire and relinquishing the post in Eastbourne.

"Why don't you make it your aim to come home in time for Christmas?" I urged Aunt Olive. "That gives you four months in which to recover. You've no idea how much pleasure your return would bring."

"On condition you don't put me under pressure, I'll see what I can do," she said. "I'm not making any promises."

Not in my wildest dreams had I expected her to offer the slightest cause for hope. I drove back to Harrogate with the distinct impression she would achieve the Christmas target.

My uncle had made great strides with his walking. When early in September he was discharged from hospital, his consultant praised his tenacity, saying he wished all stroke patients were prepared to work as hard as he had done.

Duncan and I helped him negotiate the steps at the Oxton House main entrance. The reception committee of Elsie, Miss Roberts and members of the domestic staff gave him a rousing welcome. Emma, who had been preparing for this moment, stumbled forward eagerly, burst into tears and covered him with kisses. To avoid the use of stairs, Uncle Don had asked for a bed to be installed in his study. Rails had been strategically placed by Mike Jennings to ease access to the downstairs cloakroom. Pleased with the arrangements made on his behalf, to show his approval he managed a lopsided grin. "There's nowhere like home," he professed. "It's great to be back."

Duncan and I wanted a letter to be written to the Oxton House parents to put their minds at rest. Concurring with this view, my uncle believed an upbeat stance was what was wanted. A week before the start of term, the letter was sent. In it he confirmed he was on the road to recovery, preferring to regard his disability more as a challenge than a flaw.

"It's business as usual," he wrote. *"It will, however, mean burdening Mr Duncan Knott with extra responsibilities during the next few weeks. The part he plays in what we do here is so valuable that it is impossible to pay tribute adequately to his loyalty and hard work."*

No mention was made that Duncan and Miss Roberts would later be departing for Australia. It was imperative to keep this information private. Were the news to get out before alternative arrangements were in place, the school's future was in jeopardy.

— Nineteen —

EARLY DECEMBER BROUGHT with it some hope. Aunt Olive returned home, assuring everyone her recovery was complete. Uncle Don's walking had improved so much he decided to stop using his study as a bedroom. During the Michaelmas Term Catriona and I were secretly engaged. She had at last agreed to meet my family and was coming to stay for the New Year celebrations when we planned to make an official announcement. These developments led me to think Christmas in Harrogate was going to be quite special this time. All that was needed to complete the feeling of optimism was for Emma to be fit enough to enjoy the festivities.

I had been looking forward to joining the family in giving Emma a taste of festive cheer. She adored colour, sounds of music, dressing up, sparkling tinsel, paper chains, baubles, lights and the fairy on the tree; gift-wrapped parcels with large gold ribbons; the infectious laughter of the adults, and above all she loved to be noticed, appreciated and applauded for the things she was clever enough to be able to achieve. None of our plans came to fruition because Emma was taken ill. Looking peaky at first, a troublesome sniffle developed into a chesty cough, Soon she was wheezing and gasping for breath, a high temperature inducing her to twist and turn restlessly under the sodden sheets. Dr Taylor did not think she had the physical reserves to combat the pneumonia. Strong doses of penicillin were prescribed too late to be of any consequence.

On Christmas Day a whisper of a smile appeared on Emma's parched and blistered lips. She had made it to the age of ten. This, in itself, was an achievement. She might have fought on to face another set of trials and agonies, hundreds of them judged by normal standards. But no! She'd had enough. Now was the time for her to say goodbye. I cried for Emma. I cried for myself. I cried in frustration at the unfairness of it all, I prayed that she might somehow, somewhere meet up with my parents, her aunt and uncle, in a vastly better place than the unequal world she had so stoically inhabited.

Clouds of despair closed in on our tight-knit community, symbolizing the finality of our loss. Death of any human being is always hard, but to lose a child whose potential can never be fulfilled, whose goodness never truly valued, is the cruellest of all happenings. Deciding to opt out, Aunt Olive refused to eat. Hysterical sounds emerged from her room. "I'm the one who deserves to die, not my sweet baby," she repeatedly lamented.

Uncle Don tottered about aimlessly, a broken man, his bloodshot eyes revealing the blackness that engulfed him. He asked me to organise the funeral, saying he lacked the emotional resilience to attend to the arrangements.

In need of someone to assist, I approached Elsie Chapman, whose practical skills never failed to impress in an emergency. With stiff-upper-lip predictability, she was glad to be of use rather than mope around like a useless dummy. "I think we should make the funeral a tribute to Emma's wonderful giving nature," she commended. "Let's concentrate on the positive aspects of her life and thank God for all her attributes. Had she lived on to adulthood, I'm convinced she would have ended up a saint."

What the funeral did was to demonstrate that sympathy and support existed in abundance. Distant relatives, friends from Harrogate, most of the staff and large numbers of the Oxton House parents turned up in their droves at the local church. The vicar spoke stirringly of Emma's qualities, describing her as a generous, unselfish, valiant and loving child. "We must rejoice in her release from suffering," he said, "knowing as we do with certainty that she has been welcomed into God's heavenly kingdom, where she is deservedly at peace."

Giles was the one person to be conspicuous by his absence. When he informed us he was too busy to attend, I was filled with a seething anger, which brought back bitter memories of his repugnant behaviour in the past. Unwilling to let the matter rest, I wrote him a letter. Concentrating on two main issues, I pointed out that for him not to join the family at his sister's funeral was an act of callousness that defied all reasoning.

I concluded by telling him he had caused uncountable heartache by failing to visit his parents and Emma in the summer at a time of crisis.

"Considering the lessons in basic humanity you were taught by your parents in your youth," I wrote, *"your neglect of duty and disregard for the feelings of others is barely credible. Shame is not a sensation you are likely to aspire to. Perhaps one day, if you ever grow up, you will learn to spare a thought for those to whom you are indebted."*

Giles had left home to seek his fortune in London. Working as a stockbroker since doing his national service, he had ceased to take an interest in his Yorkshire family, so enamoured had he become with the glamour and razzmatazz of the metropolis. My letter must have hit a raw nerve. Responding with typical aggression, he telephoned me two days later.

"You pompous twit," he began explicitly. "What makes you think you have the right to give me a lesson in morality?"

"Can't you see we're grieving?" I said. "By not showing up on Wednesday, it hurt your parents more than you will ever know."

"At least they had their blue-eyed boy to take my place," he sneered. "You always were the favourite."

"That's rubbish. You know how much they dote on you. All that was needed was for you to show them a little affection and respect. By absenting yourself, the humiliation could not have been more obvious."

"The reason I stayed away was because I didn't want to steal your thunder," he said contemptuously. "A word of warning. If you ever stick your nose in my business in future, I shall make no excuses for my actions."

Having had the last word, he rang off, convinced he had put me in my place. There was a time when the very sight of Giles had terrified me. I now saw him as a worthless bully, who took advantage of the underdog. Never again would I allow him to attempt to wreck my life, knowing I had the cerebral skill to outwit him with my arguments.

— Twenty —

ON NEW YEARS' Eve I met Catriona at York station. My face glowing with excitement, I rushed over to help with her luggage as she stepped down from the train. Oozing sophistication, she was wearing a striking red coat that fitted her to perfection. I found it hard to believe this tantalizing beauty was the girl I was to marry.

"You look incredible," I said. "I've not seen you in that coat before."

"My mother gave it me for Christmas. She says she can purchase anything from Harrods. It's a pity she can't buy a recipe for love."

On the journey to Harrogate, I avoided the irksome subject of her mother by describing Emma's funeral and my contretemps with Giles. "Your cousin's a rotten bastard," she said. "What we ought to do is lock him in a room with my odious stepfather, then throw away the key."

I had warned Catriona that lack of space meant she would have to sleep in a dormitory on the nights she was to stay. Well aware our school was in a different league from the flourishing Taunton Hall, she was under no illusions. Before introducing her to my uncle, I gave her a further word of warning. "You'll find we're very subdued and still in shock. I'm afraid Friday's dinner is going to be a bit of an anticlimax after all the planning."

As long ago as October, 2nd January was the date chosen to give a number of key people the opportunity to meet Catriona. Cook had planned a special menu and nine places were laid at what in term time was known as the dining hall top table. Uncle Don, wearing his college blazer, was in a light-hearted mood, having first provided the guests with sherry in his study. After applying make-up to her face for the first time in months, Aunt Olive surprised us by abandoning her sickbed. Clad in a sensible purple suit, Aunt Maude kept a proprietorial interest in her sister. Also present were Duncan

Knott, attached to a gooey-eyed Jean Roberts, and Miss O'Sullivan, who had braved a stormy Irish Sea to be at Emma's funeral. Elsie Chapman, the one remaining party member, made herself useful throughout the evening by liaising with the kitchen.

Whilst coffee was being served, instead of announcing cheerfully the news of our engagement, I stood up to give a shortened speech. "Catriona and I thank you for supporting us tonight," I said. "We want you to share the joy of our news, even though the circumstances leading up to this evening could not have been more harrowing. Catriona so much wanted to get to know our darling Emma. Sadly this was not to be."

Overcome with emotion, I then left it to Uncle Don to propose the toast. "To the happy couple," he beamed. "We wish Paul and Catriona a long and rewarding future when they tie the knot."

As I watched the smiling faces, I knew each member of the group genuinely cared about my family and would welcome Catriona warmly to the fold. I was privileged to be a recipient of their love and friendship.

My uncle and aunt were surprised Catriona and I were in such a hurry to get married. Persuading them there was no sinister reason for the rush, I repeated I was the luckiest man alive and that we could not wait to be together.

"We think Catriona's a lovely girl, stylish and attractive," said Uncle Don. "Does it not worry you her parents are divorced? Our fear is she might get bored living in rural Yorkshire."

"You're worrying unduly," I insisted. "Catriona and I are very much in love. I *know* she'll settle here and enjoy being part of a community."

In preparing for the marriage, my biggest handicap was lack of cash. Unlike Gavin Jones, who had been putting most of his earnings aside since leaving university, I had to admit I had been overly extravagant, what with taking Catriona out for meals and the cost of my car. By moving to Oxton House, my salary would be halved. From an income of fourteen pounds a week, I was going to have to find a home, as well as provide an acceptable standard of living for my wife.

Uncle Don came up with a solution to the problem. "I've not told you this before," he said. "When your parents' house was sold and the estate wound up, after the payment of legacies the balance was put into a trust fund naming you as the principal beneficiary. The will stated specifically that any money not used by the trustees for the purposes of your education was to be handed to you when you reached the age of 25 or on your marriage, whichever took place sooner."

"It never occurred to me that my parents left me anything," I said excitedly. "Surely there can't be much left over after all the expenses you've met on my behalf."

"The good news, Paul, is that Olive and I never did draw from the fund. As our adopted son, we wanted you to be treated exactly the same as Giles. In other words, the trust fund remains intact. Including any interest, on your marriage you will receive a cheque for approximately four thousand pounds, which is more than enough for you to buy a house."

I was shocked to learn my uncle and aunt had deprived themselves of financial resources to which they were entitled. One day I would attempt to repay the debt. Meanwhile Catriona was going to be thrilled to learn of this unexpected windfall, which could not have been a better wedding present for us both.

Before I returned to Eastbourne, important decisions were made concerning future staffing arrangements at Oxton House. The plan was to inform all the parents of these changes by letter during the Easter holidays.

His tone reassuring, Uncle Don set out the facts concisely in his message.

Oxton House School
Harrogate
Yorkshire
4th April, 1962

Dear Parent

I take this opportunity to thank you for your forbearance at what has proved to be a particularly challenging time for everyone connected with Oxton House. Last year was an horrendous one. Illness plagued the Elliott family throughout the summer. The sudden death of Emma at Christmas knocked us for six and we are still endeavouring to come to terms with what has happened. As many of you will know, Emma's unselfish and loving nature epitomized so well the emphasis on caring we strive to engender here. During the latter part of 1961, it was Duncan Knott's expert management that kept the ship afloat. He was, of course, ably supported by our dedicated staff. Perhaps I should stay away more often as the academic and sporting results were better than ever: two public school scholarships, a good crop of common entrance passes and an unbeaten cricket XI. I am extremely grateful to those who were responsible for producing achievements of such excellence.

I am sad to report that Duncan Knott will be leaving us at the end of this term, having served the school as my deputy with great distinction for four important years. He will be returning to Adelaide, to take up the position of assistant headmaster at Pultney Grammar School, one of the finest schools in Australia. A schoolmaster of the highest calibre, he will long be remembered for his diplomacy, his organization skills, the quality of his teaching, as well as his ready sense of wit. It was recently announced that Duncan and Jean Roberts are engaged to be married. In voicing our pleasure, the unfortunate consequence is that Jean, too, will be leaving us. Since joining my staff in 1946, she has been like a member of the family. Her patience as a teacher is legendary and her concern for each and every member of our community is quite exceptional. A testimonial fund has been set up for Duncan and Jean. I do hope that parents and friends will wish to contribute generously. Cheques should be made payable to the Oxton House Special Projects Account.

I am delighted to inform you that my nephew, Paul, is to become my deputy in September. After graduating from Cambridge with an upper second in history, he completed his Dip. Ed. at York. More recently he has been teaching at Taunton Hall Preparatory School in Eastbourne, where he has achieved considerable success. He is keen, energetic and full of ideas. I know he can be relied upon to carry out his duties with integrity and diligence.

Another good piece of news is that Paul is to marry a Miss Catriona Benson in August. The couple will live in a cottage to be built alongside the kitchen quarters. Catriona, a qualified secretary, will take over the school's secretarial duties from Elsie Chapman, who is to be in charge of a new kindergarten class we are setting up for four-year-olds in September. My dear wife has thankfully made a full recovery from her illness. She is thrilled to be back in harness and is enjoying every minute of it. To complete our team, a replacement is being sought for Jean Roberts. Interviews commence next week.

This is a time of change, of new beginnings. As Olive and I approach retirement, we want to think Oxton House will remain a family school. With Paul's appointment, continuity is guaranteed. The educational *arena in this country is fast developing. You have my assurance that not a stone will be left unturned in meeting the many challenges we have to face.*

Yours sincerely
Donald Elliott
(Headmaster)

I gave Maccy a term's notice of my intention to leave Taunton Hall at the end of the summer term. He tried hard to persuade me to change my mind, but was generous with his praise once he appreciated the circumstances surrounding my decision. Wishing me luck, he was kind enough to say he thought I had potential as a leader. "After pinching all my ideas, you are bound to succeed," he joked, a mischievous grin brightening his face. "Should Oxton House fail, which I'm sure it won't," he said, "I would be pleased to have you back."

This was praise indeed coming from a man I had long regarded as a maverick in the prep. school world.

— Twenty-One —

CATRIONA'S MOTHER WANTED nothing to do with the wedding, complaining that her daughter was mad to marry a nondescript academic whose family ran a down-at-heel prep school in the backwoods of Yorkshire. "She'll be buried alive and will hate it up there," she said. A guilty conscience pricking him, her father agreed to give Catriona away, but he failed to make even a token contribution towards the cost of the reception. Once again it fell upon my uncle and aunt to take control of the proceedings.

The wedding was held on the 15th August at St Peter's Church in Harrogate. Apart from her father, the only people to be invited by Catriona were some chums from her ballet school days. My Cambridge friend, Stuart Pennington, who performed the duties of best man, arrived in a vintage Bentley, accompanied by his debutante fiancée. A bedraggled and disparate crew, we stood outside the church in pouring rain after the ceremony, waiting for photographs to be taken. Champagne and nibbles back at Oxton House were followed by the usual speeches. The first, containing humorous anecdotes about my past, was delivered by Stuart, whose skill as an orator had greatly improved since his years as an undergraduate.

Counting the minutes throughout the day, I was thrilled to think at last I was going to make love to Catriona. For the first night of the honeymoon, a suite with a four-poster bed had been booked at a hotel near York. It was here in a perfect setting, after months of patient waiting, that I believed I was finally going to have my wicked way.

Ordering supper in our room, the waiter delivered a three-course meal, supplemented by a bottle of wine with the compliments of the management. I begged Catriona to hurry, promising she could eat till she burst during the fortnight's honeymoon in Devon. After a hasty brushing of my teeth, I slipped under the bedclothes, suspense killing me, eager to consummate our union. Taking more than an hour to have a bath, she finally appeared wearing a see-through negligée, at the sight of which my physical needs could not have been more frantic. As she climbed into the bed, the elation I felt was instantly removed by one stark sentence.

"I'm sorry but I can't," she said.

"What do you mean, you can't?"

"I can't make love tonight, I've got my period."

I could so easily have strangled her. What deflated me most was the callous way she made the blunt pronouncement. Trying not to show disappointment, I stroked her breasts and managed to relieve the tension by uttering sounds that amounted to a tacit acceptance of the demeaning let-down. Failing to respond to my caresses, using the vast space provided by the bed, she slithered like an antisocial eel as far away from me as she could get. "I'm sorry," she said again. "I'm tired. I'm not in the mood. When my period's over, I promise it will be better."

Agonised by the abrupt rejection, I blamed myself for failing to prepare Catriona for this moment. From the start of our relationship, I had respected her quiet modesty, her moral backbone, the single-mindedness with which she had kept herself in check. That night was different. Even a man as inexperienced as me knew she had no right to keep me at a distance. She presented a silent defiance that lacked either debate or explanation. I needed to make love to be able to express my passionate adoration of her. The urges were so strong, the intensity so profound that I knew no other person could ever transcend the enchantment of the young woman I had asked to be my wife.

It had been brave of Catriona to agree to marry me, I'd supposed. To lack the support of her mother and receive only half-hearted backing from her father had damaged her self-confidence. I knew this because each time I attempted to raise the painful subject she had difficulty in conquering her tears. So I defended her behaviour. Having read a book on the psychology of sex, I thought it conceivable that hurt had turned to guilt and this was why she was unable to relax. I remember my mother saying that patience was a virtue. Accustomed to having to restrain my lustful urges, I persuaded myself no harm would come by waiting a little longer.

The following day we drove to Devon. We had arranged to stay at an old coaching inn situated in Dartmoor's National Park that was famous for its food. We both enjoyed rambling and this was an ideal centre from which to attempt some of the walks advertised in the hotel brochure. As we marvelled at the silent beauty of the landscape, the bracing moorland wind blowing on our faces, we managed to regain a small part of what had been lost resulting from the bedroom failure. We were spiritually at peace, able to show affection with innocuous gestures like holding hands and our arms around each other. Apart from a drawn-out nightly kiss, I left it to Catriona to tell me when her period had ended.

Following a whole week during which there was no reaction on her part, I asked whether the time had come for us to try again. "I've still got my period," she said, sounding innocent enough.

"I find that rather strange," I answered, a hint of condescension in my voice. "Don't you think you ought to see a doctor?"

"I understand the workings of my body even if you don't. Can't you see I'm scared? How do I know it isn't going to hurt?"

"I accept I'm no expert, but I promise to be as gentle as I can," I said limply.

Her body rigid, she trembled with the fear one might expect had she been confronted by a rapist. All she had to do was try to please her self-effacing husband whose love had never been in doubt. An inevitable tension prevented either of us from relaxing. Had she been shaking less and more amenable, I might have won her over with experimental foreplay. "I suppose you'd better get on with it," she said, exhaling a sigh of resignation, the quivering movements becoming more convulsive as I drew myself towards her.

On entering Catriona, I did the unthinkable of coming inside her in an explosive thrust that caused her to writhe in agony. There had been no warning for the ill-timed penetration. It was then all hell let loose. She screamed and cursed, but not from any pleasure or excitement. All she could communicate was her sense of horror and revulsion.

"Get away," she yelled, kicking me like a stallion with her powerful dancer's legs.

— Twenty-Two —

E XPECTING THE COTTAGE to be ready on our return from Devon, we were in for a shock. Damp had been discovered in all three upstairs bedrooms. Rather than disturb us on our honeymoon, the builder had played safe by doing nothing. Catriona blamed Ted Smythe, the architect. The father of two Oxton House boarders, Mr Smythe had offered his services at a substantial discount as a good-will gesture. I advised Catriona to be cautious and polite in her treatment of him. Taking no notice, she bawled him out, saying he was incapable of running a piss-up in a brewery.

For the time being our furniture was stored in the gymnasium. Before the start of term we had to find another place to house it. But worst of all, as a temporary expedient, the only room available for we newly-weds was a space in the attic with a minute bed barely large enough to hold a midget. Here we spent weeks of sleepless, sex-starved nights, waiting for the builder to fulfil his many promises.

For me to fit into Duncan Knott's shoes was, I realised, a fanciful ambition. About to celebrate my twenty-fifth birthday, I was well aware my youth and immaturity would militate against me. There had been critical noises already. One parent had threatened to take his son away, saying never in his life had he seen such a flagrant example of nepotism. "Donald Elliott's barmy to appoint his nephew in place of a seasoned veteran," he complained to other parents.

Critical eyes would watch my every action. The most effective weapon I possessed was the stamina to work like a Trojan in an attempt to prove my worth.

Anyone involved in education will be familiar with the buzz and bustle that accompanies the start of a new school year. It's not unlike the opening chapter of a book, except that those involved in running an institution have it in their power to influence the outcome of the narrative. In spite of my fears, I relished the challenge of refashioning Oxton House in line with modern practices, to build it into a prominent and successful place of learning. One day I hoped it would be a school where parents would clamour to send their treasured offspring.

It was a comfort to know my uncle remained in charge, albeit a frailer version of the man who had purchased the run-down school eight years before the outbreak of the war. Having cut his teaching to the minimum, he was seen about the school less often. What mattered was he was still available to dispense his wisdom and support. Never patronising, he was happy to consult, advise, cajole and spur me on. It was a privilege for me to be his advocate. We had gone to great pains to find a suitable replacement for Jean Roberts. Our final choice was David Banks, a young graduate, who hailed from nearby Leeds. His bachelor status was regarded as a bonus by my uncle, who said married masters put in far less hours than did their single counterparts.

"Is that a dig at me?" I asked.

"As deputy headmaster, you'll be expected to work all the hours God sends," he warned.

Like any new arrival on the staff, David Banks was an unknown quantity. Capable of teaching a wide range of subjects, he had won us over by his enthusiasm and willingness to work beyond the hours of nine to four. Gut instinct made us confident he would be an asset.

It was not until half-term that Catriona and I were able to move into the cottage. Most of the wallpapers we had chosen had been ruined by the damp. The builder blamed the architect, who wrongly claimed we had issued instructions for the decoration work to be carried out before the plastering had dried. Catriona was furious and there was much gnashing of teeth as the dispute rumbled on for months. The positive outcome was removal from the garret to our new home where we could enjoy peace and quiet away from the commotion of the school. A major advancement was the provision of a capacious double bed. Showing artistic flair, Catriona acquired most of what we wanted by buying articles of furniture at rock-bottom prices, including a sofa costing five pounds which she had reupholstered in linen. Aunt Olive donated some of her cast-off items. These I deposited randomly about the cottage, much to the annoyance of my wife, who immediately hid them out of sight in one of the empty bedrooms.

Getting to grips with managing the school office, Catriona wasted no time in criticising her predecessor's methods. "Elsie Chapman had no proper filing system, no records and God knows what she's done with half the letters. The whole thing's a total shambles," she bitched.

"We think Elsie is a gem," I said, risking her wrath. "She may lack your qualities but she's very popular here. You must be careful not to upset her."

"I'm telling *you*, my husband, not all and sundry. And by the way, the school needs a better typewriter. The one I've got should have been thrown out with the ark!"

Renowned for his reluctance to spend money, to keep her sweet Uncle Don took the exceptional step of purchasing a machine that met with her approval.

Putting her stamp on the job, Catriona introduced a number of procedures that finally brought the school's administration into the twentieth century. Soon she had my uncle wrapped around her little finger. Instead of grumbling about the changes introduced, he sang Catriona's praises, referring to her as the miracle office worker. So quick was her output that by lunch time she had nothing left to do. Refusing to sit twiddling her thumbs, she managed to negotiate a reduction in her hours. In consequence, she worked a four-hour day for which she was to be paid the not ungenerous sum of twenty-five pounds a month. Free afternoons left Catriona with time on her hands. I had imagined she would want to assist Aunt Olive by immersing herself in the life of the school. Preferring to do her own thing, she disappeared for hours, sometimes returning as late as boarders' supper time. On Tuesday afternoons and the Sundays I was not on duty, we escaped from the confinement of Oxton House, often to the Yorkshire Dales, where we sought to recapture the tenderness we felt for one another, an expectant love that events on the fateful wedding night had interrupted.

After busy days I returned home late, eager for Catriona's company. Preparing tasty meals, she delighted me with her culinary skills. Relaxed evenings spent in an atmosphere of mundane domesticity, we valued the hours we spent together, hours that were exclusively our own. We were fast learning marriage was about sharing, companionship and above all trust. To achieve a fuller understanding was going to require much effort from us both. Having embarked on a hazardous journey, true happiness seemed still within our reach.

In conversations covering a variety of subjects, we rarely disagreed. Where there was discord, it was through possessiveness on both our parts. She complained I was fanatical about my job, imagining herself to be excluded. I blamed her for taking an insufficient part, bewailing the fact she regularly went into hiding without divulging where she went or how she passed the time. As a compromise, she volunteered to take charge of a group of budding boy artists after prep one night each week. Apart from this one diversion and her morning office chores, she avoided school involvement.

I couldn't get her to talk about our sexual problems. The fact she was inhibited and tense was a handicap to progress. A solution could only be found by our joint willingness to learn. Seeing lovemaking as an obligation rather than a thrill, she made lukewarm efforts to oblige. Bracing herself, her whole body cringing with distaste, she would shiver like a leaf, turning herself into a creature of sheer terror. The moment I was satisfied, it was my inability to please that took away the feeling of rapture I'd expected. The challenge was to unwedge the door that frigidity kept locked. Difficulties at the outset of a marriage were surely not unusual. By facing the hurdles and learning to adjust, assuming there was sincerity in our actions, the relationship was destined to improve. There were signs of an awakening, a remodelling that I believed would in time reward us with a long and stable union.

Early one morning, there was a loud banging on the front door of the cottage. There stood a tearful Aunt Olive in her nightdress, her face a ghostly white. "You must hurry," she said. "Your uncle's very ill. Elsie's keeping watch and Dr Taylor will be coming any minute."

An hour later Uncle Don was rushed to hospital.

"A second heart attack is often fatal," advised the doctor. "If he recovers, on no account must he ever work again. The stress would kill him." Turning to me, he whispered in my ear his stark opinion. "From now on the survival of Oxton House lies within your hands. A tall order for a man as young as you, but you have no option."

So it was, after nine months of marriage, the comfortable routine to which Catriona and I had become accustomed was ended by this shock happening. Headmaster in all but name, burdened with responsibilities I was unready to undertake, I failed to consider how the changes were likely to affect my sensitive and solitary wife.

— Twenty-Three —

TO BE ASSISTANT to my uncle was hard enough. To be forced to manage the school on my own meant unknown territory and pretending to be something I was not. Even though he would never work again, the one element of hope was that he would stay around to help guide me through the crisis. On evening visits to the hospital I begged my uncle to continue to battle on, stressing how much we wanted him back home. Elsie Chapman and Miss O'Sullivan took over my aunt's duties without a murmur, an expression of dependability that exemplified their worth. Free to visit her husband, Aunt Olive's constant presence at his bedside made all the difference. On the critical list for days, at last he earned the right to live through a compulsive ambition not to let us down.

Once he was back home, it was his resilience that strengthened my resolve. Getting stuck in, I devised a plan to deal with the emergency involving a workload that left no time for leisure. The entire staff responded to the challenge and nobody objected at having more to do. The one exception was Catriona. Instead of backing me up, retiring more into her shell, she became resentful and aloof. On the evening I told her I would have to give up my half-day and work on Tuesday afternoons, she turned on me, a flash of fury colouring her cheeks. "You're taking away the few bearable moments of the week," she said. "You make an arbitrary decision without discussion. In future I shall do the same. Don't expect me to sit around and wait!"

"You're being unreasonable," I argued. "Today a group of parents came to see me, all of them worried about the future of the school. They gave me grudging support, saying they would remove their sons if standards are seen to drop. In other words, I'm on probation. You've no idea of the strain I'm under. Why can't you understand?"

After a dismissive shrug, she withdrew from the room, failing to give an answer. For weeks she refused to speak. Sulking like a child, she seemed not to care that I needed her more than ever. Cursing the school and criticizing my obsession with its welfare, she kept her distance. A row might have cleared the air, but she preferred to maintain an unforgiving silence. Frozen out, dejected and alone, I tried to persuade her to open up a dialogue. Then all of a sudden she broke the deadlock.

Dressing early one Saturday, she cooked breakfast of the kind reserved for a birthday or a special treat. She was actually smiling. I wondered what had brought about her rapid change of mood. Was she schizophrenic, or judging by her look of cunning, was something sinister afoot?

"I'm skipping work today," she said. "I have a surprise for you. A surprise for us both, in fact."

"A surprise? What surprise? Tell me what it is."

Refusing to answer, she departed from the cottage, humming as she went.

As the evening turned to dusk, Catriona not yet back, I began to worry. Unsettling thoughts brought home to me my sense of agitation. Where had she gone? Had the cold war ended or was she at this very moment planning to escape, to leave her useless husband? My dreams were startled by the turning of a key. A door banged shut, followed by a breathless panting sound. A dog was barking. I could hear talking in the lobby. Catriona had invited a man into the cottage, a man with a dog. It was long past ten o'clock. What was going on?

"I want to introduce you to a friend," she called. Hurrying downstairs, I found myself staring at a handsome stranger, who looked young enough to be a student. Smooth-skinned, with thick curly hair blonded by the sun and dazzling white teeth, he looked like a toothpaste advert. "This is Tim," she said. And pointing to a frolicsome Labrador puppy, she added, "He's the surprise. His name is Krissa."

Bounding towards me, Krissa resumed his barking, a reverberant yelping that simply would not cease. As he took his leave, Tim made a courteous bow. "Bye Cat, nice to meet you, Paul," he said, the smile still fixed in perfect symmetry,

Calming the puppy with water and some leftovers, Catriona talked about buying pet food in the morning.

"Tomorrow's Sunday," I said, weary at the thought of the obstreperous intruder. "Where's the dog from? Who is Tim and why does he call you Cat?"

"You can get off your high horse for a start," she said. "Tim's a smashing chap. I'm sure you'll like him once you get to know him. He put me in touch with a breeder and I bought Krissa with my savings. Seventy pounds he cost. I think you're going to love having a puppy about the place."

"I'm not sure I even like dogs. Why didn't you consult me first?"

"I took an arbitrary decision, just as you did." There was no answer to that, much as I wanted to belittle the logic of her argument.

Endeavouring to find out more about Tim, I questioned her further. "Has Tim got nothing better to do than find dogs for married women? How did you meet him? Does he work and what else do you know about him?"

"Steady on," she said. "He recently lost his father and is living with his mother. He's been a brilliant friend to me and no, he doesn't have a job."

There was ambivalence in my attitude to the events that evening. It was a relief that Catriona was safely home and was prepared to talk to me again. If Krissa added a new dimension to her life, all well and good. It was Tim's involvement that bothered me. He was unemployed and available, a convenient playmate for my wife, whilst I was hard at work. Jealous of his influence, I decided to watch him like a hawk. One foot wrong and he was for the high jump.

Krissa required training and the opportunity to rid himself of surplus energy. I accused Catriona of working him too hard, expecting too much, not that I was an expert in the matter. Every afternoon she left the cottage, the lively puppy pulling on his lead.

Aunt Olive was not one to gossip. Since recovering from her breakdown, she'd become a model of discretion. Only if she had good reason would she indulge in telling tales. One day she seemed particularly anxious. Motioning for me to follow, she led me to her private sitting room. "I hate to bring bad news," she said, "but I've twice seen Catriona out walking with a man. Yesterday they were holding hands. Donald insists I tell you."

The shock left me speechless. The brazen chancer woos a lonely married woman, he flirts with her, seduces her, she falls in love and the marriage is at an end. It's happened time and time again. Impulsive action on my part would, I knew, ruin everything. To win her back, I was mindful of the need to play it long.

At the end of the summer term, I came up with the idea of renting a cottage in Wales. Catriona seemed pleased, making it a condition we took Krissa rather than deposit him at a kennels. It was vital for us to have time away together to allow us to communicate free from the distractions of the school.

Even in the rain, Wales was splendid for us both. When the sun shone it was magnificent. We walked for miles, uplifted by the peace and solitude, the intoxicating air, beguiled by the richness of the views. Grey towns and villages, each one endowed with a gloomy fascination, held us in its spell. On distant promontories wild ponies roamed unfettered, their silhouettes printing faded images on the unbroken skyline. Emptiness and desolation pervaded the hillside regions, where farmers toiled to scratch an honest living. Krissa was in his element. He splashed across streams, glad of the open spaces and the freedom to explore. He almost came to grief after being challenged by a guard dog on one of our scrambles on a steep ridge near to an isolated farm.

We discovered secret havens, which in our imagination belonged to us alone. We felt young. Romance was beckoning again. A fresh awareness was enlivening our senses.

The thrill vanished the moment Tim arrived to stay. I had needed to possess Catriona, but that moment had been lost. I never did learn whether she had been manipulated into asking Tim along. Overjoyed to see him, she prepared the spare bedroom with uncalled-for care. The best towels, the cleanest sheets, soap to wash his face, books by the bed for him to read, a brush to scrub his nails. And to cap it all, she lent him my favourite razor, a minor issue in normal circumstances. I blew my top. Outrage spewed out of me, unable as I was to disguise my hatred of him.

Failing to take the hint, the shameless visitor remained with us until the day the holiday ended. Few men would have forgiven Catriona's conniving actions. I had to bide my time and make allowances as I was still helplessly in love. Even my humiliation had a bitter-sweet edge. Yet as time went by, she began to display a hardness that ruled out any chance of restoring the relationship to one of stability and the most basic form of trust. There was an inadequacy in her make-up that prevented her from admitting she was ever in the wrong. No matter how hard I tried, she was unrelenting, insinuating I was not entitled to a point of view.

I would have liked a friend with whom to talk about my private torture. Uncle Don would have been the ideal confidant. Because he was so frail, I did not want to risk adding to his burdens. Although Aunt Olive understood what I was going through, there had always been a barrier that made her unapproachable. There was nothing for it other than for me to put up with the loneliness and cope as best I could.

One night in bed we were arguing, as we often did, about nothing in particular. This was one of the occasions Catriona was threatening divorce. Marriage to me was sacred, partly because of my parents' deep religious faith. I knew also it was up to us both to make it work. I suggested we might attend church together to help get the relationship back on track. Her venomous reply hurt and angered me. In retaliation and wanting to frighten her, I banged my right elbow onto the pillow next to her face. To my horror I had knocked her eye instead. She yelled and threatened, blaspheming with horrific savagery. That one inadvertent blow had destroyed a crucial thread that was keeping our flimsy partnership intact.

Three weeks later Catriona left for Brighton. She did not bother to leave behind a note. If my High Wycombe upbringing had taught me one essential lesson, it was that marriage is for keeps. Heaven knows my parents experienced problems in the early stages. Through self-sacrifice and perseverance they developed a rock-solid bond that built itself on attributes which, when totted up, amounted to the harmony of love. On the day of her departure, Tim paid me a visit. In the privacy of my home, like the vulture that he was, he came to scrutinize my thoughts, to observe my state of mind, using the guise of sympathy. I did not want his patronising prying, conscious he had only come to gloat. He had known in advance of Catriona's plans. How dare he pretend to be my friend! "Go to hell," I said, ushering him out and slamming the door in his face.

— Twenty-Four —

A T FIRST I was too stunned to take in the implications of what had happened. Innermost feelings bore no relation to the brazen part I played for the benefit of observers. Only Uncle Don and Aunt Olive were aware that Catriona had walked out on me.

Were it not for the fact she had left Krissa behind, the sense of betrayal would have been unbearable. To have failed to take with her the pet she idolized was proof her departure was temporary, that she wouldn't be gone for long.

As the days became weeks, my despondency grew, yet I didn't give up hope. Not until she was able to convince me the marriage was at an end would I dispel thoughts of forgiveness and a second chance. But her intentions were made plain when a letter arrived from Twining, Taft and Pledge, a firm of solicitors based in London. I remembered Sue Twining had been at ballet school with Catriona, who had more than once remarked that her friend's father was a lawyer specializing in divorce. In disbelief I read the contents of the letter, my heart thumping with such force it was like experiencing inside me a detonated bomb.

The first sentence stated that Catriona was seeking a divorce on the grounds of physical and mental cruelty. Without prejudice and pending a later financial settlement, I was advised to offer to pay her no less than seven pounds each week and to expect in due course to have to make over a capital sum from my parents' inheritance. The final paragraph raised my hackles further:

At 11.30 a.m. on Saturday, the 3rd March, a transport van from Edwards and Sons of Hove will collect all clothes, furniture, pictures and personal belongings known to be the property of our client. A list is enclosed herewith. We request that you allow proper access and do not impede the work of the removal men. Failure to co-operate would incur our client with extra costs for which you would be held responsible.

Appalled at Catriona's conduct, Uncle Don put me in touch with a solicitor he had known during his time as a Rotarian. "Spriggs is of the old school and is as honest as they come," he said. "He has no connections with Oxton House and I can vouch for his discretion. He won't stand any nonsense from Catriona's smart-alec London people."

Lionel Spriggs was a diminutive man in his fifties, with a bald head that was so shiny it gave the impression he had polished it with oil. A bushy white moustache twitched each time he laughed, a nervous habit he seemed unable to suppress. Wearing an ill-fitting tweed jacket, his appearance was of a disorganized don rather than the businesslike professional I'd expected. His desk, though, was neat and uncluttered, indicating he liked order and precision in his work. He shook my hand, a surprisingly firm handshake for a man of his size and build.

"Donald's filled me in enough to explain why you're here," he said. "But before we go delving into the rights and wrongs of your situation, I must ask you one important question. Is it your wish to have a divorce or would you prefer the marriage to continue?"

"I love my wife. I want her back. Of course I want the marriage to continue, but the letter from Catriona's solicitor gives the impression she's never coming back."

I handed him the letter. As he read, he scribbled notes on a pad, making grunts of disapproval as he did so. "I can see why you're upset," he said. "The letter is callous and unethical. It's only when a marriage breakdown is irretrievable that one sues for a divorce. Any lawyer worth his salt knows that. Our first responsibility to a client is to encourage a reconciliation. Leave it to me to write to Twining, Taft and Pledge and ask some pertinent questions. As soon as I can make sense of what they're up to, I promise to tell you what I think."

"I have a specific request," I ventured. "On the list of possessions to be collected, there is no mention of my wife's dog, Krissa. This I find surprising because she paid more attention to the dog than she ever did to me. I've tried to telephone her in Brighton, but her father refuses to let her speak."

"It does seem odd she's forgotten about the dog," he said. "I shall make enquiries and let you know what I discover."

The common belief was that my wife had gone away to look after her sick father, a notion I was happy to go along with. Schools are such places of gossip that it suited me well for my marital problems to escape the limelight. Elsie Chapman took charge of the school office each day in place of Catriona after the kindergarten pupils had been collected at lunchtime. Uncritical and diplomatic, not once did she query my circumstances or complain at having a second job to do.

Peace was disturbed by a rumour circulated by the milkman. He informed cook that Catriona had left because I preferred being with the boys to the company of my wife, inferring I was homosexual. After numerous winks and giggles, the story spread beyond the confines of the kitchen. Soon it was common knowledge in the staff room. The insinuation was so offensive that I was at a loss to know how best to react. Uncle Don acted promptly. He held an emergency meeting for all the school's employees. He addressed them thus: "You may have suffered the embarrassment of hearing some defamatory remarks concerning my nephew. Not only are they untrue, they are wicked, hurtful and hugely damaging to the school, an establishment which, and I must emphasize this point, provides you with employment. I don't believe in threats, but threaten now I will. If I hear of anyone repeating an insult of this nature, I promise to sue for slander and shall not rest my head until justice is done, no matter what the cost. I cannot imagine what nasty mind would be capable of inventing venomous falsehoods and scandalous untruths about a man I respect and trust as I could no other. Now go about your business, the lot of you, and let me not hear another word."

He stood up, walking unsteadily, a dignified exit from the room. The audience remained seated, speechless and bemused. Heads bowed, one by one they departed, each registering an expression of unease. To have been deserted by my wife was calamitous enough. To be accused of being morally defective, of harbouring a weakness that made me unsuitable to teach, was so degrading I was left concussed with horror at the shock. For years I had dreamt of improving Oxton House, preparing to devote myself with total dedication, using every device at my disposal to create a school of excellence. My reputation had been ruined overnight. Irrespective of my uncle's action, how could I remove the seeds of doubt in colleagues' minds? And when pupils' parents cottoned on to what was being said, they, too, would desert me, firstly withdrawing their support, then finally their children. I had two choices. Either to give in to the emotional pressures or unleash reserves of character that enabled me to keep my cool and ignore the innuendoes, the unkind whispering, the furtive glances. My best plan was to carry on as normal. By refusing to disclose the substance of my thinking, critics would be left with nothing on which to focus other than a rumour concocted by a mischief-maker with an axe to grind.

Lionel Spriggs was not surprised to learn about the gossip. "I've had a letter from this Twining fellow," he said. "He sounds a nasty piece of work. He claims you were violent throughout the marriage. Apparently your wife says quite openly you are homosexual and that your sexual indifference was the reason why she left."

"Talk about the fucking pot calling the kettle black," I said, uttering a crude expletive that expressed the state of desperation I had reached. "Now I know who started the rumour! Catriona was frigid. She never wanted to make love and on the few occasions she allowed me near, you would think she was being tortured. No wonder I felt humiliated, unwanted and a failure."

"I'm sorry to have to ask intrusive questions," Spriggs persisted, "but if I'm to be of help, it's essential for me to know the truth. *Are you homosexual?*"

"Good God, if I was homosexual, teaching is the last career I'd choose. I owe my uncle far too much to bring shame on his school with a scandal of this kind."

"I believe you, Paul, but have to know the facts. What about the violence? Did you ever behave violently towards your wife?"

"Only once. And it was a complete accident. Catriona knows perfectly well what happened on that occasion."

Lionel Spriggs frowned. Looking down at his papers, he sighed deeply before he shuffled them into a more orderly pile. "We've got to consider a suitable defence," he said, "because your wife has a medical certificate to vouch for the fact she was assaulted."

The law as it was gave three possible grounds for divorce; adultery, mental cruelty and desertion. Desertion applied only after one of the partners had been absent for a three-year period. If Catriona was not prepared to wait, she would be sure to use the cruelty option. In that event, the damaging content of the allegations would leave me with no choice other than to challenge her in court.

"I can well understand your anger," said Lionel. "I must stress that to contest the claims would be very costly. Your wife's barrister would savage you with his tongue, describing you as the lowest specimen on earth. A court hearing, with all the attendant publicity would be personally destructive and upsetting. It could ruin everything you've ever stood for. For your defence, we would need to engage the services of an equally accomplished counsel. Were you to win, and there's no guarantee of this, you would most likely end up paying your wife's costs in addition to your own."

Close to tears, overcome by the unfairness of my plight, I had to bite my tongue to prevent self-pity from taking over. Chastened by the severity of his opinion, I asked him what I should do next.

"My advice is to do nothing." he said. "Let *them* be the ones to take the action. To keep them sweet, however, I suggest you agree to pay maintenance to your wife in the sum of seven pounds a week."

"That's monstrous, it's half my salary," I protested, fuming at the idea of a far-too-generous offer.

"Don't forget I'm on your side," he said, his tone conveying genuine concern. "If you come across as reasonable, it's more likely to work in your favour later on. To pay a proportion of your income is far better than having to find a sum of capital based on the value of the cottage. In my view the money you received from your parents' will should be yours and no one else's."

When I asked whether Catriona's dog was to be collected, along with her other possessions, he shook his head. "I know you've always regarded Krissa's presence as a good omen, leading you to hope your wife was coming back," he said. "I'm sorry to have to disappoint you. I've been told Catriona will shortly be taking up a job in London where she will be unable to look after a pet. She wants the dog to remain with you in Harrogate."

So the cottage was stripped bare of many of the worldly goods we both shared. Krissa waited disconsolately for the return of his mistress, unsettled by the comings and goings of strange men, who carried away large packing cases. The home of which I had been so proud had been violated. I no longer gained pleasure from the empty dwelling, knowing Catriona's personality remained etched into the very fabric, her unique stamp now erased, and precious reminders ripped out, dismantled, leaving me with a sense of isolation I feared would never go away. This was worse than a bereavement. Death in the physical sense is final, whereas accompanied with that loss can be memories of sweet moments, treasured sentences, images that stay alive in the minds of those whose lives are as yet unended. I was aware of Catriona's new existence, a separate existence from mine, but an active, sensual life involving relationships, fresh hopes and perhaps fulfilment. I naively perceived myself to have failed her miserably. I became increasingly aware of the depth of my love, determining to use every tactic I could think of in my bid to get her back.

— Twenty-Five —

BETWEEN MOMENTS OF self-pity and remorse, I soldiered on as best I could. Taking care not to show my emotional fragility, I preferred to mislead critics by adopting an inscrutable aloofness that kept them in the dark. After weeks of mental anguish, it finally crossed my mind I was the one at fault; not because of the perversion some suspected or that I was neglectful of my work, but because of the depression. When Aunt Olive retired into her shell for months, unwilling to be reached by family or friends, none of us could help. To avoid this happening to me, I tried to dismiss all thoughts of self and by becoming more focused on the school was better able to fulfil the promises to my uncle.

For as long as I can remember, the people who cared about Oxton House had worked hard for its survival. The saving grace had always been the family atmosphere created by my aunt and uncle. Times were changing and modern parents expected for their boys a great deal more than what we had to offer. Gone were the days when private schools could get away with employing unqualified teachers and paying them next to nothing. A public school education was more sought after than ever. As a result, the most popular ones were able to raise their entry standards to ground-breaking levels. To meet the challenge, preparatory schools either had to modernize their outlook or face the risk of going under. Uncle Don could see the writing on the wall, but was too scared to come up with an answer. For this reason, he commissioned me to formulate a plan.

Putting myself in the shoes of a prospective fee-paying parent, I began to consider what mattered most to the majority. Some would go for facilities: updated dormitories, new classroom blocks, swimming pools and state-of-the-art laboratories; or spacious grounds with innumerable pitches, catering for a plethora of sports. Others would base their selection on the academic record of a school, choosing the one that could guarantee results. Although we couldn't offer any of these features, what we did have was a team of enthusiastic teachers and ancillary workers. If only we could build on that strength by improving the working conditions of the staff, I was confident the downhill slide could be averted.

Before committing my plan to paper, I decided to speak to every member of the staff, asking for candid views on their conditions of employment. Matron O'Sullivan and Elsie Chapman were more than happy with their lot. Like nuns, they regarded work as a vocation. Such selflessness meant it never occurred to them to grumble about their pay or the cramped and dingy rooms they looked upon as home in term time.

At the start of his appointment, I had been undecided about David Banks. Of powerful build and well over six foot tall, like a drill sergeant on parade his bearing was so ramrod straight that colleagues and boys alike were made to feel very much in awe by his intimidating presence. Thick horn-rimmed spectacles added to the severity of his appearance, giving him a no-nonsense air that deterred even the most delinquent pupil from misbehaving in his classes. Quiet and introverted, he mostly kept his opinions to himself. I was often at a loss to know what he was thinking.

During three years at Oxton House, he had taught a variety of subjects, insisting on high standards and achieving results that placed him a cut above his fellow team-mates. Organisation was another of his strengths. For any task that demanded originality and clear thinking, he led the way, leaving not a stone unturned as he strove to complete it to perfection. Because he was indispensable to me, it was essential to find out what made him tick, what he thought about the job and whether he planned to move to pastures greener. When I asked him how he saw his career developing, he shocked me with his answer.

Oxton's a happy little school," he said, "but it has its limitations. I can't see myself staying here much longer."

"You sound as if your mind's made up," I said, disappointment showing in my voice. "Let's assume for just one moment that changes can be made, radical improvements. Were this to be the case, what do you consider to be the main priorities?"

"To put it bluntly, there are four serious drawbacks here. The salaries are below even what is paid to state school teachers; moreover, there is no pension scheme in place. The accommodation for resident staff is uncomfortable and poky. My room is barely big enough to hold a bed and six of us have to share the only bathroom. And because the school is having to accept some boys with no academic pretensions whatsoever, standards are low. In the entire school there can't be more than half a dozen able pupils. There's no incentive for a schoolmaster with ambition."

Despite his bleak assessment, I sympathized with what he had to say. I told him in confidence that my uncle had asked me to come up with ideas that would stop the rot and help the school move forward. Emphasizing how much I valued the contribution he was making, I urged him to delay making a decision, at least until he had the chance to see what resulted from my actions. "Please give me one more term to start to make things happen," I said. "If after that you still think you're in a rut and see no sign of changes for the better, you'd be foolish not to move."

"You work hard, you've got good standards and intentions and I like and respect the Elliott family," he confided, "but it would take a miracle to bring about the turnaround you hope for. Of course I would want to stay to be part of an exciting programme of improvements. As a token of goodwill, I'm prepared to remain here long enough to give you the chance to prove me wrong. After that, I'll have to make a move."

By taking no action, I would be certain to lose the most valuable assistant master on the staff. So strongly did he feature in my plans that his departure would not only spell disaster to morale, but would further inflate the fears of cynics who were already making negative predictions. I had to move fast to stop the decline and think up a workable strategy for survival. After busy weeks spent meeting architects, builders and managers of banks and building societies in Harrogate and York, I was ready to submit my findings as a basis for discussion with my uncle. In my report there were five separate headings, each of which was accompanied by detailed explanations, with facts and financial estimates as appropriate.

STAFF SALARIES

STAFF ACCOMMODATION

TEACHERS' PENSION SCHEME

NEW PROSPECTUS

FINANCE

I waited with bated breath for his response, knowing the idea of intemperate borrowing was anathema to my uncle.

Sitting at his desk, he was definitely on edge. The last time I remembered seeing him with that desperate look was when he was in hospital recovering from his second heart attack. "You say in your report you want to borrow a huge sum of money to provide a few basins and a couple of extra bathrooms for the staff," he said, working himself into a fluster. "When I worked as an assistant master, I wasn't wrapped up in cotton wool. I had to pay the rent for a shabby bedsit from a salary of fifty pounds a year."

"You are harking back to the 1920s when conditions were entirely different from today," I said. "If we are to attract an efficient staff and want to keep them, we've got to look after them properly."

"What do they expect? Gold taps, their own lavatory and a maid to bring an early morning cup of tea? I've never heard such nonsense."

Finding it hard to remain calm, I reminded him he was the one who had asked for proposals and the least he could do was to hear me out. Once I was able to convince him we were in danger of losing David Banks and two of the other masters, he began to take me seriously. "If we pay David his Burnham Scale entitlement, it might encourage him to stay," I said.

"How about the rest of the staff?" he asked.

"I suggest we treat David as an exception. The other salaries can be increased as soon as we can build up pupil numbers."

Again my uncle looked sceptical. His jaundiced view had always been that any kind of risk-taking was a recipe for disaster.

"I've had estimates from four builders," I continued. "For the cost of two thousand three hundred pounds, we can modernize the upstairs landing. By adding the store area, which is a waste of space, we can provide five large bedrooms, each with its own basin and two extra bathrooms and lavatories."

"This is extravagance gone mad. You need reminding your aunt and I bought the school, including the goodwill, fixtures and fittings for less than three thousand pounds in 1931," he recalled pointedly.

"I know that, but we can't keep living in the past," I said. "To attract quality people, we've got to make their living conditions more comfortable. And by the way, the work can be carried out in the summer holidays. You needn't worry about the noise and mess as I'll be on site to ensure the smooth running of the project."

For two hours I reasoned with him, trying to get him to look upon the future in a new perspective. At last he gave in, saying he was tired of putting up obstacles, accepting that to stand still would not solve the problem. Once he had agreed the best means for financing the various schemes was to extend the period of the mortgage, we were almost home and dry. Having visited the building society in advance, I knew the funds would quickly be provided. Surprisingly, he did not oppose the pension scheme idea. When I explained the advantages of joining the government teachers' superannuation programme, he seemed impressed. For my uncle to agree to anything that would increase the school's outgoings was virtually unheard of. "If mollycoddling the staff is going to remove some of the unrest, I suppose it's worth the sacrifice," he said. "I'd give my eye teeth to be able to retire with a decent pension."

Less well received was my proposal to update the school prospectus. "There's nothing wrong with the one we've got," he moaned, his patience fast receding. "Why in heaven's name would you want to change it?"

"Because instead of serving as an effective promotion tool, it's dull and lifeless. Parents I've spoken to think we could brighten it up. What's needed is a glossier version with lots of photographs featuring the boys themselves, all happily engaged in some activity or other. Taunton Hall has a splendid prospectus. Maccy said it made all the difference to recruitment."

"Taunton Hall, that's all I ever hear about," he muttered angrily. "Having survived two world wars and the depression, life's been far from easy and I make no excuses for being cautious. That said, I can see you're determined to make a name for Oxton House, which is why I feel obliged to give your plans my blessing. But if you don't succeed and the house comes tumbling down, all of us go with it."

Not for one moment had I expected such a generous, if cautious, reaction from my uncle. By placing trust in my arguments, he and Aunt Olive were putting their personal security at risk in favour of a reckless gamble. Conscious of the debt I owed them and of the responsibilities I bore, I prayed for the capacity and strength to help bring about a reshaping that would help make their dreams come true.

— Twenty-Six —

NOT A DAY passed when I did not think about Catriona. For months I tried to get her back. Twice she gave the impression she was going to return, then at the last minute changed her mind, dashing the chances of a truce. Even so, she was reluctant to press ahead with the divorce, which still gave me cause for hope. As soon as she had moved to London, it was easier to keep in touch. No longer living with her father, she was free to behave exactly as she wished. I wrote numerous letters, begging her to return, stressing she had given my life a meaning and that without her there was no longer any purpose.

Apologizing for the times she had felt abandoned, I tried to convince her the hard work at school was to build a future for us both and hopefully a family. The breakthrough came when she chose to write to me. It was a confused letter from a desperately unhappy girl. Much to my surprise, she gave me her telephone number, saying she wanted us to meet. My first call was answered by a female, who introduced herself as Andrea, Catriona's flat-mate. Learning who I was, she threw aside the charm and became abusive. "You've a bloody cheek to bother my friend," she fumed. "She's been an emotional mess following two miserable years with you. My advice is to leave her alone or you'll have me to answer to."

Knowing success was not for the faint-hearted, I kept on trying until I was able to speak to Catriona. At last I found her in. Andrea's description of her mental state must have been an exaggeration because Catriona's speech was calm and lucid and I was left with the distinct impression she was glad I'd been in touch. It was agreed I would visit her one Friday in August. Booking myself into a small hotel, I drove to London, emotions wavering between trepidation and elation, a nervous stabbing pain tightening my chest. By the time I pressed the bell at the entrance to her basement flat in a smart Belgravia street, my heart was pounding so frantically that I nearly took fright and ran. It had been seven months since my wife's departure and I was scared beyond belief at the reception I was likely to get.

The door was opened by a sullen young lady, who I took to be Andrea. Of striking appearance, she was big-boned, square-jawed and tall enough to be a man, the kind of person that would stand out in a crowd. Glossy auburn hair was her finest feature. Wild eyes as black as ink stared at me unflinching and unyielding, dark caverns that conveyed a frightening air of menace.

"Catriona's getting changed," she announced coldly; "I know all about the things you've done. You'd better not unsettle her again."

She was about to say more, but suddenly went quiet when Catriona emerged from what must have been a bedroom. Wearing a close-fitting black cocktail dress, an anxious smile lighting up her face, she looked as beautiful as ever. Ill at ease in the presence of her flatmate, all she could manage was a token greeting. It was not until we had left the flat and were about to hail a taxi that she pecked me on the cheek.

"Andrea tells me I've made you an emotional mess," I said. "To tell the truth I've not seen you look better."

"Take no notice of her," she laughed. "She's like a mother hen, possessive and protective. She thinks she's my minder."

Taken aback by the frostiness of Andrea's welcome, I wondered about the nature of her relationship with Catriona, how they had met, what they had in common and why she saw me as a threat. To my mind, the two women couldn't have been more different, what with Andrea's rudeness and aggression, compared with my wife's more feminine demeanour. Rather than ask questions at this stage, I decided to bide my time before leaping to conclusions. Catriona had chosen a restaurant in Soho for our evening out. "I've booked a table at the Dolce Vita," she said. "The food's genuine Italian and there's dancing to a band."

It was obvious she knew her way around London and to live it up was second nature to her. I was put out to think I regularly sent money to supplement her busy social life, whereas what little spare time I had was spent listening to the radio, attempting to write a novel or reading another book. My last proper night out had been when I'd taken her to the cinema in Harrogate and dinner afterwards two months before she'd moved to Brighton. Rather than ruin the evening by boring her with news of my nondescript existence, I decided to throw caution to the wind and let my hair down for a change. Seating ourselves at a table next to the dance floor in the ornately decorated restaurant, I ordered a bottle of champagne. A little inebriation did wonders for the conversation. We spoke openly and with affection, nearby customers seeing us as a normal, happy couple. None would have realized we'd been daggers drawn for months and were on the brink of a divorce.

As the meal progressed and the wine flowed freely, Catriona became flirtatious. After she'd kissed me fully on the lips, her mood turned from a manic state of animation to the gloomy resentment she had exhibited so often in the past. She had never been one to express her feelings like a normal person. I remembered an occasion her father had been taken ill, the man she loved more than any other. She had remained detached, almost as if she was unaffected, unable to exhibit her emotions. Tonight in Soho she was letting go of her defences, which was definitely a first. To my horror, I noticed tears were clinging to her cheeks.

"Whatever's wrong?" I asked.

"I was safe with you, Paul. Why has it come to this?"

As the evening drew to a close, she got up from the table, eager for us to dance. A skilled performer, her intricate movements and sense of rhythm soon attracted the attention of the other diners. Joining her on the floor, I shuffled clumsily in time to the music. The band struck up a romantic, soulful tune. She held me close, sad eyes fastened on mine, registering a despair that she alone could stifle. Clasping her tightly in my arms, I longed for the world to stand still to give me the time to savour the wonder of this moment. In the taxi afterwards, she clung to me like a leech, unwilling to let me go. She kissed me harder now, the familiar sweetness soured only by the taste of alcohol sharpening her breath. As I fondled her thighs, her breasts, her neck, she responded by snuggling closer, deft fingers delicately massaging my groin.

She had never before taken the initiative in the sexual sense, not with me, at any rate. I wondered whether there had been a man on the scene, a seasoned philanderer, who had taught her what to do, and having extracted what he wanted, ditched her for someone else. Maybe she was still pining and needed a safe pair of hands, a patient ex to restore her self-assurance. My thoughts were interrupted by her downcast voice. "I don't like being on my own, tonight especially. Please let me stay with you." I needed no persuasion, seeing her request was for me a wish come true.

The hotel porter eyed us up and down, smirking cheekily as if to say it was not unusual for male guests to be joined by ladies in the middle of the night.

"How dare he look at us like that," I said, as I walked Catriona to the lift. "He obviously thinks I'm playing around with someone else's wife."

The bedroom scene brought back memories. Memories of rejection, of frustration, of feeling inadequate and unwanted, nightmare recollections of a misery too horrible to bear. Catriona was forever an enigma, her motives impossible to figure out. Either the change in her was genuine, spurred on by the stimulus of drink or she would impede my advances once again by choosing to resist.

There was no explicit loving nor did I feel deprived. Her naked body wrapped around mine, she lay whimpering, begging me to stay close throughout the night. Rocking her like a baby, I knew for certain she had changed. She had done her best, but equally I was convinced her inability to react was not her fault. There was some form of blockage, an experience in her past that had stultified her sexual growth. With my help I believed she could be cured. It would take time and effort, patience and encouragement. She fell asleep, innocently trusting in me to guard over her and help save her from herself. A frantic shaking movement woke me with a start. It must have been late as the sun was flashing rays of light through the flimsy bedroom curtains. Already dressed, Catriona, who admitted to a hangover, was in a panic, complaining I shouldn't have agreed for her to spend the night.

"Andrea will be livid I didn't get in touch," she said.

"She's not your keeper. You're a grown woman, and perfectly capable of making decisions for yourself. I've travelled a long way and hoped we were going to talk."

"I've got a lot of sorting out to do. People, situations. It's complicated. Impossible to explain. Isn't it enough for you to know I still love you and that my feelings haven't changed."

"Of course it's not enough. You know I want you back. It's not unreasonable to expect an answer after all this time."

There was an awkward silence, after which she went on to make a statement that at long last gave me cause for hope. "I'm definitely coming back. I can't say when as this will depend on how soon I can sort my problems out."

"Don't keep me dangling. Are we talking about a week, a month, a year?" I asked.

"Not a week, but almost certainly within a month. This is a promise, Paul. Meanwhile don't contact me, I beg you. No letters, phone calls, messages or pressures of any kind. I must get back to Andrea before she does something crazy like phoning the police."

In vain I waited. Early one morning I thought I heard the sound of high-heeled shoes treading on the path outside the cottage beneath my bedroom window. It must surely have been Catriona. I went downstairs to investigate. It was another false alarm. Each night I remained alert, willing her to return in answer to the transmission of my thoughts. Not one to give up, I was still convinced one day she would be back.

After three months of waiting, I was furious. After breaking her promise, it seemed reasonable that I should write to her again, an action she had begged me not to do. I wrote letter after letter. Each expressed the exasperation I felt, the love I had to give, together with a potted day-to-day version of events in Harrogate. I implored her to make up her mind, admitting life was unbearable without her. Just as I was about to surrender all hope, I received a letter from Catriona that answered the question I'd waited for so long.

Dearest Paul,

I am sorry to have messed you about, my darling. Events beyond my control have been the cause of a number of unexpected upsets. The coast is now clear and the problems I referred to when you visited me in London have at last been solved.

Assuming you still want me back, I plan to return to the cottage on Saturday, the 2nd December. I cannot be specific about a time. Please let there be no questions, no recriminations and no delving into what has happened in the past. I shall come with just a suitcase. My other belongings will follow in a week or two.

Let us start afresh and learn from our mistakes. I promise to play my part and know you will want to treat me with as much considera-tion as you do your precious school.

Am counting the days.

With all my love,
Catriona
xxx

— Twenty-Seven —

T HE NEW ACCOMMODATION was welcomed with enthusiasm by the resident staff. Goodwill abounded. It was not pure imagination that team spirit amongst the employees as a whole had moved up a notch or two. David Banks expressed his delight in fulsome terms. "A year ago I was pessimistic about the future of Oxton House," he said. "To have achieved so much and so quickly is quite remarkable. The pension scheme decision is an inspiration to us all. If it's support you're after, you're going to get it."

The improvements were already being talked about by potential customers. The new prospectus had done much to encourage parents to pay us a visit and the increasing number of registrations indicated that the school was growing in popularity. Six new pupils were due to start in January, making the total on roll sixty-eight, ten more than a year ago. Entries for the following September were already well up on the previous year and it appeared that it was going to be necessary to employ another teacher. I invited David Banks to help me study the applications with a view to drawing up a shortlist. I wanted him to meet the candidates so he felt his opinion was taken into account before Uncle Don made the final choice. Ideally we wanted a mathematics specialist who could teach up to public school scholarship level. Able mathematicians were in short supply and for this reason our prime concern was to select the right person rather than rule out applicants with qualifications in other disciplines.

Having widely advertised the post, we only received four applications. One was from a disabled woman; the other three were from men, none of whom would be capable of teaching maths to an advanced level. When we scrutinized their *curriculum vitae*, one stood out above the rest and was felt to be worth interviewing, Still in his twenties, after qualifying as an accountant, Stephen Rice had discarded the boredom of a desk job in favour of teaching. He had

151

since qualified at a teachers' training college with excellent references and was thirsting for a challenge. Rather than risk letting him go elsewhere, Stephen was appointed to join the staff in January. From the outset he worked with an energy and will that quickly enabled him to make his mark. Nothing was too much trouble and within weeks he had introduced a number of new activities: youth hostelling expeditions, a drama club, as well as ambitious preparations for a Christmas carol service, which involved the formation of a choir.

On games afternoons he put his accountancy skills to good use by helping Uncle Don streamline the payment of bills, as well as taking charge of the boys' fee accounts at the end of each term. Like a whirlwind, he dashed from one pursuit to another with such speed that it was little wonder his slim build carried not an ounce of surplus weight. Brilliant in the classroom, he maintained the boys' interest by his entertaining personality.

Given the backing of two first-rate assistants, my ambition to further strengthen standards was no longer a fanciful pipe dream. Now that we had the makings of a strong team, I knew almost anything was possible. My uncle was overjoyed with the progress in evidence. His suggestion to make David Banks my deputy was a shrewd one. Reinforcing his loyalty, the promotion inspired David to go the extra mile.

But I worried about academic standards. The main trouble was that the school had been forced to accept a number of pupils of low intelligence, some of whom were incapable of coping with the demanding prep. school syllabus. I felt it was dishonourable for us to take boys lacking the necessary brainpower simply in order to cover costs. Time and again I remonstrated with my uncle, endeavouring to express my point of view.

"You mustn't forget we're running a business," he would say testily. "If we removed all the dunderheads, we wouldn't be able to pay the bills."

I could understand the point he was making, even though it riled me every time he made that statement. One boy, in particular, stood out like a sore thumb. Not only was he educationally subnormal, his difficulties were such that he was in need of intensive private help. To have placed the poor lad in an environment to which he was so obviously unsuited was as near as you could get to committing an act of cruelty. Charlie Pick had boarded at the school since the age of eight. His widowed mother wanted him to follow in her late husband's footsteps and become a doctor. Charlie's intelligence quotient was so low that at the age of eleven he had a mental age of seven. Barely able to read, he came bottom of his class in every subject, in spite of working with boys two years younger than himself. Mrs Pick refused to accept he was retarded and was convinced the penny would suddenly drop and he would transform into a genius once he became a teenager.

Charlie was no games player, nor was he keen on art or music. No matter how much effort was made to encourage him to pursue a hobby that might help build his confidence, he soon lost interest and retired into his shell. This was before Aunt Olive discovered his interest in gardening, a disclosure that brought fresh hope to his otherwise moribund life. My aunt's self-restraint was undeniably saintly on the occasion he was first introduced to the delights of floriculture. After pulling out her most colourful antirrhinums, he watered the weeds he was supposed to be removing from a path. An essential lesson having been learnt, it did not take him long to become something of an expert. Quickly he acquired knowledge about compost, pruning and the way to feed the plants. He could hoe, bed out and water, and in no time was a deft hand at trimming the edges of a lawn, greenhouse care and gathering up the leaves in autumn. He followed Aunt Olive about like a devoted shadow, listening to every word she uttered about his favourite topic. To everyone he met, he repeatedly announced that when he grew up he was going to be a gardener.

On a sunny afternoon in May, Mr Angus Fothergill, a wealthy factory owner from Leeds, paid a visit to the school. The father of three potential boarders, he had heard that Oxton House was on the up and up and, in view of its convenient location, was well worth looking at. Mrs Fothergill's one and only concern was her boys' happiness. Pleased with what she saw, she was especially taken with Matron O'Sullivan, whose philosophies coincided closely with her own. Mr Fothergill, on the other hand, was insistent about the need for high academic standards, saying that his aim was for all three boys eventually to go to Eton. The tour of the school complete, I offered our visitors tea. Mr Fothergill began to relax and remarked how impressed he was. He said he was particularly pleased with the sense of energetic purpose detectable everywhere, adding that it was good to see a number of keen young masters rather than a collection of has-been eccentrics like the ones he remembered as a boy. "Once my wife and I have had the chance to talk," he declared, "I think you can take it I shall be getting my secretary to return the completed application forms."

On their way out, they were confronted by a small boy clutching a menacing-looking implement that looked like a scythe. Sidling up to Mrs Fothergill, the boy managed a befuddled grin before proudly handing her the muddy tool. When Charlie began to speak, I knew it was too late to limit the damage that was done. "Do you like gardening?" he asked, dribbling saliva. Appalled at the thought of sending their precious darlings to a school catering for the mentally unhinged, they hastily departed from the school. Incandescent with rage, I was thoroughly disheartened. How could the school broaden its appeal if we continued to take boys like Charlie? He was a nice enough child but because he was so backward he received much more than his fair share of the teachers' time. The situation worsened when two fathers threatened to remove their sons because of Charlie.

Despite Uncle Don's reputation for being a fair man, some people thought he was too even-handed. Aware of his stubborn streak, I was mindful of the need to assemble arguments that did not ignore what was best for Charlie. "Do you honestly think it's good educational practice for a boy to be taught Latin and French when it's as much as he can do to read a few basic words in his own language?" I argued.

"I assume you are referring to Charlie Pick," said my uncle. "What we are doing is a great deal better than treating him like a dum-dum or for him to be made to attend a state school with forty in a class. He'd be lost in next to no time and would quickly go downhill." I could see he was spoiling for a row, so decided to let him have his say. "It's all very well for you to suggest chucking Charlie out," he persisted. "We have a duty towards every boy in the school, not just the bright ones. I'd not be able to look Mrs Pick in the eye, having promised never to give up on her son. Her husband was a good friend, which makes my undertaking all the more significant."

I told Uncle Don it was hypocritical to claim that Charlie's interests were being properly served. Reminding him of his comments about the payment of bills, I made the point that his reasoning was no longer valid, bearing in mind Charlie's presence was a deterrent to recruitment. "Mr and Mrs Fothergill are a case in point," I said. "Had Charlie not met them in the corridor, we would have had three more registrations."

"Aren't you overdramatising the situation?"

"No, I'm not. The boy's an embarrassment. We all know him, but to a complete stranger, he's like a village idiot. Sensible parents aren't going to want their sons to mix with a boy like that."

"You sound like an unfeeling snob," he snapped.

"And *you* talk as if we're living in the dark ages. Be realistic, for heaven's sake! The obvious decision is for Charlie to be sent to a school better suited to his needs. Rather than spend money on fees, Mrs Pick could then pay for extra tuition at home. By avoiding the subjects that are useless to him, he would be happier and more fulfilled. He can do as much gardening as he likes and one day I expect he will opt for some sort of horticultural training."

"So you basically want rid of him. Isn't that rather callous?"

"It's all very well for you to dictate what I can or cannot do. How do you expect me to run the school profitably if I have little or no authority? I'm not sure I can carry on like this much longer."

"You always were able to wheedle me round your little finger," he said, his expression softening. "Some of your ideas may differ from mine, but for the most part I'm more than satisfied with what you do. You have my permission to carry on as you see fit. Only in exceptional circumstances shall I interfere again." He then placed a hand on my arm, a gesture of sincerity and warmth that left me in no doubt he was giving me his backing.

Shortly afterwards I arranged a staff meeting to discuss a number of issues involving academic standards. Setting a minimum attainment target, it was decided that new entrants to the school aged seven or over would have to pass a simple admission test. In view of the fact demand for places was insufficient for us to be very choosy, the new policy was a start in the right direction. Another brave step was the decision to offer each year two partially-assisted places for gifted boys, advertised as scholarships. Announcements in national and local newspapers attracted nine candidates at the first of these examinations, as a result of which two boys of exceptional ability were offered places at the school.

We all agreed Charlie was not benefiting from what we had to offer. After a long and painful conversation with his mother, I was eventually able to convince her it was in his best interests to attend a school that offered a more practical approach to learning. Months later, by which time Charlie had become a distant memory, Mrs Pick wrote to my aunt to say how grateful she was for her help in encouraging Charlie to develop his special interest. Enclosed with the letter there was a drawing of some roses, coloured in crayon, with a message meticulously inscribed underneath.

Dear Mrs Elliott
Thanks to you I still want to be a gardener.
With love from Charlie.

— Twenty-Eight —

I COULDN'T UNDERSTAND why Catriona had been so vague about her return to Harrogate. What mattered was she was definitely coming back on the 2nd December, an expectation that had replaced my feelings of despair with irrepressible delight. I could not help myself. The florist made the promised delivery that morning: bunches of carnations, a profusion of reds, pinks and yellows, as well as an enormous bouquet of white lilies, which I placed in a decorous vase on the dresser in the now sparsely furnished sitting room. Having hoovered the carpets, cleaned the windows and dusted the surfaces with the care of a dedicated skivvy, I made sure the cottage sparkled with a freshness that expressed my good intentions.

To mark her homecoming, I intended to cook a special meal. Culinary skills had never featured on my list of priorities; in fact, Catriona in the past had often complained at my inability to fend for myself. In order to impress her, I had been practising like mad to show just what I could achieve through tenacity and perseverance. The planned menu consisted of scampi, succulent steaks, a gooey dessert and a bottle of burgundy. I was eager to celebrate in tangible form her decision to try again and let bygones be bygones.

As the day progressed, I became more and more restless, bewildered to think I had lacked the sense to insist on having more detailed news of her plans. It was dark by four o'clock and as the minutes ticked by I harboured negative thoughts: thoughts of her change of heart, of an accident, a new man in her life or of her final recognition of my worthlessness. To add to the frustration, I knew there was nothing concrete on which I could base my forebodings because she had always managed to shroud her activities in a web of secrecy.

Discarding ideas of a celebration, I began daydreaming in a world of introspection, trying to comprehend what had led Catriona to make a promise she had chosen not to keep. It was not until Krissa began to bark that I realised he was hungry and was fretting for a walk. Placing the uncooked steaks in his bowl, I patted him fondly, glad to think he at least was a lucky recipient on this most miserable of days. Taking him round the block, my anger increasing, I decided, come hell and high water, to find out what had become of my wife. Late that night I phoned her Belgravia number. The line was dead and after making further enquiries, I was told there was no longer a subscriber, nor was there any help the exchange could give in helping me trace the whereabouts of either Catriona or her flatmate. On Monday I went to see Lionel Spriggs, explaining my dilemma. We considered engaging the services of a private detective. "If Catriona has moved, which is highly likely," said Lionel, "you could find yourself throwing good money after bad. My recommendation is to confine any investigation to one visit only and see where we go from there. London's a big place and you could come back empty-handed. If you can't find out where she is, she can't expect any maintenance payments!"

Colin Heep, the private investigator, travelled to London that same week. Lionel was right. On his return, before producing a substantial bill, Mr Heep presented a report that revealed Catriona had left both the flat and her job and nobody, it appeared, knew where she was now living. A week before Christmas I received a letter from her from an address in Camden Town. Sickened by what she had to say, I again went to see Lionel before deciding what action I should take. In the letter she said after receiving advice from friends and her lawyers, she had come to the conclusion the marriage was over. She thought it only fair to warn me in advance of her decision to divorce me on the grounds of mental cruelty. The letter continued: -

"I was close to coming back, but something stopped me, be it common sense or my inability to trust you. I know you will not admit to being homosexual, but having lived with you for 2½ years, I can hardly fail to know the truth. My lawyer advises me that I have ample evidence and witnesses to prove my case.

Please don't think of me unfairly because I consider you to be honourable in most respects. We are all aware, however, that a leopard cannot change its spots. You had a choice to make: between me and the boys whose morals you were supposed to protect. You chose the boys and I am unable to live with that decision.

I am ill, unhappy and living in squalid conditions. It would have been so much easier to take the coward's way out by agreeing to come back. But this would not have been a permanent solution. Meanwhile you owe me thirty-five pounds in alimony back payments, a meagre sum that will help to pay my rent and provide me with some food.

How could you be so heartless as to leave me in such an appalling mess?

Catriona

After months of waiting and hoping, I wasn't prepared to allow the marriage to end without a meeting with Catriona. "I've decided to go to London," I informed Lionel. "There are too many unanswered questions in her letter. To be accused of homosexuality is so monstrously absurd that I've got to have it out with her."

"My advice is to try to take things calmly," he said. "Avoid doing anything impulsive. To shoot off to London could prove to be a wild goose chase. For all we know, she may be using the address for contact purposes only. There's no *proof* she's living there. If I were you, I'd sit tight and do nothing until we hear from Twining, Taft and Pledge."

Ignoring Lionel's advice, I decided to do my own detective work. Leaving Harrogate early one morning I drove with daredevil haste, guilty repeatedly of exceeding the speed limit on the recently opened M1 motorway. By lunchtime I was searching for St. Paul's Crescent in Camden Town. I parked outside what I assumed was Catriona's new home, a large Victorian dwelling with shabby green paintwork and a decaying cement frontage badly in need of repair. I clung on to the rail as I climbed the uneven stone steps leading to the dingy entrance. There was no bell to press, so I gave a loud knock on the door to attract attention. After a pause, I was aware of movement from within. Moments later, I was confronted by a furious-looking Andrea.

"I thought we were rid of you," she said. "Catriona never wants to see you again. I suggest you bugger off back to Yorkshire."

"I'm not leaving until I've seen her. What I have to say has nothing to do with you."

"Let me be the judge of that," she warned. She then led me into the hallway before entering a room on the right of the front door. I could hear muffled conversation, followed by angry exchanges involving more than two people, one of whom was undoubtedly Catriona. I could tell there were several people living in the house, judging by the noise of voices coming from the kitchen and sounds from the floor above.

When Andrea reappeared, she was accompanied by a smartly dressed middle-aged man, who was smoking an enormous cigar that was dangling precariously from his mouth.

"Catriona will spare you five minutes," Andrea said. "If you overstay that time, we shall ask you to leave."

I was shown into a large, untidily furnished lounge, with miscellaneous chairs of different size, shape and colour, a threadbare carpet, an assortment of pictures and two bookcases full of classics and encyclopaedia, which were randomly stacked alongside a number of well-worn paperbacks. It was like entering a chaotic students' den rather than the living quarters of a fastidious and sophisticated woman. The room could comfortably accommodate at least a dozen and the atmosphere was what one might expect to find in some weird commune as opposed to a normal family home.

Shocked by what I saw, I moved towards Catriona, who sat on a grubby sofa close to the door. Her glazed expression made me wonder whether she was drunk. Clumsy movements and trembling hands added weight to my suspicions. Lacking its usual sheen, her hair was tangled and unwashed. Her face a jaundiced yellow, I'd never seen her look so ill. Wearing a stained tee shirt and crumpled pair of slacks, the woman of fashion who in the past always took a pride in her appearance, had ceased to bother. She pushed me away, emitting muffled words of distaste.

"Unless you've come with a big fat cheque, there is nothing I want to say."

"I've not come with a cheque, but I do have a question," I said.

Focusing on her libellous accusations, I wasted no time in telling her how I felt.

"To have kept me on a string was bad enough, but to attempt to destroy my career with your wicked assertions goes way beyond the bounds of basic decency. Give me one grain of evidence that shows I'm homosexual. You know damned well that if the people of Harrogate believe this myth, Oxton House will close and I could end up in the gutter."

"I've never condemned you for being homo," she said. "What I object to is the hypocrisy of the pretence and the fact you claim to be something you are not."

Finding it hard to refrain from physically assaulting her, I struggled for suitable words to make her see reason. "You are living with a sinister woman whose morals I would question, yet without a scrap of evidence, you accuse me of actions that could send me to prison. You've a twisted mind with an imagination gone mad. I want names, dates and facts to support your claims. Failing that, you either shut up or I shall challenge you in court."

I got up to leave, preferring to go of my own accord rather than wait to be ejected.

Disconcerted by Catriona's changes in mood, I remained puzzled by her relationship with Andrea. Where did the man with the cigar fit in? Who else was living in the house? In her letter, she referred to advice given by friends. I presumed Andrea was the main protagonist, but was Tim still involved, and if so, had he also played a part? Standing close to Catriona before setting off back up north, I could smell not a trace of alcohol. So clumsy were her movements that I began to wonder whether she was taking drugs, which would explain why she had no job and was in need of financial help. She wanted a quick divorce, a goal she ruthlessly pursued whilst disregarding the effect on me of her vicious allegations. From now on I resolved, and not before time, to give pride of place to my own self-interests.

The visit to London forced me to conclude that any more attempts to try to entice Catriona back would be a waste of time. Enduring the most wretched Christmas ever, I spent ten anxious days before Lionel was due to return to work. "It's action time," he asserted, when finally we met. "Twining is keen to put the frighteners on you. He's determined to get you for cruelty, saying you were known to be homosexual throughout the marriage and he claims that you caused your wife actual physical harm. It's a ploy to get you to act fast and dissuade you from defending."

"My honour's at stake," I said. "Of course I must defend."

"If you do there is a strong possibility the case will be reported in the press. Surely you don't want the whole of Yorkshire to read about your marital problems at their breakfast tables. No parent would want to risk educating his son in a school where it's contended the headmaster is a danger to his pupils. Even the most liberal-minded would run a mile. No, Paul, you cannot risk it. There is another way, a much better solution, one that holds far fewer risks." He went on to advise me that it would be much safer to admit committing adultery than to contest a cruelty action.

"I haven't committed adultery," I complained indignantly, desperate nonetheless for my private nightmare to reach a fair conclusion.

"There's nothing to prevent you from *pretending* you have," he said, his moustache twitching more noticeably than ever. "All you have to do is agree to be seen in a compromising situation with a woman. Heep will take the photographs and assuming you admit to being unfaithful, your wife will be entitled to an immediate divorce."

"Why should I let Catriona think I've been cheating on her when I've done nothing wrong?"

"Sometimes in life you have to be devious to achieve an equitable result," said Lionel thoughtfully. "Providing the case is heard in a London divorce court, the chances are Catriona will be awarded a decree nisi without a murmur, along with the dozens of other adultery cases. To challenge a cruelty action would be a totally different matter. As you know, adverse publicity could bring about your personal and financial ruin."

"Heep's an expensive bloke," I said. "Surely to stage an artificial liaison with a disreputable woman is going to cost me a lot of money."

"A hotel bill, a payment to the woman, plus Heep's hourly rate. That's the extent of it, apart from my bill, of course, which will be very modest compared with the huge costs you would incur if you decide to defend."

Colin Heep was skilled in providing evidence that satisfied divorce courts that infidelity in a marriage had taken place. Boasting of client satisfaction in the past, he declared there was no other private investigator in the north of England with his experience or expertise.

A few days later, I received a letter from Heep. He instructed me to be at the Crown Hotel in Leeds at 6.00 p.m. on Friday, the 11th February, where a room was to be reserved in my name. After registering at reception, I was to go to the room and would be met shortly afterwards by Heep and a woman. The whole business, I was told, would take only a few minutes. *"It could not be more simple,"* the letter concluded. *"I promise it will go without a hitch."*

After collecting the key from the hotel receptionist, I thought I recognised a man standing at the far end of the foyer. Believing him to be the father of an Oxton House boarder, I made for the lift, feeling very self-conscious and blushing like a beetroot, hoping I'd managed to avoid being seen. By the time I had entered the room, I was shaking with fear, eager for the sleazy mission to be over and done with as speedily as possible.

At a quarter past six, there was a knock on the door. Having checked the identity of the caller, I opened up to Mr Heep, who was accompanied by a young woman wearing what looked like a khaki trench coat. Though not unattractive, rouge on her cheeks and heavily painted lips gave her the appearance of a tart, which I supposed was what she was.

"I want you both to remove your clothes down to your underwear and lie on the bed together," said Heep. "All you have to do is make it *look* as if you're being amorous. I shall do the rest."

He clicked away with his camera for two or three minutes, after which he made noises of approval before advising the unknown woman she was free to leave.

"I told you it would go without a hitch," he said, his chest puffing up with pride at the thought of another job well done. "Mr Spriggs will have the photographs on Monday."

Much to my relief, Lionel wrote to say Catriona had withdrawn the cruelty claim and had decided to petition for divorce on the grounds of adultery. The case was to be heard in London and because I would not be defending, there was no need for me to attend.

Late one afternoon in May, I received a telephone call from Lionel in London. "It's good news," he said. "The judge has awarded a decree nisi. I'm pleased to be able to confirm the court was empty, apart from Catriona and that Twining fellow. There was not a reporter in sight."

"Thank God for that," I said. "Was a decision made about the maintenance payments?"

"The judge is content for the payments to remain unchanged unless your income alters. You will have to pay half Catriona's costs, but there is no question of you having to make a capital settlement on top in view of the fact there are no children. The result couldn't be fairer. In three months, you'll be a free man."

I should have been pleased and grateful. Instead I felt a sense of failure and despair. Not a quitter by nature, I had always believed the marriage could be saved. To capitulate was to have registered acceptance of that failure. Tongues would wag for months. Narrow-minded critics would have a field day. To enable me to cope, I needed to plunge myself more deeply into my work and pray for courage and resilience, the qualities best suited to repair my fractured heart.

— Twenty-Nine —

CONSTANT THOUGHTS OF Catriona and what might have been plagued me so mercilessly that I often cried myself to sleep. I would wake up in the middle of the night, only to find the pain worsening, my thoughts wandering in a void. I still yearned for the security and love I remembered from my parents' marriage. No matter how much this was my goal, I knew it would take years before I dared, if ever, to tie the knot a second time. The scandal of the divorce led me to wonder whether I was doing my uncle and aunt a disservice by remaining at the school. Yorkshire folk were known to be generous, honest and straightforward. For all that, many were quick to condemn the unfortunate few whose marriages failed. When people became aware that Catriona was never coming back, their reactions to me changed. A small number shunned me altogether, refusing to look me in the eye, as if my now single status was a hideous act of treachery. Others treated me with suspicion, while many whose friendships I had valued became indifferent and remote. I was at a loss to know how to repair the damage I unwittingly had done.

Uncle Don could understand my private struggle. Possessing amazing insight, he must have read my thoughts. One day he raised the morbid subject of death duties, warning how the penal tax might affect the survival prospects of the school. Seeing my distress, he spoke gently and with feeling, "Steady on, old chap. I've no desire to upset you, but we have to face facts. I'm not a fit man and one day I'm going to die."

His words again highlighted the affection I felt for my dedicated patron, who had loved me as much as any blood father could have done. I needed him always to be there, to witness changes for the better and to live long enough to be proud of my achievements. It was unthinkable that the time would come when he would be taken from us.

"I don't want to talk about death or dying," I said. "The thought's too painful. You and Aunt Olive are the very essence of this place. So fundamental is your influence that without you both an essential part of what's best at Oxton House could never be replaced."

"You've already filled my place, and with distinction," he said. "Nothing stays the same. What we did ten years ago is no longer relevant. With you in charge, Oxton House has a splendid future. You *are* the future, our investment and our pension. We could wish for no fairer deal than that."

What he said next shocked me to the core. Having carefully discussed the subject with my aunt, he told me they had decided to give the entire school business and premises to me with immediate effect. The purpose of this step was not only to avoid death duties, but to provide me with a greater measure of protection and security.

"I find it hard to take this in," I said, struggling for words. "The divorce has brought disgrace on the school, yet you plan to give me everything. It doesn't make sense."

"It makes a great deal of sense. We've made the decision to demonstrate our trust in you and our belief that under your leadership the school will thrive. The divorce was not your fault and believe you me it will turn out to be a seven-day wonder."

Brushing aside a tear, I admitted that to be accorded such generous backing boosted my confidence at a time when I was feeling particularly low. "What about Giles?" I asked. "He's going to be livid to think you are depriving him of his birthright. He's never liked me and such action would give him cause to hate me with a passion."

Giles had landed on his feet. Having married Philippa, the only child of a wealthy businessman, his father-in-law had purchased for the couple a house in Mayfair as a wedding present. Successful in his own right, Giles stated openly he would soon be a millionaire and he gained pleasure telling everyone he met that he was already earning more than the prime minister.

"Of course we've consulted Giles," said Uncle Don. "He's never shown a scrap of interest in the school. I'm not in the least bit surprised he's happy for you to own it."

"That's very magnanimous of him," I said. "What if he changes his mind?"

"I've instructed Spriggs to attend to the paperwork. Giles can change his mind, but if he does it will be too late. He says he wants to create his own destiny and make his mark without any help from us."

"You've answered my concerns," I said. "Five years ago he would have throttled me rather than let me have anything he felt was rightly his."

So the documents were duly signed at the office of Lionel Spriggs. At the age of twenty-eight, not only had I become heir to everything connected with the school, I was also a lawful partner, with the right to have my say in the making of decisions.

"Providing Donald and Olive live for seven years," said Spriggs, "there will be no imposition of tax, whereas should one or other of them die within this period, death duties will apply on a sliding scale, reducing as each year passes. It's up to you, Paul, to see they avoid stress so that they live long and happy lives!" Shaking hands with the three of us, beaming a mischievous smile, he went on to advise us further. "Whenever you purchase more assets for the school, make sure they are in Paul's name," he said. "Even though all three of you are partners, it's essential for him to be the sole owner in property acquisitions and for his name to be the only one to appear on any of the deeds."

Lost for words by their big-hearted gesture, I racked my brains to come up with an idea, no matter how small, that would enable me to reciprocate their kindness. Inspiration struck one night as I lay restlessly awake. It occurred to me that throughout their married life my uncle and aunt had never had a home they could call their own. They had always shared their living quarters with the pupils, having denied themselves the right to personal space and privacy. The answer was obvious. By allowing them to live in the cottage, I could then move to the main school building, where I would be on the spot to take on more duties and reduce their daily burdens. After airing my proposal, I discovered they were divided in their views.

"The last thing I want is to be forced to budge from what is familiar," protested Uncle Don, noticeably put out. "I like being in the thick of it and can't stomach the thought of living in a place no bigger than a box."

"You're selfish and ungrateful," accused aunt Olive. "You know how much I've always wanted us to live separately from the school in a home of our own."

"I'm not moving and that's final," he said, refusing to listen.

"If that's the case, we shall have to live apart," she threatened. "For all these years I've put you first. This time I won't give in."

As the argument became more heated, I regretted having made the suggestion in the first place. What irritated was that I knew perfectly well once he moved he would soon value the advantages. I needed one good incentive to get him to change his mind.

Ever since Catriona's departure, Uncle Don had gained pleasure from taking Krissa out for walks. These were only gentle saunters because the old man's disabilities prevented him from moving fast, a fact uncannily understood by the perceptive Labrador. The two were the best of pals and when I was at work Krissa would lie at my uncle's feet, panting with pleasure, idolizing his new-found master. The solution was self-evident.

"If you decide to live in the cottage, Krissa can then belong to you," I said.

"He's your dog, you can't give him away."

"I wouldn't part with him to just anybody. Besides, the two of you are inseparable. By having him all the time you can increase your daily exercise, which will help to extend your life. Remember what Lionel Spriggs said about living another seven years."

"Alright, alright," he said. "You win the debate. I've told you many times I'm putty in your hands."

Aunt Olive was now smiling, amused to think her husband had reversed his decision on account of an affectionate canine creature.

"I don't mind sharing the cottage with Krissa," she said. "But I draw the line at feeding him. This will be Donald's job and if I find dog mess or hairs, I refuse to clear them up!"

As the months passed, I was forced to accept I was on a lonely journey and that the woman of my dreams had discarded me for reasons I would never understand. Although news of her occasionally filtered through, it was difficult to assess whether what I heard was fact or fiction. When it was rumoured Tim had moved to London and was living close to Catriona, it was pointless for me to check the truth behind the story, knowing any research I carried out could only lead to further heartache. The marriage was over.

A chapter in my life had ended. A new one was beginning. The responsibilities of school helped to focus my attention on issues over which I at last enjoyed generous autonomy, freed from a fickle wife's disruptive influence. Despite the breakdown of my marriage, numbers at Oxton House continued to increase. With facilities overstretched, the school was visibly bursting at the seams. Having taken on more teachers, it was frustrating to have to turn away bright pupils on account of lack of space. There was an urgent need to expand the size and scope of the business. At a private meeting with David Banks and Stephen Rice, we decided to form a committee of key staff and some influential parents, to determine the best way forward.

I held firm opinions about what was needed. So strong was the demand for boarding places that I had secretly begun to look for additional accommodation. When a large property next door to Oxton House came up for sale, it was essential to acquire it. My aim was to convince committee members that such a development would help to raise standards in a much more spacious physical environment.

The committee included seven parents: Julian de Vere Standley, who was a bank manager in York; a solicitor; an accountant; an estate agent; and three mothers, among whom was Lady Boddington, wife of a baronet and a fervent believer in boarding. Joining David, Stephen and myself as school representatives was Miss O'Sullivan, our highly respected matron. On the night of the first meeting, committee members were invited to a dinner at the school. For the main course, cook served up her famous pigeon pie, accompanied by wine selected by my uncle. By ensuring everyone was suitably fed and watered, I hoped to generate an atmosphere of support and friendliness that would bear fruit later on. Assembling after dinner in the library, I explained how the acquisition of the house next door would relieve congestion in the main school building. By moving the boarders to more suitable premises, space would be released to allow for additional classrooms and specialist facilities for art and music.

"Before making a commitment, I wanted to seek your views," I said. "It's been estimated the entire project will cost somewhere in the region of twenty-two thousand pounds, to include alterations and improvements in both buildings."

"Sounds a lot," moaned the solicitor, Donald Grumball, whose name seemed to encapsulate his griping personality.

"Please let me finish," I said. "What I want to stress is the effect all this will have on numbers. We could take another twenty-five boarders and from the third form upwards it would be possible to introduce a two-stream system which would dramatically improve academic standards."

"How many more boys would this allow you to take?" asked Mr Standley.

"A total of two hundred on roll would be our target, an increase of sixty."

"I hope you will permit me to make a couple of points," ventured David Banks. "In a short time we've all seen Oxton House develop from a tiny school to one with the potential to compete with the very best. The benefits to be derived from growth are indisputable. The opportunity to acquire next door may never come again."

"I concur with that," said John Sharpe, the estate agent. "I know for a fact the previous occupants lived there for the best part of twenty years." During a pause there were nods of approval, indicating that the committee as a whole supported the concept of expansion.

"What will you do for games with the extra numbers?" demanded Lady Boddington.

"A fitting question. We shall continue to play in the park," I replied. "Having said that, I'm well aware we need our own playing field and I promise you this will be our next priority."

"Good show," enthused Lady Boddington.

"This talk of enlargement is all very well," cautioned Mr Grumball. "If the extra numbers you talk about don't materialize, we shall be in a frightful mess. The school might close, in which case the boys would have to leave and the staff lose their jobs."

"You are talking rubbish, you witless idiot," said Lady Boddington. "We have here a thriving school, ripe for growth, supported by a dedicated staff, with everything going for it. All you can do is put obstacles in the way of progress. You can rest assured, headmaster, that all sensible people present will give you their one hundred per cent support."

Before closing the meeting, I asked for a show of hands to indicate those favouring the plan. Backing was unanimous, except for the sardonic Mr Grumball, who remained the sole dissenter.

— Thirty —

A WEEK LATER I received a telephone call from Julian Stand-ley, asking to see me as a matter of urgency. Lacking his usual bright and breezy manner, he gave the impression I had done something to upset him. Perturbed by his unaccountable impatience, I cancelled a social engagement to make myself available to see him that same evening. Julian was just the sort of parent we wanted to attract. Young, ambitious and enjoying a formidable reputation as a financial whizz-kid, he managed the largest bank in York and was clearly going places. It was only a matter of time before promotion took him to a more senior position somewhere else. His two sons were all-rounders, gifted academically and good at sport. The elder boy, Charles, played the violin with sensitivity and skill. His brother, Daniel, at the age of nine was already the most talented artist in the school. I was conscious it would be no less than a calamity to lose two boys with such potential.

At the start of the interview, Julian cleared his throat before coming to the point. "I'm going to withdraw Charles and Daniel from Oxton House at the end of this term. I know I'm supposed to give you a term's notice, but circumstances beyond my control have made this impossible."

Taken aback at the news, I asked him what had brought about this sudden turn of events. Cold fear gripped me. Was this Catriona's latest attempt to ruin my reputation?

"Barclays want to move me to Birmingham," he said. "Much as we like living in Yorkshire, the offer is too tempting for me to miss. I'm sure you will understand that if I turn the offer down, I'm unlikely to be given a second chance."

Relieved to hear nothing at the school was to blame for his decision, I began to think up a rationale that might encourage him to board his sons. Stressing that to uproot the boys was bound to set them back, I urged him to think carefully before transferring them

171

to another school. The main thrust of my argument was that this could be the first of yet more moves and each time this happened Charles and Daniel would be further unsettled.

"Janet and I have always wanted to play a full part in our sons' education," he said. "That's why we chose to send them to a day prep. school."

"I appreciate your reasoning," I told him. "What you've got to decide is whether you are prepared to sacrifice their happiness and success for the sake of your career."

"I resent that remark," he said, vexed to think I had the temerity to accuse him of being a selfish parent. "It's perfectly in order for you to offer advice, but I get the feeling your attitude is grossly partisan."

"Meaning what?" I asked.

"It's obvious you are trying to get me to enrol Charles and Daniel as boarders because you're intending to open a new boarding house and need pupils to fill it."

"Would that be so bad? There are three prep. schools in Birmingham and one in Solihull, none of them better than Oxton House. Charles and Daniel are settled here and doing well. Why upset the status quo by moving them to a school where they might no longer excel? My recommendation is for you to keep them here for one more term and see how they fare. If they enjoy boarding, my view is you should let them stay, on condition you remain happy with their progress."

"Birmingham's too far away for them to board," he said. "Janet and I would be miserable without them. An empty house at weekends would be unbearable."

Reminding him of his family's affection for Yorkshire, I suggested that regular weekend visits to coincide with seeing the boys could be the ideal compromise. Looking at me quizzically, he told me I was the most manipulative schoolmaster he'd ever met. Casting a wry smile, he said: "Give me time to think about it."

Regretting I might have overstated my case, I assumed Julian's mind was made up and no matter how convincing were my arguments he was unlikely to change his view. My relief was immense when before assembly the following morning he phoned me with an unexpected answer. Having discussed the situation with his sons, they were so upset at the thought of moving to another school that Julian and Janet de Vere Standley were left in no doubt as to what

172

to do. "We've opted for them to board," he said. "As a trial to begin with, but I have a strong suspicion you are going to be lumbered with us for another four years."

This fact of itself was cause for a celebration, but his next statement was better than a win on the football pools. Reiterating his approval of the school's development programme, he went on to say he was prepared to consider granting a loan for up to twenty-five thousand pounds.

"This would be on condition the bank has a charge on both properties," he said. Using the pragmatic language of a banker he added: "I shall need a detailed business plan, showing estimated income and how you propose to repay the loan with interest over an eight-year period."

To avoid the sale of the property next door to another buyer, I had to act fast. Staying up all night, I worked on the business plan, helped by Elsie Chapman, who always turned up trumps in times of crisis. By six o'clock next morning the draft was ready. After some minor editing, she then typed the final version. Knowing Julian always dropped the boys off at eight-thirty, I stood waiting for him on the drive.

"I am impressed," he said as I handed him the envelope.

"There's not a moment to waste. We can't afford to lose the house," I said, still on a high, despite my lack of sleep.

"There's no harm in getting the ball rolling with the agents," he said in an attempt to calm me down. "It will take a few days before I get back with a definite decision." Pleased to think he was playing an important part in providing financial backing for the school, after depositing his sons, he drove off.

By pulling strings and with a vested interest, Julian must have quickened up the process. To my delight, later that week he phoned through the news saying the bank was prepared to loan the school the sum of twenty-five thousand pounds. "What's good about the deal," he confided, "is that the bank is to charge 1½ per cent above base rate, which is not much more than what is offered to our blue-chip customers. I can guarantee that any other lender would charge 2½ per cent and possibly as much as 4 per cent. I congratulate you on your perseverance and suggest you get on to the agents straight away and put in an offer for the house."

Success in the business sense, I was fast learning, depended a great deal on who you knew. Luck also played a part and it was good fortune indeed for me to have Julian batting for my team. Making a deliberate attempt to subdue any outward show of eagerness, I went to see Victor Turrell, the estate agent handling the sale. I told him I thought the asking price of just under ten thousand pounds was too high in view of the poor standard of upkeep at the property. Assuring him I was in a position to exchange contracts at once, I put in an offer for nine thousand, two hundred and fifty pounds. He informed me the vendors were sticking to their price and that another prospective purchaser was about to carry out a survey. Aware of the disastrous consequences should the school fail to acquire more land and buildings, first thing next morning I upped my offer to the full amount.

I instructed Lionel Spriggs to attend to the legal work. One month later, Wyvern Lodge, a nine-bedroomed residence, situated in an acre of garden immediately adjacent to the school, became part of the Oxton House empire. By early January I was in possession of the keys. This left us with eight months before the start of the new school year to complete building work and renovations. Plumbing for the extra bathrooms was a major undertaking.

At the end of the contract we all agreed the facilities, which included ten light and airy dormitories, were impossible to fault. As well as decorating the entire house, an extension provided accommodation for a married housemaster and his family. The expansion also required changes to the main school building: the conversion of dormitories into classrooms and the allocation of space to provide an office and reception area. An annexe was built next to the kindergarten, equipped as a music classroom, with six soundproofed teaching and practice cubicles. After a mad scramble to get the builders to complete on time, the school opened its doors at the start of the Michaelmas term with a full complement of boys and only three remaining vacancies for boarders.

Lady Boddington enjoyed being the centre of attention. Nothing gave her greater pleasure than when she arranged charity events or was supporting one of her many worthy causes. After the school's expansion plans had been announced, she came to me with a proposal. "No doubt you have your share of whingeing parents," she said. "What I'd like to know is how many offer you practical assistance and are prepared to be of help."

174

"We provide a service for which a termly fee is paid," I replied. "The most I ever hope for is for our customers to recommend us to their friends."

"That's a load of nonsense," tut-tutted Lady Boddington, who began talking about her current craze. "Anyone with a grain of sense knows that to run a show like this is bloody hard work. The parents are in partnership with the school and it's up to us all to pull together."

I wasn't quite sure what she was getting at until she touched on the controversial subject of appealing to the parents to help raise funds for the expansion.

"We are a privately owned business; it would be immoral to go begging in this way," I said.

"You've a lot to learn," scoffed Lady Boddington. "When I was at Cheltenham Ladies' College, there were masses of appeals and nobody objected."

"Unlike Cheltenham, we are not a charity. You can hardly expect the Oxton House parents to donate money, which would be the same as putting money in the pockets of the Elliott family."

"The trouble is you are frightened of upsetting people. You need to be more assertive," she said, eager to stake her claim as ruler of the roost.

Had anyone other than Lady Boddington made this remark, I might have taken it as an insult. She was, we all knew, a nonconformist, an exception to each and every rule. In full flow, she turned on me with typical directness. "You may not feel able to agree to an appeal, a stance I must accept, but I'm damned if you're going to stop me from raising money on the school's behalf."

For months she worked tirelessly, aided by a committee of her choosing. She arranged coffee mornings, a sponsored walk, bring and buy sales, two dinner dances, a barbecue, and an equestrian event. Her money-raising efforts concluded with a summer fête, held in the grounds of her husband's estate, and opened by an earl whose imposing presence added a touch of class to the event.

At the end-of-year assembly, Lady Boddington presented me with a cheque for seven thousand pounds. Restating that only the best was acceptable for the boys of Oxton House, she instructed me to spend the money on luxury items that might not otherwise be afforded by the school.

"There's enough in the kitty to purchase musical instruments, a kiln and potter's wheel, sports equipment, perhaps a trampoline, a television set and furniture for the boarders' common room. Don't skimp on the quality of what you buy and get exactly what is needed," pontificated Lady Boddington, who was clapped and cheered by her admiring audience.

Other private schools in the area had begun at last to regard us a threat. In a short time we at Oxton House had travelled far, given the support of several influential parents. Little did I know this period of change was to herald the beginning of an expansion that would surpass my wildest expectations.

— Thirty-One —

TO SURVIVE IN the ruthless world of commerce, private schools have to make a profit. Empty desks and beds offer proof of the potential to generate more income. Acting as ambassadors, the teachers have an enormous part to play in marketing these institutions. They are the people responsible for bringing about success or failure. Once parents are satisfied there is a stable staff in place, they come knocking on our doors, eager to secure places for their children. My ambition to make Oxton House the best school of its kind could only be achieved with the help of a first-rate workforce. The expansion in numbers necessitated some new appointments. As well as advertising nationally, we placed notices in some of the local papers. To persuade strong candidates to apply, we offered a number of perks, including a concession in fees for staff children and free accommodation for those preferring to be resident.

I had planned to advertise for a housemaster to take charge of the boarders. David Banks was keen to be considered, announcing to my surprise he was about to marry and that the self-contained flat was exactly what he wanted.

"Wouldn't the extra responsibilities detract from your other duties?" I asked him warily.

"You know I'm committed heart and soul to this place," he said. "You have my word that if you give me this chance, you won't regret it."

So it was with confidence I offered him the post. By Christmas, he and his wife, Fiona, a trained physiotherapist, were running the boarding house like clockwork, aided by Miss O'Sullivan and her assistant.

Boys of high intelligence benefited from our policy of singling out the ablest pupils early on, ensuring they were suitably stimulated, whilst allowing no time for boredom. By the age of thirteen, a gifted prep. school child was covering work in advance of the 'O' level syllabus. In striving for the highest standards, it was vital for me to employ good honours graduates with the capacity to cater for the needs of some of the brightest children in the land.

Proof of an exceptional school is that it has no weaknesses. Prior to the expansion, I knew perfectly well that much of what we did could be improved. Although academic standards came first, it was commonly accepted that a pupil who achieved success in other areas went on to make better progress with his work. For this reason, standards in games, music, art and drama mattered greatly in our quest to provide each boy with the opportunity to excel at something. A dynamic director of music was sought to head what I hoped would be a thriving new department. And to vitalize a lacklustre physical education programme, I wanted a skilled athlete with passionate ambitions. The music post was the most difficult one to fill. The adverts brought such a poor response that not one applicant was felt to be worthy of an interview. Then out of the blue came a letter from an unemployed musician, who had taught for five years at a rival school in Harrogate. Possessing the desired qualifications, he stated he was well versed in what a director of music's role entailed. The drawback was he had fallen out with his most recent head, who refused to recommend him. It all sounded very fishy, but there was something about the application that intrigued me.

A heavily built forty-nine year old with a flamboyant personality, Herbert Bond was no shrinking violet. Articulating his words with clarity and style, his powerful voice drew everyone's attention. During the interview he convinced me, given sufficient freedom, he had the ability to achieve superlative results, an opinion shared by David Banks. Uncle Don was less enthusiastic. "To take on someone else's reject is a risk I wouldn't take," he said. "By doing so could mean inheriting a burden. I'll grant he's an accomplished musician and has a lively sense of humour, but I can't see him taking kindly to working under someone so much younger than himself." Notwithstanding my uncle's reservations, we decided to offer Herbert Bond the job.

Of the three physical education applicants on the shortlist, Andrew Brooke was by far the most impressive. After training at Loughborough College, he had worked for three years at a grammar school in Hull. Married with a baby daughter, he hungered for promotion. Unlike most games teachers, whose toned physiques exemplified the nature of their trade, Andrew was a weedy-looking specimen, whose mop of ginger hair matched the goatee beard that sprouted from his chin. In spite of his appearance, he was a fine sportsman. His references described him as a hard-working teacher, whose management skills would be difficult to match. When David and I asked him whether he liked the idea of working at the school, he seemed uncertain. Criticizing the lack of provision for physical education, he said he was surprised to learn there was no swimming pool and that games were still being played in a public park a ten-minute walk away. He blushed noticeably before continuing to make his point. "The department is clearly underfunded. Do you plan to allocate more money for its development in the future?"

I pointed out that Rome wasn't built in a day and that we were spending a vast sum on improvements. David confirmed progress recently made had been nothing less than staggering. To help influence Andrew's decision, I made a proposal. "Prove capable of achieving the results you say you can and I promise the PE department will be the next priority as far as spending is concerned."

"That being the case, you can count me in," said Andrew, delighted to think he was about to face the challenge of his life.

Several parents had grumbled about poor standards in French. Complaints were well justified because leavers taking the common entrance and scholarship examinations had for some time performed badly in the subject. Apart from the top classes, which were taught by a tired, elderly part-timer, lower down the school the boys had been receiving an inadequate grounding from a master who could claim no more than a basic knowledge of the language. A complete overhaul was needed to raise the subject's dismal profile to a higher level. Nicole Tyler, a French woman in her twenties, submitted the strongest application. Graduating at the Sorbonne, she had trained as a teacher in Nice, where she met and married Steve, an Englishman, who returned with his bride to live and work in Yorkshire. Four years later Steve deserted Nicole, leaving her to look after their three-year-old son in what was to her a foreign country. It was not until her widowed mother moved to England that Nicole was able to seek a job. What she lacked in experience was more than compensated for by her determination to produce results. A competitor by nature, she was not one to be satisfied with second best. "Give me a year," she said. "After that time, I guarantee

French will be the most popular subject in the school and should any boy fail to pass the common entrance in my subject, I would be happy to receive a reduction in my salary. That's how confident I am!" It's little wonder that we opted to give Nicole the chance to prove her worth.

To complete the appointments, Jean Rourke, trained as an infant teacher, was chosen to head the team of mistresses responsible for the youngest children in the school. Her brief was to ensure each boy could read, write and cope with basic number work before embarking on the rigorous prep. school syllabus. To strengthen administrative efficiency, Elsie Chapman was moved from kindergarten to become my full-time secretary and a young woman with bookkeeping skills was employed as assistant to the bursar. Much to my relief, all four new teachers settled in speedily and after the first four weeks of term each one was proving to be an asset.

Herbert Bond's greatest strength was undoubtedly the singing. Daily choir practices, conducted with disciplined precision, swiftly achieved results. I had to admit the sounds emanating from the music room were hard to distinguish from the tuneful utterances made by cathedral choristers.

If enthusiasm was anything to go by, one would have thought the 1st XI football team trained harder than professionals. Pushing the boys to the utmost of their limits, Andrew Brooke would accept from them nothing but their best. Strutting about the pitch like an army general, whistle at the ready, he made a daring boast: *The first three games we've won, with not a goal conceded. I'll eat my hat if we lose a single match!*

Nicole Tyler soon earned the reputation for working the boys so hard that they were left with little time to cope with preps set by her colleagues, a habit that caused some ructions in the staff room. "I've had to start from scratch," she said, defending her policy of setting huge lists of words and verbs to be learnt by rote. I was fortunate to be an observer at some of her early lessons. A resourceful teacher, she used compulsive powers, instilling in each child a love of French and a desire to do his best.

At the most junior level, the boys' happiness had to be the prime consideration. An expert at knowing how to respond in any situation, Jean Rourke was capable of playing a variety of parts. She could be compassionate, patient, resourceful and long-suffering, but when strength was called for, she was capable of firmness.

Above all, she cared deeply for the boys and staff for whom she was responsible. Managing her department with attention paid to the minutest detail, she was professional through and through.

Recent developments had been so numerous and far-reaching that a casual observer would have been justified in thinking the original Oxton House had disappeared. Functioning with well-ordered efficiency, the school was at last able to offer the quality of service I had always wanted. I owed this entirely to my employees, each of whom played an important part, no matter how menial, with commitment and devotion. Rather than hide our light under a bushel, my next aim was to broaden the school's appeal by spreading the word beyond the horizons of the neighbourhood.

Up until then advertising had been a dirty word in the sheltered world of private education. Attitudes were changing. Not before time more blatant marketing techniques were being used. I must have been one of the first headmasters to use the services of a public relations firm. I nicknamed Geoff Parker of Parker Enterprises, Mr Fixit. Not only was he on good terms with influential Yorkshire journalists, he knew how to place a good story in the nationals. For a monthly fee, he arranged for articles about the school to feature in magazines, and eye-catching pieces began to appear in newspapers as far afield as Sheffield, Leeds and York.

"For a special news item," he crowed, "I have friends in high places at the BBC, television and local radio stations."

True to his word, he suggested opening the new music building with a flourish. To mark the occasion, a celebrated concert pianist, an old boy of the school, gave a recital before an audience of parents, boys and local VIPs. After being provided with enough alcoholic refreshment to satisfy a paparazzi regiment, photographers snapped their cameras and the reporters scribbled notes. Most valuable of all was a slot on Yorkshire television that allowed me two minutes to answer questions about the school's dramatic growth,

Consistent with the policy of trumpeting our achievements from the rooftops, we began sending regular press releases to all the newspaper editors in the region. By drip-feeding news of our successes in this way, what had once been an unknown school came to be seen by members of the public as a trendsetting place of learning.

— Thirty-Two —

CAUTIOUS BY NATURE, my uncle hated the thought of owing money. He constantly warned against the perils of ambition, openly admitting he would not have had the guts to saddle himself and the school as I had done with debts that might never be repaid. *What if there's another depression? What if pupil numbers drop? What if the government legislates against this type of school?* These were some of the questions he would ask. In his younger days, he'd taken the occasional chance and tried out schemes that failed, too timid to risk investing for the future. The situation now was different. Not only was the school much in demand, it accommodated as many boys as we could take and there was a healthy waiting list.

Despite his original misgivings, Uncle Don was proud to share in the success from the position of adviser. Relieved of most of the stress, like a benevolent chairman of the board, he dispensed direction wisely. When he and I disagreed, it was done with gentlemanly tact, each of us respecting the opinion of the other. Over one matter we were unanimous. We agreed this was a time to consolidate, knowing it would be foolhardy in the extreme to expand the school any further for the present. But once in a while a too-good-to-miss opportunity arises.

It began with a phone call from our nearest neighbour. Jack Letts and his wife, Margaret, owned the market garden adjacent to the school. For three years their son, Austin, had been a pupil at Oxton House. Prior to that he had attended another private school in Harrogate, where he was very unhappy. Gaining confidence in leaps and bounds, young Austin blossomed way beyond the limits of his parents' expectations. So grateful were they for what seemed to them a miracle, they were effusive in their praise, saying they wanted to donate a prize to express their gratitude. When Jack came to see me, I assumed it was to talk about that offer or some equally mundane matter. His weather-beaten face indicated he led an open-air existence and I could not help noticing his cheeks were especially red that morning.

"We've decided to sell up," he announced with typical northern bluntness. "It's a bad time for market gardens. Margaret and I have slaved away for nigh on twenty years with little to show for profit. We've enjoyed the life, but we aren't getting any younger. The last thing we want is to keep the business going for Austin's sake. He's destined for something a great deal better, thanks to the start you've given him." Describing in detail his reasons for wanting to quit, he coughed nervously before coming to the point. "Do you want to buy my land?" he asked.

In its present state, the land was of no use to us. A number of greenhouses lay randomly scattered over a site of 9.7 acres. There was a paddock and stables, a store area, an office with a counter that gave the appearance of a shop, two derelict barn-like buildings and a car park accessible from a narrow track. Some of the land was unused and therefore unproductive. A big advantage was that the entire area was flat, with no evidence of an incline.

"I'll not try to pull the wool," said Jack. "After father popped his clogs, he provided for us well. We were able to pay off the mortgage on the house and there's enough left over to cover the remainder of Austin's education. We live frugally, so as you can see our needs are not that great." I had to pinch myself to believe what I was hearing. The possibility of acquiring a large strip of land immediately next to the school was so fortuitous it would have been pure madness not to jump for joy and put the wheels in motion straight away. *But, hang on,* I thought, *how is a market garden business valued and why hasn't Jack applied for planning permission to develop the land for housing?* He must have been reading my mind.

"You obviously want the facts," he said. "Taking into account our profits for the last five years, the goodwill of the business and agricultural values, we've been advised to put everything on the market for eleven thousand, seven hundred and fifty pounds."

"Is that all? I don't pretend to know anything about your kind of business or land values. Have you not considered the development of housing?"

"We've had meetings with planners, solicitors, a barrister and every conceivable expert you can name. Each time we've drawn a blank. Without better access, we are fighting a hopeless cause. That's why I've come to you. You've been so good to us and Austin that as a special favour I'm prepared to reduce the asking price by 10%. Quite tempting, don't you think?"

The prospect of having our own playing field filled me with such excitement that I failed to give sufficient consideration to the financial implications. The acquisition of the land alone would require more borrowing. For a specialist firm to carry out the levelling and drainage and to provide pitches of professional standard, including a cricket square, would be a major additional expense. Naively thinking Barclays would be happy to oblige, I told Jack that, subject to the bank's approval, I was ready to go ahead. Even though Julian Standley was now living in Birmingham, I still looked upon him as a business adviser, whose opinion I respected. He of all people would understand why I had set my heart on embarking on another innovative project. Outlining the relevant facts in a letter, I ended by saying there was a further borrowing requirement of a little in excess of fifteen thousand pounds and I was sure he would want to help. In his reply Julian reprimanded me for contacting him direct, saying I should first have approached the manager in York. The letter continued in pessimistic vein.

I have taken the liberty of studying the figures provided for the bank by your accountant. You will have seen for yourself that, after meeting your commitments, the surplus left over is insufficient to justify more borrowing. In my view, no bank would agree to lend you the sum of fifteen thousand pounds to finance a scheme that will not increase your income. Speaking as one of your strongest supporters, I urge you to forget the whole idea. Cash flow, or lack of it, is a serious handicap. Believe you me, I have seen many good businesses come to grief when expenditure exceeds the income. I am sorry to disappoint.

On a more cheerful note, Charles and Daniel are exceptionally happy at your school and we continue to be delighted with their progress. The best thing Janet and I ever did was to keep them on as boarders.

Kindest regards,
Yours sincerely,
Julian

Outraged by his response, I hated Julian for his patronising dismissal of a fantastic proposal. By playing God and lacking the courage and imagination to back me up, what he'd done was to strengthen my resolve. It was all very well for him to sit in his ivory

184

tower presiding in smug judgement over others, pushing paper, destroying dreams and sticking to his rigid formula. To hell with bankers! No matter what it took, I *had* to find the money for the land.

After Lady Boddington got wind of what was happening, she came hurrying to the school. She delighted in telling me more than I knew myself. "We've done some calculations," she announced. "Mr Brooke and I have worked out the positioning of the pitches."

"What *are* you talking about, Lady Boddington?"

"It's no secret you are about to buy the plot of land next door. Someone's spilt the beans, as practically all the parents are privy to the gossip. Once more unto the breach, I say, with all hands to the pump! You can count on us to back you to the hilt, even if it means seeding the field with our own bare hands."

"Your loyalty is overwhelming, but nothing's been decided. The bank isn't prepared to lend us a penny more, at least not until we can increase our income."

"That's absurd," she muttered scornfully. After drawing breath for a brief moment, she delivered some more advice. "My husband doesn't trust bankers, never has. What you should do is remain positive and determined, put up the fees and not allow a bunch of po-faced idiots stop you from making Oxton House a place we can all be proud of." On saying her piece, she stood tall, nose in the air, and made her customary regal exit.

After a busy day, within minutes of placing my head on the pillow, I was fast asleep. I can't say I never had an interrupted night, but for the most part I enjoyed seven hours of rest and was able to get up refreshed, prepared to meet whatever challenges came my way. Worry about the field changed all that. There were two points of view, both of which made sense. On the one hand, it would have been crazy not to grasp what was a golden opportunity, no matter what it cost, a development that would be the making of the school. Yet there was this terrible doubt. Failure to meet the costs would risk endangering everything the Elliotts held dear, and could lead to the destruction of a dynasty. Indecisive thoughts disturbed the pattern of my sleep. Menacing images in the form of recurrent hallucinations highlighted the wavering doubts in my subconscious. Involving two familiar characters, the dream started in the unlikely setting of the school gymnasium. There was a boxing match in progress.

Lady Boddington had the advantage of carrying a spade, which she repeatedly smacked onto the head of her opponent, who must have been Julian, because as he begged for mercy he was clutching a giant-sized cheque. By the time the referee declared Lady Boddington the winner, his head gashed wide open from the blows, Julian fell to the floor, blood oozing from him like a tap. Then someone blew a whistle, followed by the arrival of the fire brigade. Amidst smoke and chaos, they battled to rescue burning pupils from the flames. Waking in a sweat at two o'clock each morning from the same repetitive nightmare, I couldn't get back to sleep for thinking about the decision I had to make. I did not dare discuss the problem with my uncle.

Sidestepping him completely and feeling like a traitor, I spoke privately with David Banks. His appointment as my deputy had been a significant success. Dependable, level-headed and known for his plain-spoken views, he was just the man to help me find an answer.

"If it's any comfort," he said, "all the staff want the school to buy the market garden."

"Do you share their opinion?" I asked.

"There's no mistaking it would be a major improvement to have more space, but not if it results in the school going bust and us losing our jobs. I've seen how tired you look. What you mustn't do is overcommit yourself to please the likes of Lady Boddington. Any decision you take has to make financial sense."

"That's the problem," I said. "The fact is we *can't* afford to go ahead and if we don't we shall probably be stuck in a rut for years."

David was silent for a while, deep in thought. Seized with a sudden inspiration, he leapt to his feet before making a suggestion. "Why don't you ask Stephen what he thinks."

When I approached the school accountant, he agreed with Julian's view, repeating there was insufficient collateral to justify the extension of the loan. Stephen Rice was less dogmatic. As our enterprising part-time bursar, he possessed more creative imagination than all the puffed-up money experts put together. Why had I not sought his opinion sooner? David was right. No harm would come from giving him a hearing.

Stephen had already considered an alternative way to raise the funds. He said his scheme was by no means foolproof, but handled intelligently the chances of success were high. Intrigued to hear more, I arranged for the two of us to meet. He asked, was I aware that public schools offered a discount of five per cent to parents who elected to pay fees in advance to cover the entire period of their children's education? "I haven't a clue how many take advantage of these schemes," he said.

"Not many," I concluded. "The incentive is not that great, except perhaps for grandparents wanting to avoid death duties. If I parted with thousands of pounds up front for a period of five years, I'd expect a damned sight more than five per cent."

"That's exactly what I think. What I'm about to suggest would be vastly more attractive to a parent." Excitement rising, I was beginning to guess what was coming next. Why hadn't I thought of it myself? "It's a matter of cash flow," he continued. "Using approximate figures, boarding fees amount to four thousand five hundred pounds over a five-year period, whereas for a senior day boy the figure is three thousand pounds. It only requires four lots of fees, two boarders and two day boys, to be paid in advance, for the school to receive sufficient capital to buy the market garden and carry out the preparation of the field."

"We've already agreed a five per cent discount is nowhere near enough," I pointed out, unable to conceal my doubts.

"You know how Yorkshire folk are always looking for a bargain. You can imagine how many takers there would be were we to devise a scheme that excluded all fee increases until the agreement is completed."

"That's an incredibly attractive proposition," I said, applauding his ingenuity. The drawback, though, was obvious. When fees increased, which happened annually, the loss of revenue would merely postpone the problem of the cash flow deficit to a later date. Perceiving my concern, Stephen uncovered yet another of his revolutionary ideas.

"If, for example, fees are paid up front for ten boys, producing a capital sum of sixty thousand pounds, all we have to do is take on ten more pupils. In a school the size we are, an extra desk here and there would make no difference to our image or to standards. With so many names on the waiting list, in next to no time we would fill those extra places."

"The words of a true genius," I exclaimed excitedly, patting him on the back. Imagination running wild and with optimism returning, I instructed Stephen to draft out a specimen agreement. "Ask one of your public school bursar friends to show you the document they use, then amend it to form our own tailor-made agreement."

"The matter's in hand already," he said.

"That's brilliant. You think of everything. Before letting me see the final draft, you'd better get Lionel Spriggs to check out the wording from the legal point of view."

A fortnight later, letters were sent to all the parents, inviting them to participate in the scheme. In view of the substantial discount offered, numbers were to be limited to a maximum of ten. Those seeking a quotation were advised to write directly to the bursar. So the die was now cast. In no hurry to proceed with the sale of his land, Jack Letts had kindly kept his offer open. I hoped soon to be able to let him have my answer.

— Thirty-Three —

S TEPHEN'S SOLUTION WAS absolutely right. Born in the black country town of Wolverhampton and not overly familiar with the Yorkshire frame of mind, it was clever of him to have gauged so accurately parental reaction to his scheme. First to apply was a grandfather, Mr Reginald Briggs. A hard-headed businessman, not content with the advantages on offer, he was cheeky enough to demand a five per cent discount in addition. His plea rejected, he was not to be deterred. Within days he submitted the agreement duly signed in respect of grandsons Paul and Neil, both of whom were boarders. Enclosed with his letter was a cheque in the sum of seven thousand, three hundred and sixty pounds, a response that served as an assuring augury for the future.

Three months later, the fees for nine boys had been paid upfront, totalling fifty-six thousand pounds. This was considerably more than what was needed to purchase the land and establish a playing field on the soon-to-be expanded site. To take on extra pupils was less straightforward. Certain rooms were already full to overflowing, with no space to hold another desk. In three of the largest rooms, two more desks could easily be installed without giving the appearance of overcrowding. Skill was required to ensure that waiting list pupils who were to be offered places matched the age groups where there was space to squeeze them in. With careful rationalization, reinforced by the bursar's inventiveness, the school was able to accommodate ten more boys without undue disruption. There were no complaints about the extra numbers except, that is, from the troublesome Iris Bott. Feared by the staff and a constant trial to me, Mrs Bott, the most obnoxious of the parents, used her acerbic tongue in the manner of a weapon. She specialised in nit-picking and when I spied her one day advancing in my direction, her face hardened and morose, it was too late for me to find a hiding place.

"At last I've tracked you down," she said, her voice conspicuously tetchy. "I thought you were an honourable man, headmaster."

"Have I done something to suggest I'm not?"

"Indeed you have," she thundered. At great length and noisily she reminded me how at our initial interview I'd assured her no class would contain more than fifteen boys. "You are a liar and a cheat," she accused. "I'm disgusted to discover you are taking money under false pretences. Joshua has seventeen in his class and I understand next term numbers in the Kindergarten are to rise. My husband and I demand an immediate reduction in our fees."

Embarrassed and angry to be carrying out this heated conversation in a passage, I escorted her to my study, quietly closing the door behind us. No matter how hard I tried, she was unprepared to accept that to improve the amenities from which both her sons would benefit, it was still up to me to see the business made a profit. Exercising the maximum self-restraint, I suggested coldly perhaps the time had come to arrange for her sons to attend a school that lived up to her exacting expectations.

"How dare you talk to me like that," she screeched. "And I thought you were a gentleman!" After using some choice profanities, she flounced from the room, huffing and puffing as she went.

Later that same morning, Jean Rourke informed me that Mrs Bott had removed Joshua from his class, together with his personal possessions. She had stated moreover he would not be coming back, nor would his brother be starting in September.

Her departure from the scene was like a tonic. The incident taught me an important lesson. I was fast learning it took one rotten apple to contaminate a pile: a disruptive parent, a sadistic teacher, a mutinous cook, an untrustworthy secretary. These were all rotten apples in their way and the school was better off without them. Determining in future to be intolerant of troublemakers, I saw it as my duty to attempt to expunge any subversive elements that threatened to disrupt the peace of our community.

Planning permission for the playing field was easily obtained. Despite my impatience to press ahead, I was warned it could take up to two years before the work would be completed. Meanwhile I had to decide how best to spend the balance of the money. Ideas came flooding in from a variety of sources. The recommendations were wide-ranging: a theatre, a science block, the enlargement of the gym, a war memorial, another boarding house, a swimming pool, a separate junior school, two tennis courts. These were only some of the suggestions. Unable to make the decision on my own, I sent a questionnaire to all the parents, asking what new facilities they would be in favour of supporting. Whether Lady Boddington and Andrew Brooke were in cahoots, canvassing together behind the scenes, I did not know, but the physical education department topped the list by far, with a majority opting for a new gymnasium.

Rubbing his hands with glee when commissioned to oversee the work, the architect wasted no time in presenting a visual impression of a gargantuan building shaped like an airplane hangar that would fit nicely in one corner of the field. "This fine hall will be the talk of the county," he confidently predicted. "Not only can it be built within your budget, there's enough space for four badminton courts, a mini indoor soccer pitch, changing rooms and showers, a stage for drama productions and yes, wait for it, an indoor heated swimming pool." Taken in by his gushing language, and pleased beyond belief at the thought of an exceptional new facility that would make Oxton House unique, I gave him permission to proceed.

Planning consent was difficult to obtain. Some of the neighbours complained about the height of the building, saying it would obstruct their view. Not to be daunted, the architect intimated he had friends on the planning committee, who with a little monetary persuasion would agree to exactly what we wanted. It went against the grain to part with eleven hundred pounds in a grossly dishonest act. That said, however, the workings of the world were never fair and if that was what it took, I hold up my hands and make no excuses for my actions.

Past dealings with builders had been reasonably free of stress. As soon as work started on the sports hall, one problem followed another. First the measurements were wrong, a mistake that almost caused a stand-up fight between architect and builder. Next there was a shortage of materials, for which the architect blamed the builder, who downing his tools, withdrew all his men from the site. To cut a depressing story short, and to overcome the standstill, I engaged the services of a quantity surveyor. In a practical sense, this tactic proved successful, but there was, of course, a downside. Charging an exorbitant fee for his trouble, the surveyor, acting with the impartiality of a judge, insisted we paid compensation to the builders to persuade them to resume their duties. At regular intervals stage payments were made to the builder in accordance with the contract. These were duly met, but because the architect's specification was insufficiently precise, almost weekly there were queries concerning the number of coats of paint, the design of brick, the make of the showers to be installed, lockers and pegs, equipment storage, the style of roofing, the treatment of the floor, the dimensions and quality of the stage, but worst of all was the swimming pool that presented so many snags that I was close to giving up. Unwilling to accept anything less than the best, I reminded the architect of his promise to build the perfect hall within the budget.

After thirteen months of discrepancies and aggravations, with a dwindling bank balance to bear testimony of our ills, the most ambitious project ever to be undertaken by Oxton House was ostensibly completed. I say ostensibly, as there was more and worse to follow.

The playing field contractors complained that some of their work had been ruined by the builders and that it would cost a further nine hundred pounds to repair the damage done. Shortly afterwards, I received the final certificate for payment from the architect. Exceeding the quoted figure by eight thousand pounds, there was a covering note to say the extra charges resulted from my frequent requests to change the specification, involving more expensive materials and last-minute alterations, all of which added to the costs. The bank was unsympathetic. Having seen large sums disappear from the school account, the manager was concerned about the loan, warning me of the action he would take in the event of my failure to stick to the schedule of repayments. No, he wouldn't extend the loan, nor would he as a special favour alter the arrangement, which he described as generous to a fault. The writing was on the wall. Unless I could raise the sum of ten thousand pounds and fast, everything I'd worked for was under threat and in danger of collapse; the toil, the heartache, the sleepless nights, the desire to be the best, the energy expended. And all for what? Ashamed of my inability to think things through, to use financial nous, to practise common sense, I had to make amends, if only to preserve the security of my aunt and uncle. Time was running out. In my attempts to save the day, I devised another action plan, knowing the future of anyone who had a part to play in the workings of our school was dangerously at risk.

Since the divorce, my income had increased substantially. I was now drawing a monthly salary of one hundred and ninety pounds, a fact I was forced to divulge to Catriona, who demanded half my additional earnings as her alimony entitlement. At a meeting with Lionel Spriggs, he agreed it was a monstrous request that was morally unjust. In his letter to her solicitors, he reminded them there were no children from the marriage and that because Catriona was back at work and earning good money, she had no need of the extra income. Dismissing Lionel's argument, Twining telephoned him to say this time their client would not be lenient. Unless fair play was seen to be delivered, he warned he would ask for a full disclosure of my assets, having heard I had become sole owner of the school. Rather than be subjected to interrogation by a judge, with the possibility of a large forfeiture of capital, I increased my payments from seven pounds a week to ninety-five pounds a month. Through reckless action I had manoeuvred the school into a state of financial jeopardy. This was bad enough, but to be deprived of half my earnings when I was working such long hours, doing what was by any standards a very stressful job, seemed totally unfair. On receipt of her first new payment, Catriona wrote me a letter that contained surprising news.

Dear Paul

I do not believe in concealing the truth and I want you to be the first to know I am to marry again. My husband-to-be, Humphrey Green, is a Harley Street doctor, who I have known for over a year. He is twenty years older than me, is kind, tolerant and has done much to restore my faith in men. Despite the gap in our ages, we are a perfect match and I am certain he will make me happy.

The wedding is to take place in two months' time, after which we shall be moving to a house near Sloane Square. This lets you off the hook. I chose to write to you rather than do it through our solicitors. As you know, they often distort the views of the people they represent.

You were good to me in a number of ways and the break-up was hurtful to us both. I should like to think we shall bear no bitterness to one another and that in time we shall retain only the good memories. I wish you happiness and success in the future and hope you can find it in your heart to want the same for me.

Affectionately yours

Catriona

I didn't know whether to be pleased or upset by Catriona's plan to remarry. I had no wish to support her for the remainder of my life, but her engagement represented an allegiance to a newcomer, a man of evident substance, who had it in his power to succeed where I had failed. It was perverse of me to have gained satisfaction from sending her the regular maintenance payments, an action that enabled the two of us to remain in touch. Realizing this contact was about to cease, I was left with a feeling of rejection. The new beginning would mark for me a final dispossession, and not least remove the opportunity to decipher some of the riddles posed by her weird persona. There were so many unsettled questions. What had become of Tim and how had Catriona managed to escape from Andrea's controlling clutches? It was unlikely I would ever know the answers.

Having already raised money for the school by introducing an advanced payment of fees scheme, I had assumed the same method could be used a second time. Lady Boddington was unconvinced. "As a one-off idea, it worked well," she said. "Don't you think you may have killed the golden goose?" She was furious with the architect, seeing him as the prime offender. Convinced that my best remedy was to sue him, she urged me to consult my solicitor at once. For the second time in a month, I sat facing Lionel in his office. His nervous twitch more noticeable than ever, he listened intently as I outlined the problems I had encountered with the architect.

Applying his usual honesty, he again gave me wise advice. "Had you questioned the architect at the outset about the adequacy of his specification, you might have had a case," he said. "I sympathise with the situation in which you find yourself, as it's clear to me he may have acted improperly. To prove negligence, however, is quite another matter." I told him it was wrong for the school to suffer financially as a result of his incompetence. "Incompetence is not the same as dishonesty. In my view, you do not have a leg to stand on in a court of law," he repeated.

"Is there nothing you can do to help?" was all I could say.

"I could find you any number of solicitors who'd be only too pleased to take your money and fight what is an extremely doubtful case. Your time would be far better spent considering how to rectify your indebtedness to the bank."

Whilst Stephen and I were trying to work out the best way of covering the debt, Lady Boddington came up with a proposition. She said her husband was prepared to loan the school ten thousand pounds and would charge the same interest as the bank. For the deal to go ahead, she said they insisted on a reduction in their school fees by an amount equivalent to the value of the interest. On the face of it, this was a generous offer, but as a business transaction it was hazardous. Once the Boddington boys had moved on to Harrow, would Sir Edmund still want the arrangement to continue? And what would happen if I fell out with Lady Boddington or if she became so big for her boots that she began to make demands? We all knew she liked nothing more than to be queen bee and delighted in lording it over others. We concluded it was far better to stick to the original formula and try to persuade more parents to pay the fees upfront. This time, with inflation on the increase, the scheme was even more attractive. Three parents eagerly applied. All that remained was for us to find places for three of the boys whose names were on the waiting list to reduce cash flow problems later on. Taking on more boys required strategic thinking. In view of complaints already made about overcrowding, we had to choose with care where the extra desks would cause the least upset. With numbers already in excess of what was a comfortable quota, we knew this was the last time we could get away with a strategy such as this.

Still wanting to be in the thick of it, Lady Boddington paid me yet another visit. After acclaiming the merits of the sports hall, she made an awkward observation. "I'll grant you it's a fine building, but you must be warned the consensus of opinion is that it's no more than an empty shell."

"That's an exaggeration," I said. "The building is already in use and as soon as the school can afford it, extra items of equipment will be bought."

"You must have forgotten I'm an impatient, obstreperous mother. Rupert is off to Harrow next year and when Dominic follows him two years after that you'll be shot of us for good. I want to see all the facilities in place *now*, rather than for the benefits to be reserved for the next generation."

"I'm not a magician, Lady Boddington," I protested.

"That's a silly thing to say. I think I can do a great deal better," she declared. "Give me a shopping list showing exactly what is needed and you have my word the money will be raised before you can catch your breath."

Knowing once she got the bit between the teeth there would be no stopping her, I did as she asked, appalled to think I had allowed an overbearing parent to dictate what I should do.

It didn't take Andrew Brooke long to itemize his needs, which included apparatus to provide an indoor assault course, parallel bars, diving boards for the pool, gym mats, badminton nets and rackets and four table tennis tables. As well as teaching mathematics and overseeing the school's finances, Stephen was a leading light in amateur dramatic circles and was dying to produce a play on the school's own stage. Given the task of deciding what was required to equip the theatre, he wasted no time in carrying out research. Tongue in cheek he presented Lady Boddington with an exhaustive list: theatre lighting, cinema projection facilities, stage curtaining, blackout blinds and an up-to-date sound system.

"There's something missing," commented a scornful Lady Boddington. "Where the hell do you expect to seat the audience?"

"Stacking chairs will have to be purchased at a later date," said Stephen. "They're really quite expensive."

"Add them to the list," she ordered. "Nobody's going to short-change the boys of Oxton House as long as I'm involved."

Presented with what looked like an unattainable objective, working with fanatical aplomb, she was unwilling to admit defeat. Supported by Andrew, who had set his sights on making the PE department the best equipped in Harrogate, she enlisted the support of a dozen of the pupils' mothers. "The fathers can write out the cheques. That's all they're good for," she said. "We women roll up our sleeves and don't mind what we do. We've got the stamina and the gumption. If we can't raise the money by the end of term, you can exterminate the lot of us."

Having a bee in her bonnet about the effectiveness of sponsored swims, she instructed her helpers to organize two such events, one for seniors and the other for the under-nines. Several boys were capable of swimming fifty lengths and sponsored at £1.00 a length by family and friends, as a money-raising exercise the potential was tremendous. Thanks to Lady Boddington's relentless efforts, the target was quickly reached and the equipment ordered, installed and put to use.

— Thirty-Four —

THE COMPLETION OF the sports' hall was a feat that justified a major celebration. Publicity guru Geoff Parker came up with an enterprising idea. "For an event as big as this, I think we should ask a senior member of the Royal Family to open it," he said. When I suggested he was being overambitious, he disagreed. "I happen to know that Princess Margaret enjoys this kind of engagement. There's no harm in sounding her out. If she refuses, we can't have a second stab at a senior royal, but we might be offered someone like the Duke of Gloucester."

"I'm out of my depth here," I said. "You understand the protocol, so how do I set about making an approach?"

"A letter should first be sent to her private secretary. At the same time it's advisable to offer three or four dates. I would suggest preceding the ceremony with a luncheon for local dignitaries, to include the Lord Lieutenant. The press love covering Margaret as she never fails to add a touch of glamour and once she's had a few drinks she can be fun to entertain." I decided to give it a try.

An invitation was duly sent. Much to our disappointment, the Princess declined with a polite response from her secretary, regretting that Her Royal Highness was already committed on the dates in question. She nevertheless extended her good wishes to all the members of the school, a message I was proud to convey to the staff and boys at a subsequent morning assembly.

Thinking our ambitions were getting out of hand, I called a staff meeting to discuss our plans in greater depth. Some interesting views emerged. Quick to venture an opinion, Herbert Bond felt it was unwise to have approached a member of the Royal Family. "I realize I'm heavily biased in favour of music and am a duffer at games," he admitted ruefully. "Having said that, I feel strongly that the opening is unlikely to be national news. It's a local event and as such should involve a Yorkshire personality. We have a few boarders from far afield and half a dozen from abroad. For the most part our catchment area is within twenty miles of Harrogate."

Andrew Brooke shared Herbert's thinking, saying caustically that Princess Margaret was not noted for her sporting prowess and that as he was on first name terms with three well known athletes, he was quite certain one of them could be persuaded to open the building.

"My uncle has come up with a specific proposal," I said. "We all seem to have forgotten one of our old boys plays cricket for Yorkshire. Richard Fells left Oxton House thirteen years ago, having been the captain of our most successful ever cricket team, and two years ago he was twice selected to play for England."

"That's a far better idea," applauded David Banks, who went on to make another recommendation that had been broached by a number of his colleagues. "Were it not for the efforts of Donald and Olive Elliott, this school would not exist. Everyone knows that. I should like to propose that we name the new sports hall the Donald and Olive Elliott Sports' Centre, and dare I say it, who better to open it than Donald himself?"

Sticking to his guns, Uncle Don was still keen for Richard Fells to be the guest of honour. "Much as your aunt and I are thrilled that the sports' centre is to carry our names, you don't want a couple of fuddy-duddies stealing the show," he said. "As a PR exercise it would be far better to have a talented youngster returning to his old school, especially if it's press exposure you're after."

"Seeing your mind's made up, I'm happy to get in touch with Richard to see if and when he's willing to take part," I was glad to say.

After more meetings with Geoff Parker, we were able to finalize arrangements. Richard Fells was pleased to accept the invitation and a date for the opening was fixed for the last Saturday of the Lent term, well before the start of the cricket season. The only amendment was that, in view of the remarkable part she had played, Lady Boddington was invited to carry out the unveiling of the plaque, a task she said she was delighted to perform.

"Just think of it," fantasized Geoff. "Local socialite, Lady Boddington, seen with Yorkshire cricketing hero, Richard Fells, shaking hands with his former headmaster, whilst you and Mrs Elliott look on proudly at the opening of Oxton House school's fine new sports' centre. It will make an outstanding picture and what's more I think I can guarantee to get you television coverage."

I was discovering that poor sleep was not only caused by worry and anxiety. Now that the financial difficulties had been largely overcome, it was the emotional adrenaline of success that kept me awake at night. Eager for each day to begin, I would get up at 4.00 a.m., not wanting to remain idle any longer. Soon I would be so busy meeting parents, staff and pupils that there would be no time to deal with the boring paperwork. The advantages of an early morning start were obvious: no appointments, no telephone, no mail, no irksome parents, no mutinous teachers. The boarders were still snugly sleeping in the safety of their term-time beds. I remember that particular morning because I was so absorbed in the preparation of a speech that when the telephone rang, I thought it was a hoax. Nobody called the headmaster's private line in the middle of the night! Not believing the reality of the noisy interruption, I allowed the ringing to continue until it stopped then started up again.

"Yes, what is it?" I barked into the mouthpiece, livid that my quiet had been disturbed.

"I've terrible news," sobbed a barely audible Aunt Olive. "There was nothing I could do to save your uncle. You must come quickly."

With alarm bells sounding in my head, I made for the kitchen exit and hurried to the cottage. Waiting for me was Dr Taylor, who silently led me up the stairs to the bedroom, where Aunt Olive was kneeling by the bed as if in prayer. Krissa lay beside my lifeless uncle, whose parchment-grey face exhibited the blank expression of a mask. Whilst trying to comfort my aunt, I cried tears of shock and torment, bringing to the fore my feelings of love and admiration for the man who for twenty-eight years had been my guiding light and inspiration. No matter how hard I tried, I was unable to give her reassurance. As the whimpering turned to panic, she began to paw her husband's body, willing the breath to return and shouting hysterically that she would sacrifice anything if it meant giving him a second chance.

Before leaving the cottage, Dr Taylor wanted me to know he was worried about my aunt's ability to cope. "She's going to need a lot of support," he warned.

His comment led me to ask a sober question. "Do you think the shock of all this will cause her to have another breakdown?"

"I sincerely hope not, but because she and Donald were exceptionally close, she's going to feel abandoned and distraught. Make no mistake, it's going to be very hard for her to come to terms with being on her own. As the only family member on the spot, much will depend on the backing you can give. I've one or two ideas I think you should consider."

His advice coincided closely with my own assessment of the situation. I had already decided to ask Elsie Chapman to move to the cottage, which was one of his suggestions. By having a cheerful companion living near at hand, Aunt Olive's state of mind could be monitored and action taken to avoid disaster.

The key to a favourable outcome lay with son Giles. For years he had remained distanced from his roots, with contact confined to no more than a card at Christmas. Having married Philippa, a wealthy woman in her own right, he appeared too high and mighty to bother with his parents, whose unfeigned love they had longed to be requited. Even after the births of Alexander and Peyto, Giles failed to keep in touch. To be prevented from seeing their grandsons was for Donald and Olive a more sadistic penalty than words were able to express.

"You must get in touch with Giles at once," said Dr Taylor. "If he doesn't support his mother at this time, it will be nothing short of a disgrace." He failed to come when Emma died, I reminded him, adding that at times like this Giles didn't seem to have a conscience. "Like it or not, you're going to have to tell him it's his duty to attend the funeral. If he doesn't, we all know your aunt will take it badly."

Not having spoken to Giles for years, I had no note of his address. Knowing that Uncle Don kept all his personal information in a file, I made for the drawer in question. A man of meticulous precision, his notes were neat and easy to interpret. In consequence, I was quickly able to discover the likely whereabouts of Giles. The family residence was shown as 49 Hill Street, Mayfair, London W1 and a second address, a villa in Gibraltar, was, I presumed, the holiday home to which my aunt occasionally made reference. Of the various telephone numbers listed, I dialled 01 793 3453, which was the Hill Street number. As it was barely 7.00 a.m., unless Giles was away on business, I was likely to catch him in.

"Giles Elliott," announced a self-important voice.

"This is Paul from Harrogate with bad news. It's with great sadness I must tell you your father died two hours ago. He passed away peacefully and Dr Taylor says it was another heart attack."

"Oh my God," exclaimed a clearly shaken Giles.

During the pause which followed, I came to an astonishing conclusion. My cousin was crying. Yes, crying. The ruthless, unfeeling son, who had broken his parents' hearts, was actually shedding tears. What was it? Shock, guilty conscience, contrition; or was it a painful reminder of his lack of appreciation for the things they'd done for him?

"Oh my God, oh my God," he repeated. "What makes it so ghastly is that I was about to ring them up to arrange a visit with the family. And now it's too late."

"It's never too late," I said. "Your mother needs you more than ever now. Why have you deprived her of the chance to get to know her grandchildren?"

"I've no excuse. Busy and selfish is what I've been."

"You can change all that and help give her life a meaning."

Hoping beyond all else that he would want to attend the funeral, my relief was immense when he stated with out-of-character sincerity that nothing would prevent him from being there to pay tribute to his father and support his mother.

"I want all of us to attend," he said. "Philippa *and* the boys. Alexander never stops talking about his relatives in Yorkshire."

This was wonderful news. A reconciliation with her son and the chance to get to know her grandsons would bolster Aunt Olive's confidence and add a fresh dimension to her now irrevocably altered world. Bearing in mind his undertakings, I swore I would hold Giles to account if he reneged on his promise by abandoning his mother at this time.

At the last minute, he informed us they would not be staying overnight before the funeral and for this reason he arranged to meet us at the church. Throughout the long journey, Alexander had barraged his parents with questions about funerals, burials and death. Frightened and confused by the time they reached Harrogate, he begged his father to turn tail and take him back to London. On arriving at the church, Philippa had the good sense to make for an empty pew well distanced from the family they were later due to meet. Bewildered and upset, Alexander was painfully aware of what was going on, whereas his untroubled younger brother regarded the event as an adventure.

The funeral took place at St. Peter's where since the early 1930s my uncle had been a regular communicant. After all the pews were taken, large numbers of people continued to pile into what was by any standards a sizeable parish church. By the time the coffin had been placed by the altar, even the aisles were filled with sombre-suited gentlemen and women dressed in black. At the front, seated next to Olive, Giles and I each held on to her in an effort to guide her safely through the ordeal. To begin with she was remarkably resilient, but when the school choir chanted Donald's favourite anthem, overwhelmed by the public outpouring of affection for her lately departed husband, she finally broke down. As we led the cortege the short distance to the graveyard, she swayed unsteadily, using every power at her disposal to stifle the outward appearance of her grief. Uniting with the family party at the graveside, Alexander gripped his mother's hand with a tenacity that emphasized his agitation at that moment. Jumbled emotions must have led him to wonder about the grandfather he had often talked about but never met. Three-year-old Peyto was quite the opposite. Totally at ease, he scrambled about the churchyard, splashing in the mud as he dodged the flustered mourners, daring them to join him in a game of hide and seek.

Diverting my aunt's attention from the most solemn aspect of the day, the sight of her unruly grandson made her laugh. A spontaneous, joyful laugh that touched the hearts of those who understood the importance of the breakthrough. After pretending to hide, she chased the playful Peyto, picked him up and, smothering him with kisses, it was as if the years of denial had never taken place. Seconds later she was wiping the tears from Alexander's cheeks and following this act of love he began to loosen up. Philippa watched her sons with pride, gladdened to think they were bonding with her husband's family and that the shock of the bereavement had brought Giles to his senses.

The lowering of the coffin induced Alexander to avert his eyes and seek solace from his grandmother. Horrified at the gruesome finality of the interment, his distress in a strange way gave my aunt a fortitude I never thought she had. Giles meanwhile stood staring at the coffin, his whole body alive with shaking movements that indicated he was desperate to maintain his self-control. In a sudden impulse, I moved over to him, placing a hand on his shoulder, to signal my understanding of his misery. Encouraged by my instinctive act of kindness, he let out a pitiful cry, begging to be forgiven.

"Christ knows I've been a lousy son. I'm sorry, dad. May you rest in peace."

Clasping me with the strength of a bear, the tears flowing freely now, he was attempting to display the brand of brotherly affection I had yearned for in my childhood. Warmed by his actions, I responded by giving him a hug, my moistened features mirroring his equally distraught emotions.

As a mark of respect, the school had been closed for the day and lessons cancelled. Members of the choir, several of them boarders, were supervised throughout the morning by Herbert Bond, who was dressed in a cassock and looking very grand. He escorted the choristers to and from the service in a well-drilled two-by-two formation. Most of the other boarders, not wanting to miss out, had clubbed together to buy a floral tribute. Their altruism earned them the right to attend the funeral under the care of Miss O'Sullivan and her assistant. Those too squeamish to cope with the melancholy aftermath of death were taken on a country ramble.

It was impossible to predict how many would turn up afterwards for sherry and a sandwich. Even after the stacking of the tables, there was insufficient room to accommodate what seemed like hundreds of people elbowing their way into the school's full-to-bursting dining hall. Unable to deal with the volume of demand, the kitchen was in crisis. Jennings saved the day by driving the van to a nearby off-licence and Marks and Spencer, returning with dozens of sausage rolls and enough sherry for an army. Stuck in a corner, unable to mingle with the guests, I found myself standing next to Philippa, who was separated by a mass of bodies from her family. She looked decidedly uncomfortable.

"It's meant a lot to have you here today," I said.

"Giles was more upset than I've ever seen him when he heard about his father," she responded. About to say more, she hesitated, blushed and thinking better of it added: "From what I've seen, you have an amazing school."

"If you've time before you leave, I should like to show you round," I promised.

She was pretty and voluptuous and was, I imagined, photogenic, judging by the high cheek bones that showed signs of Slavic origins.

Well groomed, jet-black hair matched the colour of her tailored suit. Without doubt she was a sophisticated, classy lady, unaware of the enchantment of her beauty. On casual first acquaintance she struck me as sensitive, intelligent and a strong match for her husband. The change in Giles was striking, depicting him now as a genuinely contrite man, whose new identity was certainly no act. I marvelled how hard Philippa must have worked to influence the remoulding of his character. Lucky to have an understanding partner, my cousin possessed the one essential element I lacked and wanted. Powerlessness to make a go of it with Catriona had underlined a personal failure on my part. Giles, on the other hand, had proved the soundness of his judgement by choosing a wife who was making the marriage work. Envious of his success, it brought home to me my desire for a woman in my life and a family of my own.

— Thirty-Five —

MEETING HER GRANDCHILDREN rewarded Aunt Olive with a new lease of life. Far from being embittered, the gap caused by Don's death was miraculously filled by the love she was able to give to Alexander and Peyto. This affection they returned in full, a gift that boosted her morale, adding to each day an invigorating sense of purpose.

Before returning to London, Giles let me into a secret. He told me his family planned to attend the opening of the sports' centre and he had arranged for the four of them to stay at the nearby Majestic Hotel. "I want our visit to come as a surprise," he said. "We'll do our best to divert mum's thoughts away from the sad aspects of the day and make the occasion a celebration. The opening will present the ideal opportunity for everyone to recognise dad's achievements and mum's as well." This was exactly the emphasis I had envisaged for the opening. Not only had Giles acquired qualities of thoughtfulness and tact, for the first time ever he was beginning to manifest some of his father's strengths that up until then he had stubbornly concealed.

There was another reason for my aunt's light-hearted mood. "Giles has invited me to join them at their villa in Gibraltar for part of August," she happily announced. "Philippa says I'm welcome to stay with them in London whenever I like. She's turning out to be a lovely daughter-in-law. It's hard to believe I used to think she was a snob."

A month after the funeral, Elsie Chapman moved back to her own bed-sitting room, having discovered that Olive was more than capable of coping on her own. "The trouble is," she confided, "we keep on clashing and for the two of us to live in such close proximity is not a good idea."

Another unexpected development was that Krissa's allegiance to my uncle was quickly transferred to his widow, who pampered the friendly Labrador. Dog and mistress were often to be seen on their daily walks by other canine lovers, one of whom said it was foolish to exercise a dog of Krissa's age so strenuously. It can safely be said Aunt Olive had three priorities in her vastly changed routine. First came the grandchildren to whom she wrote almost every day. A close second was Krissa, whose faithful companionship helped to keep her from being lonely; and last of all was the school, a growing institution with which she was proud to be connected, but was privately overawed by the speed and breadth of the expansion.

There was a heavy fall of snow during the night before the opening. Geoff Parker directed a photographer to take pictures of the field, remarking that the whiteness of the ground's surface matched the newly-painted rugby and soccer posts, whilst highlighting the vastness of the building in the background. I was irritated that everything Geoff did had a commercial angle to it that was a means of earning him more money.

"Surely we want shots *inside* the centre rather than an empty field covered in snow," I argued.

"You've still got a lot to learn about promotion," responded an indignant Geoff. "This is the first fall of snow we've had in months. When an opportunity presents itself, you have to take it. A photograph with a festive flavour would make the perfect Christmas card, an advert for the school. Parents would be eager to send one to their friends."

I wanted to dignify my uncle's memory and had made it plain I thought it was inappropriate to cheapen the opening by overdoing the publicity.

"You've engaged me to promote the school," he said testily. "If I pussyfoot about you will say I'm doing nothing, yet if I fire on all cylinders and achieve results, you'll accuse me of failing to show sufficient reverence to your late uncle."

The ceremony couldn't have gone more smoothly, thanks to careful preparation on the part of Richard Fells. After a couple of jokes slipped in at the beginning, the profound content of his speech left many of us near to tears. He began by making reference to his time as a pupil at Oxton House.

"My years spent here in Harrogate were, without a shadow of a doubt, my happiest by far. Public school was exciting, three years at Oxford were rewarding, but it was my family's good sense to start my education at Oxton House that enabled me to acquire some of the habits that matter most, disciplines I hope will remain with me forever. I owe a great deal to Donald and Olive Elliott. My father was a regular army officer and when my parents lived abroad, Mr & Mrs Elliott acted as my guardians, in which capacity they were considerate, kind and always prepared to listen. I owe them a lot. it was Donald who was more responsible than anyone for my interest in cricket. He taught me how to bowl, coached me in the nets and even after he'd been taken ill his encouragement continued. Never be satisfied with your performance, he would say. Always strive to be better. So when I fail to score a run or drop a catch, I remember his words of wisdom, which keep me going and stir me to exert more effort. How apt it is that this magnificent sports' centre is to carry the names of Donald and Olive Elliott. It's a tragedy that Donald himself is not here to bask in the glory. The Elliotts are a great family and Paul is doing a splendid job in continuing their work. I hope one day to board my two sons here, but shall have to score many more runs before I can afford the fees that are charged these days. It's been a great pleasure to return to my much-loved stamping ground. I'm greatly honoured to have been invited."

After unveiling the commemorative plaque to tumultuous applause, Lady Boddington spoke briefly. She said she was proud to be a parent of the school and commended the Elliotts for having the courage to choose this time to add further scope to the facilities. Describing the new sports' centre as the jewel in the crown, she predicted the amenity would be of inestimable value to present and future generations.

Geoff handled the press with a quiet dignity that was right for the occasion. Despite his subdued approach, photographs of the event appeared in the *Daily Mail* and three Yorkshire newspapers, which included a two-page spread in the *Harrogate Advertiser*. The most impressive coup was Richard Fells's interview on a regional television programme that showed excerpts from his speech. No amount of money could have accomplished a more subtle yet effective form of advertising. To follow the morning's proceedings, rather than push the boat out with an extravagant luncheon catering for large numbers, we chose instead to lay on a less formal meal in the school dining hall for special guests, which included Richard Fells, Lady Boddington and some senior members of the staff.

Aunt Olive was quick to point out a mistake on the seating plan. "Who is sitting next to me?" she asked, concerned to note there were two blank spaces on the place settings on either side of her. Not wanting to lie, but knowing the deception was about to be unearthed, I managed to keep up the pretence until just before grace was said. It was then that Giles and Philippa appeared. Aunt Olive was speechless with delight, unaware the entire family had witnessed the ceremony and speeches from the back of the hall.

When the guests had departed, the school was spookily silent until Elsie Chapman turned up with two unruly boys, the elder of whom was besieging her with questions. Having looked after Alexander and Peyto during the lunch hour, it was with relief that she was able to return them to their parents. Addressing Giles, she said she had met smart boys in her time but that Alexander was without doubt the brightest spark by far, with a mind much sharper than a knife.

"Miss Chapman," the lively boy persisted. "I'm going to ask Daddy to send me to grandpa's school as I want to be a boarder."

"That's as may be," said his mother. "Life isn't about having exactly what you want. We agree this is a marvellous school, but I don't want you to board until you're older."

Alexander was not alone in being impressed by the school's facilities. Prospective parents who paid a visit were so taken with what they saw they needed little encouragement to enrol their sons, many of whom played a part in the decision-making process. Not so long before, we had been a school fighting for survival; after seemingly no time at all, the pendulum had swung dramatically and we could no longer satisfy the demand for places.

Academic rigour was our forte. Scholarships won to leading public schools in the distant past had been few in number. In the last five years, forty-seven names appeared on the honours board, with two scholarships to Eton. Every member of the teaching staff had played a part in these achievements, but it was mainly through the gifted teaching of David Banks and Nicole Tyler that Oxton House became known for its high scholastic standards, making it a prep. school without equal in the north of England. I remember attending a meeting at a well-known public school when the headmaster took me to one side. He paid us a compliment I shall not forget.

208

"My head of modern languages tells me your boys are better prepared in French than any of the candidates from other schools. They consistently produce high marks. How do you do it?"

I recounted the story of how Nicole Tyler at her interview had boasted that under her aegis French would be the most popular subject in the school. What I failed to mention was that it was with not a little scepticism I had decided to appoint her.

Under the punctilious direction of Herbert Bond, the music department thrived. More than half the boys over the age of seven learnt an instrument and an orchestra of forty players performed at concerts and on speech days. There were two accomplished choirs. Both took part in choral festivals and carried out engagements at a number of different venues, a policy that enhanced still further the standing of the school.

The more responsibilities I thrust upon Andrew Brooke, the happier he was. Among his duties he controlled the activities of the groundsman, whose job it was to mark out and prepare the pitches and maintain the swimming pool. Delighted with the status he had earned as manager of a complex operation, he bored fellow teachers daily with blow-by-blow accounts of everything connected with PE. A man of ingenuity, he was the most passionate member of the staff. An innovator, too, he encouraged parents to help with the coaching of the games and in addition to the many teams fielded by the school, he arranged fixtures for the boys' mothers and fathers in a variety of sports. Long after I was about to go to bed, he was still in his office burning the midnight oil and, speaking from experience, I warned him that in order to preserve his marriage, he would be wise to show much more consideration to his wife.

It was unheard of for Elsie Chapman to be ill. She never had a cold and not once during twenty-five years of service did she suffer from the flu. Her skinny frame disguised a resilient constitution, a robustness she put down to a healthy diet, an aversion to smoking and the occasional glass of stout. Soon after her sixty-third birthday, two years before it was agreed she would retire, she handed in her notice. It surprised and hurt me that, in spite of our very special bond, she had chosen to submit her resignation in a letter. I wondered whether she had been squabbling again with Olive or more likely she was afraid to admit the demands of the job had become too much for a woman of her age. I was prepared to go to whatever lengths were necessary to persuade her not to leave. I asked whether it would help to find an assistant to relieve her of some of the workload. As I waited for her answer, I noticed her face bore a yellowish complexion and dark hollows under her eyes made her look much older than her years, a change so sudden that it seemed to have happened overnight.

"I'm simply not up to it anymore," she said.

"Of course you are. You're the perfect secretary, the best ever. All we need is to make a few adjustments."

"It's too late for that. I've been given six months to live." I couldn't believe what I was hearing. "You are going to have to believe me. I don't want any fuss. What's more, I don't want it to be known by all and sundry why I'm going. I suggest we advertise at once for a replacement."

Like a dagger in my side, her words struck a lethal blow, underlining fate's vicious and speedy intervention. There had been moments when, without her commitment and support, I might not have had the spirit to continue. Self-denying to a fault, she placed the needs of others before her own. Above all, she was my friend, a true, dear friend, whose loss would leave an impossible gap to fill.

Rebuffing my expressions of concern, she told me to snap out of it and focus on what mattered. "You have a school to run," she said. "If you start getting sentimental, it will only make things worse."

Seeing she would not rest until I had appointed her successor, it was decided she would draft out the adverts and make up a shortlist. Of the thirteen applicants, she thought three were worth seeing. Before the interviews, whilst supplying the candidates with all the relevant details of the post, she was able to make her own assessment of their strengths and weaknesses. Pooling our thoughts at a meeting afterwards, Elsie and I had come to the same conclusion.

"Mrs Polly Rankin is the best by far," I declared.

"Great minds think alike," agreed Elsie, who said how impressed she was with Mrs Rankin's attitude and overall demeanour. "She's obviously efficient, sets high standards and has excellent shorthand skills. What's more she's discreet and is, I think, a thoroughly decent person."

After Polly Rankin had spent a fortnight learning the ropes from the seasoned veteran, Elsie vacated her bed-sitting room and moved to Scotland to stay in Inverness with her only living relative. She refused to allow her retirement to be marked in any way, telling me she was upset enough at the thought of leaving and had no intention of making an exhibition of herself in public.

I drove her to the station. Two small cases contained her entire possessions, a pitiful reminder of her impoverishment and contempt for worldly goods. As the train departed, taking her on her final journey, the gaunt face pressed against the window, she blew me a kiss, tears dribbling down her shrivelled cheeks. She was mouthing the word *Goodbye*.

— Thirty-Six —

POLLY RANKIN HAD a mind of her own. She had the annoying habit of offering opinions on every subject you could name. Having employed her as my secretary, the last thing I wanted was to have her bossing me about. After Elsie's quiet diplomacy, it irritated me no end that everything I said or did was analysed and challenged by the new probationer. What riled me most was that her judgement was impeccable and frequently her ideas were more original than my own.

One day her arrogance went beyond the limits of my endurance. I reminded her she was still on trial and that I paid her to do as she was asked and not behave like the chairman of the governors.

"You don't have any governors," she said, eyeing me, eager to discover if her glib remark had caused more offence. She giggled playfully, and as she did so, the severe features of her face softened, drawing my attention to her even white teeth and flushed cheeks that gave her a pleasingly wholesome look. When she smiled she was like a different person. If only I could learn to be less defensive in her presence and make use of her obvious intelligence, rather than regard her as a threat, she had the potential to be an invaluable help.

"I think we may have got off to a bad start," I said. "You're too clever to be a mere secretary. If I were to regard you as my personal assistant, which would entitle you to some say in how we work, would you like that more?"

"I'm not after status or more money, Mr Elliott. I know I was too eager and pushy at the start. Don't hesitate to tell me if I overstep the mark. Call me your PA if you like. My sole aim is to please."

As the weeks passed, I found myself looking forward to Polly's arrival at the school, which was always a good half hour before she was due to begin her work. On the one day she failed to appear on time, I was inordinately anxious, realizing how much I had come to rely on her. An organizing genius, she cut corners, abhorred gossip, had a fetish about waste and was quick to identify priorities. On my return from morning prayers, she had messages and correspondence divided into sections, with the urgent pile ready for my attention. Research connected with decisions to be made, or facts for letters to be dispatched, she had the knack of fathoming out the answers with the minimum of fuss. In everything she did, she was a stickler for perfection.

It's strange how one's impression of a person's appearance can change after getting to know them better. Initially I had regarded Polly as a bluestocking, an engaging lady nonetheless, who possessed an inscrutable beauty that made her physically appealing. Was it my imagination that she was starting to wear make-up and was taking greater care over how she dressed? Her long blond hair was better groomed these days and I liked to think she was making the effort for me. On the rare occasions she appeared in high-heeled shoes and a slightly shortened skirt, I had the distinct feeling she was doing it for my benefit, a provocative display that brought to the fore lustful thoughts I had to fight hard to suppress. She was full figured, perhaps a little overweight, with ample breasts, a build that made her look vibrant, voluptuous and strong. As summer approached, and she wore less bulky clothes, I used to watch her with a growing fascination. She arrived one Monday morning in noticeably spirited mood. She told me she'd been wrestling with an idea and would I like to hear about it. Before giving me time to find out more, she reminded me of the occasion I scolded her for behaving like the chairman of the governors.

"What's that got to do with your suggestion?" I asked, curiosity mounting.

"A lot, as it so happens. If you appointed a board of governors, all of them solid citizens and pillars of the community – a bishop, a public school head, a captain of industry, and one or two titled people – think of the benefits such a committee could bring to the school."

"The idea is all very well, but considering the school is not a charitable trust, trustees would be superfluous in an organisation such as ours," I reminded her.

"Don't you see," she said, "they wouldn't be trustees? They would act in an advisory capacity. For them to be seen to play a part in managing the school would influence any doubting parents into believing Oxton House is well-established, classy, authentic, and on a par with the most exclusive prep. schools in the land."

In common with many of Polly's brainwaves, this had merit. By asking a number of distinguished men and women to become honorary advisers, we both knew the school would benefit from their specialist skills and financial expertise. Deciding to name the committee the school council, our first task was to determine who to approach. Seeing my apprehension, Polly persuaded me that anyone invited to join would regard it as a compliment.

"Most successful people respond to flattery," she said.

I suggested, "Wouldn't it be an imposition to expect them to add to their already heavy burdens?"

"A get-together once a term is all that's needed. You open the meeting with a progress report, then the chairman deals with the agenda, item by item. It wouldn't involve an undue amount of work."

"You've convinced me," I said smiling broadly. "Let's start with the appointment of a chairman."

"I think I know just the man," she said. "Sir Quentin Isaac is the tailor-made candidate. He's a leading industrialist, with a finger in all sorts of pies and a reputation for getting things done. What's more, he's mad about education."

"I agree he's all those things, but why would he want to help this school? He has no direct links with us, as far as I'm aware."

"That's where you're wrong," she said, trying to conceal her excitement. "He and his wife are on very friendly terms with the parents of two of our day boys, the Snapes to be precise."

"I rather assumed Cyril Snape had powerful connections, but I had no idea he was a pal of Sir Quentin. Why don't I invite Cyril to be on the council and get him to sound out Sir Quentin to see if he would be prepared to be our chairman? I know it's a hell of a cheek. There's no harm in giving it a try."

"Now you're talking," exclaimed a triumphant Polly.

Cyril Snape was an eminent Queen's Counsel. An expert on plan-ning, he was reputed twice to have won legal battles for Sir Quentin Isaac and it was in this context the two became close friends. A pompous little man, whose vanity was renowned, he loved the sound of his own voice and to be the centre of attention. After agreeing to become a member of the council, he boasted that he had a strong influence on Sir Quentin and was confident he could get him to agree to be the chairman.

I had often seen photographs of Sir Quentin Isaac in the press. In his mid-forties and dressed always in a stylish suit that covered his stocky build, he had a jovial face and a fine head of thick black hair. A ruthless operator, he despised time-wasters and was contemptuous of any kind of failure. Nothing would induce him to get involved with ventures from which he would not gain some benefit himself. My surprise, therefore, was considerable when I received a call from his office, requesting a visit to the school. After stepping out of his chauffeur-driven Rolls, he said he'd spoken with Cyril, but before agreeing to anything he wanted to see the school in action. Speaking with a strong Yorkshire dialect, he took pains to expound his own virtues, reminding me he was a self-made man, whose risk-taking had brought him success as well as earning him a knighthood. It was evident he was prepared to be generous with his time, but would fight tooth and nail to hang on to every penny of his hard-earned cash.

The tour of Oxton House complete, he gave me a brief summary of his thoughts. "You've got an impressive little business. I don't see why I shouldn't be of service, especially as Cyril never stops singing your praises. I'm envious of your land and buildings, Elliott. It has potential as a valuable development site. If, God forbid, the place goes belly up, it's comforting to know you are sitting on a fortune."

Late for another appointment, he was in a hurry to depart. Before stepping into his car, he said he'd soon be in touch to discuss the inaugural meeting. I had to act fast to select more members, knowing it was prudent first to seek Sir Quentin's opinion before decisions could be made. This was just as well because there were certain people he disliked and, more important still, he said bishops were a waste of space and if I wanted a man of the cloth to join the group I would need to find another chairman.

In addition to Sir Quentin and Cyril Snape, ten others, half of them parents of the school, consented to serve on the council. A garrulous Welshman, Evan David, CBE, who owned food factories in York and Leeds, agreed to be deputy chairman. The remaining places were taken up by a public school headmaster, a television producer, Lady Boddington, an accountant, a solicitor, an engineer, a marquess with a country estate in Cumbria and a second home in Harrogate, a female dermatologist and, representing the old boys,

Richard Fells, the youngest member of the group. As clerk to the council, Polly was responsible for organizing agendas, distributing the minutes and arranging supper for the delegates before the meetings. Co-opted as a fully-fledged member, she was not afraid to speak, but when she did so her opinions were precise and to the point.

I cannot put my hand on my heart and say it was the formation of the council that led to the start of a new era. Vacancies were at a premium and waiting lists were full. The harder it was to gain entry to the school, the more coveted were the places. An explosion in demand from an extended catchment area meant we were in a position to pick and choose, a policy that was to lead to raising the academic level of each intake.

Conclusions at the first meeting were not as I expected. Instead of praising the school's record of achievements, Evan David made remarks I found clumsy and mundane. "Surely, Mr Chairman, the purpose of these discussions is not to pat each other on the back and leave with nothing other than a feeling of self-congratulation. The headmaster doesn't want us to applaud what is good. What he wants is for us to point out the failings in his system."

"Don't beat about the bush," said Sir Quentin, suggesting Evan spell out exactly what he meant.

"I'm not saying Oxton House is badly run. My sons are doing well and for the most part I'm a satisfied customer. But I feel the social side is lacking and there should be more opportunities for parents to mix at dances, cultural events and so on. We pay the fees and our wives spend most of their time ferrying the boys about from one activity to another. The kids are having fun, so why not the parents?"

"I agree schooling should be an enjoyable experience," asserted Dr Porter, the public school head, keen to have his say. "Gone are the days of bullying, homosexuality and runs before breakfast. Boarding is much more popular now that conditions have changed. Fun is a key element."

After a lengthy debate, it was decided to make the May speech day weekend more action-packed by staging a play or concert, arranging a barbecue and giving every pupil the chance to display a skill at something.

"My wife keeps going on about wanting to dress up, so why not have a summer ball?" advocated Cyril Snape.

"I think a ball would be better attended in December," said Richard Fells, who promised he would work with the secretary of the old boys' association to drum up support.

An experienced chairman, Sir Quentin Isaac allowed everyone time to air their views, but he effectively cut short long-winded speakers by rolling his eyes with an expression of extreme agony before glaring at his watch. "At tonight's meeting, at least we've made a start," he said. "Whilst deciding on the next agenda, I want to make it absolutely clear we are not here to deal with trivial matters in which some may have a vested interest. Much of what's been said today has been petty and irrelevant. Our brief is to help guide the headmaster and his staff in making decisions over educational practices, expansion, financial strategy and, of course, we must give consideration to the rapidly changing needs in our society. Arrangements for dances, barbecues and concerts should be left to a committee of mothers or to designated staff."

Expressing pride in his Harrogate connections, Sir Quentin closed the meeting on an optimistic note. He said there had been talk for years about building a conference centre in the town and that he was heavily involved in the planning. He predicted when the facility was in use, Harrogate would be capable of laying on conferences and exhibitions on a par with Birmingham and London. Rallying his troops, he spoke eloquently and with feeling: "Steeped in history, Harrogate has a fascinating past and a compelling future. There's something for everyone here: breath-taking scenery on the doorstep; the green tranquillity of our parks; the Royal Baths, Betty's café and Oxton House, a school that's going places. As members of the school council, it's up to us to support events and play a full part in what's going to be a very worthwhile journey."

Asked what makes a prep. school teacher tick, cynics complain that, after enjoying sixteen weeks' holiday a year, we teach a few lessons, mark some books and spend the rest of our time either umpiring cricket matches in the sunshine or pursuing our pet interest, be it model railways, philately or fencing, diversions that are arranged to relieve the pupils' boredom. We are criticized, too, for receiving benefits in kind, of which supervising boys skiing in the Alps and taking them on cultural trips to Paris, Rome or Marrakesh are typical examples. The truth is that any teacher worth his salt derives fulfilment from what he does. He is fortunate to be able to teach subjects in which he has a special interest and the icing on the cake is if his school is progressive enough to allow him to use his hobbies for the benefit of his students. Although teachers as a group are often branded with a hang-dog image, the majority are highly conscientious practitioners, who work long hours, take pride in what they do and are competitive in the sense of wanting year by year to raise their game and improve on past performances. A parent once asked what I thought was a headmaster's most important function. "I see myself primarily as a salesman and problem-solver," was my answer.

A successful school is made up of contented staff, good-humoured and absorbed pupils and the parents, who deserve to be treated with respect. It is vital for a head to detect difficulties emerging at the outset to avoid a crisis from developing. A tearful seven-year-old in need of reassurance; a master whose wife is giving him a hard time at home or an aggressive parent with unrealistic expectations: these and other worries can be prevented from becoming disasters providing the head has the time and skill to deal with them at once. To be able to handle the unexpected, I had to be well organised. By having an uncluttered desk and ensuring every letter was answered and phone calls made before the day was over, I left myself with the capacity to cope with the emergencies.

Managing Oxton House was a way of life. There were activities I would have preferred to avoid. Attendance, however, was expected at every event listed in the school calendar: concerts, drama productions, sporting fixtures, swimming galas, art exhibitions, poetry readings, parents' gatherings, lectures, quizzes, chess competitions and debates. I attended innumerable meetings, chaired committees galore and whether in a foul mood or full of bonhomie, it was my duty to play my part with relish and commitment. Occasionally a member of staff succumbed to illness or for some other reason was forced to take time off. It was a matter of honour for me to be resistant to distractions of this kind because years of practice had taught me it was essential to lead by setting an example.

In moments of quiet I marvelled at my luck. To preside over a thriving enterprise, one that was expanding and had scope for yet more change, made each day an excitement and a challenge. Some of the day boys travelled long distances; several hailed from as far afield as Leeds and villages beyond. The fact parents were prepared to spend long hours driving their sons to and from Harrogate showed how much the school's popularity had grown. Boarding lists were full and an increasing number, mainly children of serving officers and diplomatic personnel, now came from overseas. I was humbled to think these people had chosen Oxton House, often in preference to more conveniently placed alternatives, a knowledge that highlighted the responsibility I held. I vowed never to take their trust for granted and made it my goal to emulate the clear code of ethics implanted by my dear departed uncle. Had I been granted a wish, it would have been for Uncle Don to be able to see the progress we were making. I liked to think he was studying my performance from some mystical vantage point, reunited with his brother, the father I had known but briefly. Both would be cheering me on, willing me to succeed, a source of inspiration that gave each task I undertook a valid purpose.

It surprised me Aunt Olive rarely made any reference to her late husband. Taken up with looking after Krissa and seeing as much as she could of her grandsons, she started to behave in what seemed to me a somewhat selfish fashion. "I've done with the past," she kept on saying.

Whether this was her strategy for coming to terms with being on her own, I was unable to decide. Knowing she had suffered from dark moods on and off for years, I was well aware she would not want me to ask intrusive questions. Assuming she preferred to keep her thoughts to herself, I was dumbfounded when she let rip with a wounding statement. "When your uncle and I started here in 1931, this was a happy place. The school's become too big to offer a personal service any longer."

"That's hardly fair, Aunt Olive," I protested.

In forthright fashion she expanded her scathing views. "Instead of treating each boy as an individual, too many slip through the net, forgotten and neglected. Everything's done on a colossal scale. It's little wonder you are obsessed with meeting targets, keeping the parents sweet and treating the staff like golden idols. I can appreciate the necessity for change, but to be honest, I no longer get pleasure from my work. I'm a square peg in a round hole, super-fluous to requirements."

It cut me to the quick to think my aunt disapproved of developments at the school, and worse still that she no longer gained pleasure from the crucial part she played. Her remarks forced me to confront her, and when I did so she began weeping like a child before unburdening the main reason for her ills.

"Is it that you're missing Don?" I asked.

"Of course I miss him. I miss him every minute of the day. His spirit lives in every corner. Each nook and cranny contains a part of him and the memories are so vivid that I still expect to see him standing on the touchline at a match or smoking in his study another of those revolting cigarettes."

The other concern, and it was a major one, was Krissa. The dog she had gratefully inherited was suffering from kidney failure, a malady which brought on incontinence and caused the animal considerable pain. The vet's recommendation to put poor Krissa to sleep was taken by Olive as an act of failure on her part. Blaming herself for the dog's declining health, she was inconsolable for weeks. Instead of coming to terms with the loss as a normal person would, she became increasingly reclusive and rarely left the cottage. No matter how hard I tried to reason with her, she scoffed at my suggestions, saying I was making a nuisance of myself when there were better things to do. Fearing she was showing signs of another breakdown, I telephoned Giles. This time he was grateful for my intervention and I found it useful to be able to confide in him now that he was much closer to his mother.

"The old girl's tired", he said. "She's done her bit and needs a rest. I keep telling her businesses today are run on different lines and she should leave it all to you."

"I agree she does too much, but it's entirely of her own volition. We just love having her about. What worries me is the spark's gone out of her and she is very, very down."

"It's probably her age. Now that Elsie Chapman's no longer there and Mary O'Sullivan's retired, she's like a fish out of water. The last straw was losing Krissa."

The symptoms were obvious, but what was the solution? Thanks to Philippa's constructive influence, Giles had become softer, more perceptive. Genuinely concerned and, much to my surprise, he had contingency plans in hand already.

"For some months Philippa and I have been anticipating an outcome such as this. Builders are installing a granny flat in our Hill Street property and the expectation is that mum will come and live with us."

I agreed this was a most thoughtful plan and was confident it would be the making of Aunt Olive. The only stipulation I made was that the cottage would always be hers. Speaking for everyone at Oxton House, I expressed the hope she would grace as many school events as possible with her presence in the future.

Because Sir Quentin Issac was such a busy man, I didn't expect him to visit the school except on the occasions he chaired the termly council meetings. One day he appeared unexpectedly during morning break whilst I was having coffee in the staff room. Instead of seeking me out, he was content to talk to Polly, who later told me what he'd wanted. "He came to buy a ticket for the Christmas dinner dance," she said.

"Only one ticket?" How about Lady Isaac?"

"He says she's deaf and can't cope with any kind of noise, which is why he's coming on his own."

"It's very good of him to support us at all," I said. "Are you coming, Polly?"

"I've been toying with the idea but haven't yet decided."

I knew Polly had a husband, but there was at times a strangeness in her manner that indicated she was unwilling to talk about relationships at home. She wasn't devious, but I suspected she was concealing a secret that a paranoid desire for privacy prevented her from sharing.

"You've been working with me for three years now," I said. "I find it distinctly odd that I know nothing about you beyond what goes on in this office. Surely after all this time I'm entitled to know a little more about my indispensable PA. Are you a happily married woman or is it a taboo subject never to be raised again?"

She blushed, her discomposure leading me to think I had overstepped the mark. Looking away, she answered in a whisper. "Ronald and I married ten years ago and two years later he was diagnosed with multiple sclerosis. The disease developed rapidly and now he's in a wheelchair."

"I had no idea. This is awful, Polly. How do you manage to cope if he's as ill as that?"

"No doubt you think it's callous of me to leave him to go to work. *He* was the one who insisted I got a job. It's good for us both. He has a helper who comes in each day and when I get home, he's keen to hear of all the things I've been up to at the school."

Quizzing her about the delicate subject of their finances, she assured me money was the least of their concerns. Despite his illness, she told me her husband, an avid reader of financial journals, was a wizard with investments and was comfortably off.

"Tell me if there is anything I can do to help," I said.

"Apart from asking for some time off when his condition worsens, I think you can take it we're just about managing to hold our own." She then raised a finger to her lips, indicating the discussion was at an end.

I disliked parents' socials and dances in particular. I was likely to be besieged with questions about Johnny's high IQ, the loss of Damian's tuck box key, Patrick's torn and tattered football shirt, Tom's allergy to the vegetables at lunch and Daniel's violin lessons, in connection with which was his teacher an L.R.A.M. or an A.R.C.M.? Would I please explain the difference. Many of the parents who were normally polite, obsequious even, hyped up with drink became demanding and abusive, eager to pin me down in some pointless verbal argument. There was to be one redeeming feature. This time Polly had agreed to attend the function and I managed to persuade her to be my guest and sit next to me at the council members' table.

Last year Lady Boddington had taken pity on me. Commenting I looked like the male version of a wallflower, she had challenged me to join her for all the quicksteps, complaining that her husband's gammy leg meant he could only manage the slow waltzes and a continental shuffle for the foxtrots. My clumsy attempts amused her greatly and she screeched with laughter as I tried in vain to compete with her nimble-footed efforts.

"Headmaster," I remembered her saying, "isn't it about time you chose another wife? Everyone's allowed a second chance. Would you like me to try and fix you up?"

Whether or not she would have approved of my decision to invite a married woman to this year's dance was quite another matter. Much as I had been looking forward to having Polly as my guest, Sir Quentin's behaviour aroused a jealousy that caused me later to lose my temper. Seated on her other side throughout the dinner, he monopolized her with a persistent flirting that prevented me from talking to her at all.

His loud voice boomed and grated as he flung out compliments, referring to her as darling girl, the belle of the ball and sweetheart. This was outrageous language coming from the chairman of our council. When the band began to play, he brazenly proposed: "Will this sexy creature be so kind as to honour me with a dance?"

The two were on the floor for the remainder of the evening, holding each other close, she smiling gracefully and he perspiring like a pig, a lecherous leer attached to his overfed face. During the last waltz he became more amorous. Smudging her cheeks with his kisses, she was shameless enough to keep smiling until the bitter end. It was a bitter ending because my anger was such that I could not refrain from making caustic comments to them both.

"I would have expected better from you than that Sir Quentin," I exploded. "And as for you, Polly, I thought you were a respectable married woman!"

— Thirty-Seven —

AFTER MY SATURDAY night outburst, I had the whole of Sunday to reflect on the damage I had done. Sir Quentin was bound to resign as chairman of the council and Polly, my rock, dependable Polly, the woman I privately adored, would be justified in walking out, leaving me with the impossible task of finding a replacement. She stayed away on Monday without so much as a word of explanation. Feelings of guilt were so strong that I decided by mid-morning to eat humble pie and apologize for my rudeness. I was prepared to do anything to retain her services, even if it meant condoning an inappropriate relationship with our chairman. As I was about to pick up the phone to call her, there was a knock on the door and in marched a smiling Evan David. He told me he'd come on council business.

"I've just spoken to Sir Quentin," he said. "He's going to be abroad at the time of the next meeting and has asked me to take his place."

"Does that mean he no longer wants to be the chairman?"

"He's an egomaniac, loves power and thrives on having status. He'll not step down unless it suits him."

This was getting interesting as it was quite obvious he disliked Sir Quentin. I wanted to hear more. Having always avoided close friendships with pupils' parents, in Evan's case I sensed he was different from the rest. I was sure he was a man who could be trusted with a confidence. I spoke bluntly, hoping he would respond with an opinion.

"I was very rude to Sir Quentin the other night and expected him to sever his connections with the school. He placed poor Polly in an intolerable position."

"When he's drunk he invariably behaves like that. The best way to control him would be to invite Lady Isaac to one of your school events. Why don't you ask her to present the prizes at next month's music competition?"

"What good would that do?" I asked. "I thought she was as deaf as a post."

"She's not deaf. That's one of Quentin's porkies. He's scared to death of her. He knows full well another scandal would end up with her taking him to the cleaners. He's been caught out twice already and you can take it from me she's more than had enough."

"You surprise me," I said, finding it hard to take in the implications of his startling disclosure.

He gave a conspiratorial wink before making an observation that caused both pleasure and dismay. "It's as plain as a pikestaff Polly has no time for Quentin. She only has eyes for you."

Trying to conceal my embarrassment, I admitted she was a woman of charm and intelligence without whose vital contribution my ability to function would appreciably diminish. He looked at me quizzically. "You don't have to pretend with me. You've got the hots for the girl, and can't make a move because she's married. I'm right, aren't I? Life isn't a bundle of fun for most of us, so when a snatch of happiness is within our reach, we have to take it."

Evan's pronouncement replaced my darkest fears with a particle of hope. Had my instinct been correct or was it nothing more than wishful thinking that Polly had feelings for me, secret cravings equal to my own? On Tuesday morning, she returned to work. Her face white as a sheet, dark hollows under her eyes revealed the tell-tale signs of lack of sleep. There was a sullenness in her manner I found disturbing. She murmured something about trust, which I couldn't properly hear.

"What was that? I didn't catch it."

"You've no idea how loyal I am to you."

"What are you trying to say?"

"Keeping Ronald happy, running the house, being at your beck and call, no matter what, with no time to myself. And when I give up an evening to be made a fool of by that loathsome drunk, all for the sake of keeping him on side, you treat me like a whore. You can stuff your fucking job."

Unwilling to listen to my apology, she advanced towards me, eyes ablaze with fury, and began pummelling me with her fists. The blows came in swift succession, strong fearsome blows that stung, blows expressing her frustration. The terror attacks exhausted, she stated coldly as soon as she had gathered together her things, she would be gone for good. So adamant did she appear to be that I had to act on impulse, take some action that would prove how important to me she was. Getting hold of her, I drew her closer, forcing my lips on hers, a brutal step that was unprofessional and shameful. Instead of screaming for help, she snuggled closer and returned my embrace, her sweetly moistened tongue probing the inside of my mouth with delicate, sensual movements.

The connection between us in those electrifying seconds was so powerful that had it not been for the noise of voices in the adjoining room, our lustful urges would have got the better of us. Such madness was equivalent to walking a tightrope; professionally, morally and psychologically we were taking an enormous risk. Everything we held dear, self-respect, credibility and perhaps even our sanity, were in danger of being lost.

"That's enough," she gasped. "We can't go any further."

"I'm sorry, Polly. I crossed the line, I know, but I need you, the school needs you. Please don't leave me to cope on my own. I'd rather have a small part of you than lose you altogether."

She spoke softly. "I won't leave you. I respect and admire the work you do too much for that. I can be your friend, but it can never be more than that."

My disappointment showing, it was plain a compromise was all I could ever hope for. I could tell she cared for me and that was what mattered. Being in charge of a school was a lonely path to follow. I'd learnt long ago true friends were hard to find. I had to be content with a confederate. Someone whose constancy was absolute, a steadfast supporter who told the truth, used logic to counter unworkable ideas and refused to patronize. Polly possessed all these qualities and many more besides. She would have made the perfect wife.

Schools are jealous places. It would have been more than my life was worth to let it be known that Polly was the one whose opinion counted most. Functioning as a democracy, it was essential for the staff to have a say, knowing I would listen to their feedback and suggestions. David Banks and Stephen Rice were concise and radical in their thinking, though if they had a weakness it was an inability to take into account the drawbacks from the standpoint of the owner of the business. Polly was less subjective. She could analyse and decipher, spotting at once the pros and cons of every situation. Not once had I come to fault her judgement, and not because of my feelings for her.

As a traditionalist headmaster, the idea of admitting girls was anathema to me. On a number of occasions parents had made tongue-in-cheek enquiries about sending their daughters to the school, only to be given a negative answer. The complications in accommodating girls were legion. And because we had full waiting lists, I saw no point in creating unnecessary extra work.

"You've got to consider the long-term interests of the school," opined the persuasive Cyril Snape at the July council meeting. Asking him to state his reasons for favouring co-education, Sir Quentin then called upon the other members to express their views.

With the exception of Lady Boddington, who described the thought as absolutely scandalous, all the others were keen to investigate the matter further, leaving me six months in which to report back with my findings. Forming a committee of staff and parents, we held a meeting, by which time Polly and I had done our homework. Apart from the household names, many of the lesser known girls' schools were battling to remain viable and already boys' prep. schools were jumping on the bandwagon by opening their doors to girls.

Of the senior schools, Marlborough was the first noteworthy example of transition to co-education. Other minor public schools followed suit and it was no secret that Repton, Oundle and Rugby were among those preparing for a similar upheaval. It was even rumoured that Eton had set aside the sum of two million pounds for the construction of a boarding house for girls. The facts were self-evident. What I wanted to discover was whether these changes were being made for ideological or financial reasons. If I could be convinced that my school would benefit by mixing the sexes in the way that others had, it was my duty to press ahead.

Had we at Oxton House not adapted our ideas in line with modern thinking, we would have closed by now. Cold baths, corporal punishment and the sadistic practices of thirty years ago were outmoded and defunct. Some of the harshness still survived. It was for this, if for no other reason, that the introduction of girls would make the regime gentler, less formal, allowing the unique differences of femininity to add harmony and balance to our school. We offered a service. It was up to the parents to decide what kind of change they wanted. A consultation paper was sent to all current and prospective parents. In an accompanying letter, I explained we were considering taking girls, but that no steps would be taken until the school council was convinced there was overwhelming support in favour. I emphasized it was essential for everyone to participate, warning that an incomplete survey would lessen the impact of the findings. At the bottom of the sheet there was a space for comments, which I said would be carefully considered as part of the decision-making process.

Within a month, most of the replies were back. By the closing date only three of the families had failed to respond. The results were conclusive. Seventy-three per cent voted in favour of taking girls. Of the twenty-seven per cent who were opposed or undecided, only three per cent said they would seek a single-sex alternative. The most promising sign was that more than half the parents signified it would be their intention to send one or more of their daughters to the school, calculated to be a number in excess of sixty. Written comments covered boarding, activities for the girls, separate changing rooms and additional female teachers. A view shared by most was that for the reorganization to succeed, it had to be carried out thoroughly, with enough money to provide top quality staffing and amenities. Carried out on the cheap, damage to the reputation of the school would be immutable.

Sir Quentin, whose dealings with Polly had been entirely above board since the Christmas dinner dance, was eager for the co-education debate to be concluded. At a specially convened meeting he said he was pleased with the enthusiastic reaction of the parents and he invited Dr Porter, the council's education expert, to enlighten us with his views.

Describing the background which led the governors of his school to bite the bullet, he gave some cautionary advice. "Proceed slowly. Don't expect masses of girls to enter the school at once. No matter what they say, parents are unwilling for their children to be guinea pigs. Once the system is seen to work, they will apply in large numbers and then you'll have to be selective. Girls are generally more conscientious than boys; standards will rise as it's a matter of pride for the boys not to be outsmarted. Plan a five-year programme and take it a step at a time."

"What were the financial implications?" asked the accountant member.

"Done gradually, the strain on our resources was not that great. Had we gone like a bull at a gate, the burden would have been much heavier. Very little was borrowed beyond our usual annual budget."

Evan David wanted to know whether he had regretted taking girls.

"A thousand times no. Our school is stronger, more balanced, happier, academically superior, better prepared to face an economic downturn, and most significant of all, the boys and girls, contrary to popular belief, are not distracted by each other. It's an ideal preparation for the less structured life at university."

Sir Quentin got up to speak, impatiently studying his watch. "Now everyone's had the chance to contribute, I suggest we take a vote."

"Mr Chairman. I'm disgusted with the speed of these discussions," bellowed a hopping-mad Lady Boddington. "My husband and I would never have chosen to send our two sons here had there been girls. Our daughter, now at Cheltenham, wouldn't have fitted in. Separate the sexes, that's always been my motto. Why change a proven system? Instead of being the best boys' prep. school in the county, as members of the council are we going to spend our time talking about rounders, needlework and ballet? To have girls is not only impractical, it's morally unwise. By pandering to a fad, which in ten years' time will have been rejected out of hand, I urge each one of you to be strong enough to place your vote for common sense."

Requesting a show of hands, Sir Quentin said the time had come for a decision. Of the eleven members present, nine voted in favour of co-education. Too angry to speak, Lady Boddington glared icily at Dr Porter, furious to think she'd been disregarded and outmanoeuvred after giving years of generous service to the school.

"At last we have a verdict," announced the smiling chairman. "We as a council are an advisory group and as such have no responsibility other than to make our recommendations. The advice we give is, taken slowly, a step at a time, to quote the distinguished Dr Porter, Oxton House should now set the wheels in motion. We leave it to the headmaster and his staff to act as they see fit."

Polly was worth her weight in gold. Added to her secretarial duties, she took care of the maintenance of buildings, staff contracts, the hiring of cooks, cleaners, matrons, gardeners and office personnel. Apart from the accounts and bills, which was the province of Stephen and his assistant, she was bursar in all but name. To demonstrate my appreciation, I decided to raise her salary and gave her the use of a car. Bribery, favouritism or not, she more than deserved these extra benefits. She was the one person whose wisdom, honesty and foresight were going to play a vital part in helping me meet the challenges of the future.

— Thirty-Eight —

I N SEPTEMBER, TWELVE eight-year-old girls were admitted to the school. One of the female teachers was made responsible for their pastoral care. Temporary changing facilities were provided, mixed hockey was introduced and those who wanted to could play cricket in the summer. In the junior school, which catered for pupils aged four to seven, there were twenty-one girl recruits. Polly's master stroke was to suggest the opening of a dance and drama academy. It was in connection with this innovative idea that I took the bold step of inviting her out to supper. Her reply was not as I expected. "Providing it's business only, I'd love a decent meal. I've not been out in ages." She was such a well-adjusted person it never occurred to me her home life might be drab. Not one to feel sorry for herself, she'd always given the impression her husband was gregarious, that despite his disabilities they were active socially. Now I was not so sure.

There was nothing furtive about our meeting. Arriving separately in the bar of Oscar's, a popular local restaurant, we discussed at length her dance and drama thoughts. Not only had she earmarked a building in which classes could take place, we agreed to look for someone to mastermind and run the project. "Don't you see," she said, "it would be used principally by the girls, but there's nothing to stop the boys from taking part. There could be classes in tap, ballet, speech and drama. To make it pay, why not open it to pupils from other schools? It would make us more girl-friendly."

After the aperitifs we made for our table, positioned in a snug alcove in the restaurant. A catchy rendition by Charles Aznavour played in the background, muffling the sound of the other diners' voices. I was on cloud nine, happier than I'd been in years, proud to be with Polly and prouder still to be her friend. She was always well presented, but tonight wearing a black cocktail dress, pearls and matching earrings, she exuded an aura of true elegance. There

231

was a ripeness about her like a tasty apple ready to be plucked and savoured. The signals I sensed were there, though I did not dare to reveal just how I felt. I thought of the torrid kiss we'd shared.

"You're stunning," I said. "I've not seen you look more beautiful. I think your husband is a very lucky man."

"Much as I enjoy your flattery, I thought we were here to talk shop."

"I've decided to break the rules."

"What do you mean by that?"

"For three years we've worked together harmoniously. Do you agree with that statement?"

"I agree we're compatible in the professional sense."

"The contribution you make at school is incredible, your handling of staff, your discernment, financial competence and the support you give to me."

"Where's this leading, Paul?"

"For once let's make an exception and talk about you. All I ever see is a façade, the busy executive suppressing her feelings, the unselfish paragon. You're a perfectionist with standards nobody can match. You make me feel inferior, dependent, unworthy." I flushed using such praise.

"You're a brilliant headmaster. If I didn't think that I'd have left you long ago."

I was desperate to find the words to progress our friendship beyond the grudging formality she had offered me for months. I pressed on. "Tell me what you really think, let down your guard, say what pleases you and talk about your desires and preferences. Do you have a dream? I'm scared by your silence. To hell with it, Polly, are you settled and fulfilled at home? I know things can't be easy."

I could see anger mounting in her face, an indignation so palpable that I thought she was about to get up and walk away. The tenseness easing, she gave a weary smile as if to say it was not in her nature to talk about herself.

"You know damned well it's difficult at home. It would be wrong to discuss my situation with you, or anyone, come to that."

"Why not? I thought I was your friend."

"You are. Haven't you problems of your own?"

I knew perfectly well what my problems were. Emotional frustration, sexual deprivation, a deep-rooted fear of being on my own, of reaching old age, isolated and unloved, with no partner, no children, only memories of momentary joys, successes, satisfaction. She was the one person I could trust. If only she was free. Marriage to Catriona had been a disaster from the start. Was I capable of making someone blissfully content, the fairy-tale happiness we read about in books? And had circumstances been different, how would Polly and I have been together? This time I intended to persist.

"We all have problems. I'm sure yours are more taxing than mine. Don't you think sometimes it can help to share a burden?"

"I have to be strong, put on a front, give the impression everything's just fine. That's how most of us survive."

"Are you happy," I asked.

"In a way. Happy with my work. Happy when Ronald's health is stable, but low, terribly low when he's unwell, not sleeping, has an infection or is angry with himself at the sheer effort of trying to be normal, seeming to be normal, just to please *me*."

I could sense she was removing some of the barriers that hitherto pride had forced her to use to shut me out. I had no doubt she loved her husband, but the pain of seeing him suffer was unbearable. She described it as a slow-motion agony that would never go away.

"His illness is a worsening condition. He's not going to get well and who knows when and in what form there will be an ending. Day after day I witness the price he pays, knowing there's no let-up, nothing to be done other than to console, encourage, hope. And prayers, lots and lots of prayers, none of them answered."

I, too, had known what it was to suffer, having been orphaned and later rejected by the woman for whom I'd have willingly given my life. These traumas involved the loss of precious parts of me, leaving scars that would be permanent. Polly's pain was different. Hers was a living nightmare, relentless in its prediction of a gruesome outcome. I wanted to empathize with the hurt, the loneliness, to be her prop and give her strength and comfort in the future.

"I'd like to make a suggestion," I said. She answered she was listening. "Why don't we meet socially once a month, just the two of us, to give you a break? You need the chance to breathe a little."

"I'm not sure it's a good idea, but I promise to think about it." Her voice was sharp, yet her lips quivered imperceptively until she gradually unmasked a glimmer of a smile.

We met regularly, not every month, but often enough for it to be quite normal for us to be seen in one of Harrogate's eating places on the occasional Thursday night. People who saw us together weren't shocked, nor did they make snide comments behind our backs about the headmaster wining and dining a married member of his staff. Polly was known to be high-principled and morally impeccable. Had Ronald objected to her having the occasional evening out, she wouldn't have dreamt of going against his wishes. The fact was he encouraged these meetings, claiming it did her good to have a change of scene. In any case, the school was undergoing developments that had to be discussed.

To make provision for the girls required many hours of careful planning. Polly's perceptive intelligence and eye for detail put us ahead of the game, an advantage that was reinforced by her uncanny knack for identifying problems before mistakes were made. Our target was to cater for three hundred pupils, an increase of nearly fifty per cent. To allow for the expansion we needed extra classrooms, specialist rooms for domestic science and design technology and a changing suite for the girls.

After surveying the site, Polly recommended the positioning of the buildings, liaised with the contractors, planners, architects. Once estimates had been submitted and planning permission granted, my task was to arrange a medium-term loan. With annual profits of seventy-five thousand pounds, I had no difficulty in getting the bank to lend the school, now a limited company, one hundred and fifty thousand pounds, repayable quarterly over a five-year period. The manager gave the impression he had a bottomless supply of funds and knowing the deeds were safely in his possession, with ingratiating eagerness he offered to lend an additional fifty thousand pounds at an even lower rate of interest.

"Thanks but no thanks," was my answer, remembering how unhelpful the bank had been when ten years earlier we'd struggled to meet financial targets.

The trouble often with teachers is they become set in their ways, suffer from tunnel vision and are opposed to any kind of change. Three of the Oxton House masters were strongly against the concept of co-education and weren't afraid to voice their views. They didn't want more female staff. They thought mixed sport of any kind was unworkable and dangerous. They disliked the adjustments to the syllabus and hated even more having to alter familiar routines in order to accommodate the girls.

With a divided common room, two conflicting camps had formed, which was a major handicap to progress. Herbert Bond, the most vocal of the dissenters, was becoming difficult to handle. Refusing to have girls in his choir, his influence was so disruptive that I was left with no alternative other than to issue him with a written warning. Most serious was his unwillingness to accept resolutions that had been arrived at democratically, decisions which I admitted had placed doubts in the minds of many. He was, I said, perfectly entitled to his own opinions, but that if he was no longer prepared to support school policies and was disloyal to me, I warned him I would be asking for his resignation.

Polly knew how dejected I was made to feel by the behaviour of the militants. Hers was the voice of reason. Able to see the situation from my perspective, she was also endowed with the ability to understand each problem from the other person's point of view. "I think you've misread Herbert," she said, thinking he genuinely believed taking girls was a mistake and that the school would come tumbling down because of it. She strongly advised me to reassure him by patiently repeating the original arguments. She was instinctively aware how to handle the most rebellious of the staff. Had she qualified at an early age in one of the professions, as a psychologist or as a management consultant, she would have reached the top of the tree by now. She was unassailable and tremendously gifted, never ceasing to amaze me with her quick-wittedness and the agility of her thinking.

By now I loved Polly with an intensity I knew could never be returned. It was essential to hide from her my sexual fantasies, the nightly urges, portraying as they did in graphic detail the erotic things I wanted us to do. Lack of physical fulfilment was a heartache that stabbed me like a knife, an incessant reminder of my inner emptiness. We were in tune mentally and both looked forward to our regular suppers out. Now much less formal in her manner, Polly was prepared to talk to me more openly on a number of subjects, some of them personal. I shall not forget the evening we discussed restaurants and eating when I said I was glad she enjoyed her food.

"I'm putting on weight," she grumbled. "When I look in the mirror and see all those bulges, I despise myself. I haven't the strength to say no. I just eat and eat."

I told her she suited her build, that I preferred a woman to be wholesome-looking rather than thin.

"Most men like a bit of flesh," I said.

She grinned self-consciously. "I used to have a good figure when I went running every day and got very upset if I gained so much as a pound."

"You don't need to worry. You look terrific, yours is the perfect physique. What does Ronald think?"

"He's got so many problems that the question of my figure is hardly of significance. Why all the compliments?"

"I think you know my feelings, even though I dare not put them into words."

"Am I that intimidating? I promise I won't be upset, no matter what you say."

"I'm in love with you, Polly. Can't you see? It's tearing me apart. All I do is think about you like some moonstruck teenager. When I was at Cambridge I thought I was in love, but not like this. That was practising, experimental, a part of growing up. With you it's real, only you're not available and I'm jealous of Ronald because I want you to myself. How contemptible is that?"

Silent for a moment, she then asked me a question that made me wonder what was coming next. "Do you think it's possible to love two people?"

"Apart from Catriona, I've loved my parents, my aunt and uncle and Emma, that's six in all, excluding you. Yes, it's possible to love several people in different ways. But you can only be *in* love with one person at a time."

I could see she was unhappy with my answer.

"I don't agree. I love Ronald and I love you, too. I love you as a woman loves a man, which doesn't mean my love for Ronald is any less sincere. I admire and respect him and shall always cherish the memories of how he was before his illness. He can't help how he's become, not wanting to touch me anymore. I'm nearly forty, living like a virgin and the frustration's driving me up the wall. I've never spoken like this before, but can't hide the truth. I want you, Paul. I want you desperately. I miss being held, caressed, made love to. Am I shocking you? Please say you feel the same."

I found it impossible to believe what I was hearing! The difference between desire and practical application was so vast that even in my most desperate state of need I knew it was lunacy to ignore the dangers of having a full-blown affair with Polly. There were also the feelings of guilt to consider, the knowledge that cheating on her husband could destroy the pleasures of our passion, portraying us as two self-absorbed deceivers, who deserved to be found out. In spite of these misgivings, I was still eager to make love to her, but not if it meant hiding away in some anonymous boarding house or copulating in the back of a car in a secluded lane at night.

I had become friendly with Evan David. He and I played squash together at a local club and after our encounters on the court, we would often repair to a pub for a drink and a bite to eat. He had for some while confided in me about his marriage, saying he was miserable at home because his wife had taken a lover and that he'd resorted to having girlfriends to help fill the emptiness.

"Why don't you get a divorce?" I said.

"I love the kids too much for that. If Sue and I separate, she's threatened to move to Cornwall, which would mean depriving me of the boys. In view of my wealth, she would stand to gain a small fortune. If that's not bad enough, the thought of some of my hard-earned money ending up with Harry, her smug-faced lover, is more than I could stomach."

"If she's the guilty party, surely that fact would affect the settlement."

"Guilty party be damned. She's got a duplicitous solicitor and he's up to every trick imaginable. I've decided to play a waiting game and see what happens when the children have grown up and left for university."

Whenever we met, he always questioned me about Polly and I sometimes wondered whether he fancied her and was angling for an opportunity to get to know her better, using me as the point of contact. I need not have worried. He had fish of his own to fry. Swearing me to secrecy, he told me he had met a new and exciting young lady through a business associate.

"She's only twenty-nine and a little cracker."

"What if Sue finds out?" I warned.

"She won't. Francesca lives in Burnley and more often than not we meet on her patch rather than mine." His involvement sounded even more complicated than my own predicament.

"It must feel like permanently living on the edge," I commented. "I couldn't lead a cloak-and-dagger existence like that."

"What you're forgetting is I'm a normal, healthy male, who depends on the stimulation of sex to keep me going. I love my wife, but she pushes me away. What would you do, given those circumstances?"

His words were a reminder of two wretched years of deprivation with Catriona. What was it that made Evan think I had different desires and impulses from other men, simply because I was his sons' headmaster?

In view of his willingness to divulge such personal information, I decided to let down my barriers of reserve and come clean about the dilemma over Polly. Saying our relationship had taken a different turn, I explained how hard it was for us to meet, let alone find a safe place where we could be alone together.

"If that's the only problem, I think I can help you out," said Evan. Winking at me cheekily, he said he'd purchased a flat in a discreet neighbourhood on the edge of Harrogate where he met Francesca on the occasional weekend. He then made me a very generous offer. "You have my permission to use the flat any weekday night apart from Wednesdays when the cleaner comes to tidy up. I'm happy to loan you a key so you can meet Polly there as often as you wish. This is serious stuff, Paul, so not a word to a soul. If the news got out, we'd both be for the high jump."

I'd always been cautious in matters relating to my private life. There had never been any question of allowing my image to be tarnished by reckless conduct, behaviour that could damage the reputation of the school. In view of Polly's unforeseen entreaty, there was to be no stopping me, and throwing caution to the wind, the two of us began to meet regularly in Evan's flat, an arrangement that was to continue without a hitch for eighteen sensational months.

— Thirty-Nine —

A DECISION STILL to be reached was whether or not to open a boarding house for girls. Co-education was seen to be working well, with the girls playing a conspicuous part in the advancement of academic standards. Remarks made by Mark Davenhill, a parent from Sheffield, helped make up my mind. "I've always regarded Oxton House as one of Yorkshire's gems," he said, adding the caveat that his only complaint was we did not take girl boarders. "We live too far away for my daughters to travel on a daily basis. You are discriminating against the girls by not offering them the same facilities as their brothers." Not only had he made a valid point, several other parents were using the same argument. Acting decisively, I asked Polly to start looking for a property that could accommodate twenty-five girl boarders.

Co-education in the truest sense would have meant having one hundred and fifty girls on roll, fifty per cent of the total numbers. Because Oxton House had for generations been known as a single-sex school, many people still looked upon it as a boys-only establishment. This hypothesis made it harder to recruit girls than boys and there was the added problem that some of the girls moved on to their senior schools when aged eleven, two years before the departure of the boys.

The school council considered these issues carefully, endorsing my view that we needed above all to prevent girl numbers from falling below a sensible total in any one class. The decision to take girl boarders was an important step in proving mixed education for us was here to stay and was not a passing trend. Apart from the capital expense of acquiring and adapting another property, in view of the small number of girls to be housed, we knew the running costs would be disproportionately high. Our budgeting took into account staffing and day-to-day maintenance, including electricity and gas bills. It was essential to locate a house within easy walking distance of the school. As luck would have it, Polly discovered a small private hotel just round the corner that had fallen into disrepair and was about to close. The owners, an elderly couple, were having difficulty in selling the business as a going concern. After hurried negotiations, I was able to purchase the building, which included a sizeable garden, for just under thirty-seven thousand pounds.

Polly began the onerous task of planning the extensive renovations to provide all the facilities parents would expect in a modern boarding house. My bonus was that apart from having to finance the project, I played a back-seat role, able to leave all the day-to-day minutiae with Polly. As was typical of her, she handled the builders shrewdly, combining bullying with courtesy and tact, a strategy that worked.

After months of intense activity, completion was well in time for the September opening. With all the beds filled and a resident matron and housemother in place, I was speechless with admiration for Polly, whose spectacular handling of the entire operation again exemplified her determination to strive for nothing but the highest standards.

From many points of view life for me was good. At school, Polly displayed the loyalty of a wife, one who never quibbled or groused, but was there to smooth my troubled brow at times of stress. She was not obliged to look after me if I was sick, nor did she have to endure the less seemly aspects of the man she claimed to love, such as stale morning breath, my dirty laundry or having to condone my bad habits procured from years of living on my own with no one other than myself to think about.

Away from the stiff formality of school, the private time we spent in Evan's flat provided us with precious moments of fulfilment. In bed, Polly liked to take the lead. Uninhibited and physically demanding, she knew exactly what she wanted. Surprised by my inexperience she acted as my tutor. Within weeks she had taught me to be considerate of the need first to give pleasure before achieving satisfaction myself. Compatibility grew from modest beginnings to an ardent desire for us to meet more often, bringing out in us both a possessive form of love that defied all sense of reason. The cosy arrangement was not enough. Now our relationship was on a different footing, we thought it unwise to be seen eating out together. It was as if the world would know by the look on our faces that ours was more than just a friendship. To conceal our love, except in the context of our work, was an unviable expectation.

We had for a long time been talking about a change of routine to lift us out of the rut of two regular weekly meetings at the flat for sex and sympathy. A weekend away was talked about. We had never lived as a couple, able to behave normally, doing things that a husband and wife take for granted. Activities like going for a walk, taking tea in a café, a visit to the theatre, and waking up together. These were some of the simple pleasures that we lacked. To celebrate Polly's achievements at the school, I told her I wanted to reward her by taking her away for a weekend break.

"I'm not sure what excuse I can give Ronald," she said.

"Can't you say you're going on a management course? That would sound plausible enough."

"I've not left him overnight before. His health is reasonably settled at present, but the situation is very fluid. One minute he's OK, the next he can be unwell. What if there's an emergency?" But attracted to the idea of spending some quality time together, she finally consented. What I hadn't realized was the extent of her doubts and that the thought of abandoning Ronald for a couple of days was making her feel guilty.

We decided to drive somewhere on spec rather than make a hotel booking. The priority was to get as far away from Harrogate as possible to avoid meeting someone we knew. I'd always liked Devon and Somerset and Polly, who was happy to leave the choice of where to go to me, said that if she had a preference it was for a quiet seaside location.

"All I want is your company, with only the sound of seagulls and waves crashing on the rocks to break the silence," she declared poetically. In recent days she had been pensive and of a more melancholy frame of mind than was her habit. I was greatly relieved to see she was at last warming to the idea of our clandestine adventure.

Stopping off for lunch at Cheltenham, we continued our drive in a westerly direction. Making for Dunkery Beacon, from Exmoor's highest point we admired the scenic vista of rugged countryside, perfected by the distant sea forming a decorative backdrop. Close to Minehead we discovered a sleepy fishing village at the foot of Porlock Hill that offered Polly a carbon copy of the idyllic spot she hankered after. Enhanced by the boats and two fishermen repairing their nets, the quayside was picture-postcard perfect, with few cars and no noise or bustle to detract from our desire to locate the perfect lovers' hideout. Opposite the little harbour was The Anchor Inn, a rustic pub that provided food and accommodation. Decorated with nautical artefacts, the restaurant offered an extensive menu with an emphasis on fish. We were surprised to discover lobster dishes were a special feature. Attracted by the quaint sophistication of the place, we decided to book a room.

The landlord, a snappy dresser with coiffured grey locks and a pretentious accent, greeted us at reception. He informed us how fortunate we were to secure the one remaining room. I responded by signing the register using a false identity and fictitious address. Polly was uneasy and self-conscious, convinced she had met the licencee before. Her fear was sufficient for her to make a guarded observation.

"I seem to think I know you, though I cannot for the life of me remember when or where that was."

He responded immodestly. "I get this all the time. When I was an actor on stage and television, my face was known in almost every household in the country. I'm sure we haven't met. Had that happened, I wouldn't have forgotten a lady of such charm and gracefulness."

His flattery was getting on my nerves and it was a relief to deposit our cases in the privacy of what was misleadingly described in the inn's leaflet as a superior room. The cramped bedroom contained a small double bed from which there was a view of the sea and harbour. There was only one hanger in the wardrobe and the revamped en suite bathroom about which the landlord had waxed lyrical, was painted in garish pinks and orange. The toilet flush was faulty and the plug was missing from the basin, but these were minor inconveniences compared to the thrill that we were able to live openly like an established married couple.

Before changing for dinner, we walked beside the sea, searching for shells. Like competitive teenagers, we began throwing pebbles into the water to find out how many times they bounced before sinking. Polly had a strong pitch, able to judge exactly how low to aim the shots. Sometimes the winner, she goaded me playfully, professing she would have expected my performance to be better considering I was a cricketer. Sitting on a bench, we marvelled at the perfect stillness, the pureness of the air and the spirit of calm abandonment that the mini break was arousing in our hearts. In the past our meetings had often been hurried, preoccupied and strained. Tonight the formula was different. For the first time ever we were liberated from the manacles of convention and were permitted to behave exactly as we wished.

Before the meal we thought it would be fun to have a drink in the public bar and meet some of the locals. A huge man in blue overalls with a lined smoker's face asked whether we were eating in the restaurant. When we replied in the affirmative, he gave us unsolicited advice.

"Watch out for that Quinn fellow," he said. "He's the landlord. Used to be an actor and does he love himself! My advice is to avoid him like the plague."

Intrigued to find out more, we were shown to our places in the dining room by Quinn himself. It was impossible to keep our eyes off him as he darted about extravagantly, his ear-splitting voice diverting our attention from the important task of choosing from the menu. Everything he said or did had a theatrical ring to it and by the time we had finished our desserts, we'd had enough of the charade. In actual fact he'd done us a favour. Instead of staying for coffee, we retired to bed early to indulge in some serious lovemaking.

As this was the first time we were to spend an entire night together, there was no need to eye our watches or feel under pressure to get away. We could take as long as we liked, knowing Polly didn't have to return to her husband, nor did we have to make an early start next day. Though the situation could not have been more perfect, I sensed something was wrong. I had no idea what was bugging Polly until she admitted she'd been foolish to leave Ronald on his own, saying how much she hated telling lies.

"It's bad enough cheating on him at home. To be hundreds of miles away, allowing him to think I'm somewhere else, is shameful and disgusting."

"Why don't you phone him to see if he's alright?"

"Don't be glib about it. To do that would merely add to my feelings of remorse. We shouldn't have planned this trip."

She was getting angry and I knew the more I tried to console her, the more disturbed she would get. Endeavouring to calm her down, I began fondling her breasts. Seconds later she'd stripped off her clothes and we lay naked on the bed, fastened to each other in an amorous embrace.

Up until then when making love we had stuck to a formula, an unscripted technique perfected after months of concentrated effort, the predominant aim being the need to please each other. I'd learnt how to be unselfish, how to tantalize by stopping then starting up again to increase the sexual tension. Above all, I'd discerned the significance of patience before achieving relief myself. Instead of a gentle, unhurried start, Polly led the way with aggressive, thrusting movements, willing me to come. She powered, pushed and scratched, her arms and legs tightening their grip. She was hysterical, relentless, deranged.

"I want you to come," she roared. "Faster, harder, deeper."

Exasperated, ashamed and physically exhausted, I obliged her by doing as she asked. In spite of the brief elation induced by her frenzied actions, her unwillingness to seek pleasure for herself made me very anxious.

"I can't get out of my mind a passage in the bible about the last supper," she said at last, her voice expressionless and sad.

"What's that got to do with my selfishness just now?"

"For one last time I wanted to turn you on. You're an incredible man, you're good in bed, I've loved you and I've encouraged you, I know, but it can't go on. *We* can't go on. The pretence is driving me insane."

Unwilling to believe the truth behind these words, I gripped her by the shoulders and began shaking her.

"Stop that this instant or I'll call downstairs for help," she snapped.

"How do you *expect* me to react? We're madly in love one minute. In the next you tell me it's over because you don't like telling lies. You've been lying through your teeth for two years. We both have. Surely you don't expect me to say, fair enough, it's been a pleasure knowing you, thank you and goodbye."

I instantly regretted my outburst.

She began crying, though I couldn't work out if they were tears of misery or whether she'd decided to retract her threat. Her next statement destroyed all hope of a favourable result. "This isn't something new, a whim, a flash-in-the-pan decision. Ronald hasn't said, but I think he knows about us. I can't bear the burden of betraying him any longer."

"You've never told me that."

"You must try to see my point of view. Be glad of the happiness we've shared and find someone else, someone who's free. Then you can get married and live happily ever after."

"I was hoping that person might be you. I don't want someone else. One day you'll be available. I'm willing to wait as long as it takes."

"That's a dreadful thing to say. To wait for Ronald to die is sick. Sick and not worthy coming from a man whose decency I respect. I know I've been disloyal, but I'm not capable of being as treacherous as that. You've got to move on, Paul. My job is to try to repair what's left of my marriage."

Next morning we packed our bags and left. The silent journey home gave me time to think. Too upset to speak, I sulked and brooded, lacking the desire or energy to hold a normal conversation. Bitterness multiplied as I considered the hopelessness of the emotional abyss.

By the time we were back in Harrogate, I'd come to a conclusion. Women were not for me. Three times relationships had failed. In future I undertook to leave them out of the equation and devote one hundred per cent attention to my job.

— Forty —

TO HAVE EXPECTED Polly to continue to work for me would have been an absurd assumption. I knew perfectly well she wouldn't want to remain at the school, but I had hoped she would stay on long enough for me to find a stand-in rather than be left with no help and an abundance of paperwork to unravel. After handing in her keys and returning the company car, she said she would shortly be leaving Yorkshire with her husband and that contact between the two of us must cease. Meanwhile, life had to go on.

Top-notch secretaries were a rarity and I knew no matter how hard I searched, I would never again find someone with Polly's qualities. From a professional point of view, her departure was a catastrophe. At a personal level, I had been sickened beyond belief, finding it impossible to comprehend how the woman who'd given herself to me with such love and sensitivity could have acted so harshly. Left emotionally stripped of everything that mattered, I struggled to keep myself together, aware of the need to appear to be on top of things, clear-headed and strong, when the truth presented an entirely different picture. Swallowed up with bitterness and hurt, I used all the resources I could gather to fight off the spectres of disillusionment and shame.

To Polly's credit, there was not a whiff of scandal at the school, though news of her swift exodus did raise eyebrows in the staff room.

"It's not like her to leave without any warning," said David Banks, who made plain his disapproval at the mess she'd left us in. Hypocrisy would have been taken too far had I agreed with him, which led me to defend her actions whilst covering up my own disgraceful conduct.

Evan was quick to discover that Polly and I were no longer visiting his flat. Arranging for us to meet, he began quizzing me, a mean-spirited smirk appearing on his face. "A little bird tells me Polly has done a bunk. What did you do to upset her?"

I told him I resented his tone and that it was no laughing matter. "Not only did I depend on her at school, had she been free we would have married long ago."

He still seemed amused and caused further irritation by making light of my distress. "There are plenty more fish in the sea," he quipped.

In no mood to listen to his jibes, I told him no matter how many fish there were, I was far too bruised to seek a sex replacement for Polly.

"Women are all the same," he remarked. "When they've taken what they want, they move on to pastures greener. You remember the girl from Burnley I was telling you about? She's buggered off with a younger man and now she's engaged. I've found someone better, Yvonne, She's a model, divorced and much sexier than Frankie, so everybody's happy. There's no need for you to fret. The best is yet to come."

When I challenged his remark, he said the children at school had noticed how much more cheerful I'd been during the last few months.

"Before that you were known to have a short fuse and the kids called you grumbleguts. The affair with Polly has obviously made you human."

He had hit me where it hurt. To get my own back, I took the moral high ground, saying he treated his women as if it was a game, a cruel attitude that highlighted his superficiality.

"That's an insult," he thundered. "I've done a lot for you, been loyal, supported you at school and on the council, given you the keys to my flat; and because you're unwanted and unloved, you're behaving like the bishop of the diocese."

Too late to make amends, I realized our association was over. Professional friendships were never safe and to have offended a parent of two of my pupils, and a prominent one at that, had been a mistake that could well come leaping back to haunt me later on.

I decided to use an agency to find a new PA. There was no short-age of applicants. Despite the glowing references of half a dozen, none of them impressed. I knew it was going to be an impossible task to appoint someone capable of matching Polly's competence, I offered a short-term contract to a sixty-three-year-old widow who had been personal assistant to the managing director of a building company. From the moment she arrived, she made my life a misery. She was humourless, argumentative and cold. A martinet with a penchant for controlling everyone in sight, she was impossible to handle. After months of purgatory, her contract about to end, an act of fate provided the chance to restructure the administration of the school, giving me the excuse not to have to reappoint the abhorrent office tyrant.

Uncle Don had always said he could tolerate the pupils and the parents but was damned if he could control his staff. I had some sympathy with this sentiment, although I was fortunate to have two stalwart colleagues, both of them personal friends, whose support I knew I could rely on. David Banks and Stephen Rice had given extraordinary service to the school. For eighteen years David had been the ideal deputy, dedicated and vigilant, an ally who'd backed me to the hilt. Stephen's claim to fame was his financial know-how. As part-time bursar he had streamlined outdated systems and throughout his time at Oxton House been a fantastic friend. It's not that he was unhappy, but unknown to me he had set his heart on taking holy orders.

Upset to think he'd not warned me of his plans, I made a caustic statement. "You might at least have discussed it with me. I'm without a secretary and now I'm going to have no bursar."

"I can't help it if you've forgotten conversations from the past. I've often talked about wanting to be ordained."

"I didn't think you were serious. You were speaking frivolously and I assumed it was one of those fanciful ideas that people get from time to time."

"I can assure you I'm in earnest. I shall be leaving in July. I've been offered a provisional place at Mirfield in the autumn."

My dog-in-the-manager attitude conveyed the anger I felt at the prospect of losing one of the most effective members of my team. Instead of congratulating him on his self-denying choice, I treated the decision as a personal affront, thinking only of myself and of the inconvenience his departure would produce. Forgiving my uncharitable response, he came up with an ingenious idea. By adding Polly's bursar's duties to his own, he said there would be enough work to create a full-time post. He made it sound so easy. After getting him to prepare a detailed job description, we agreed to advertise for a bursar, a position that would ideally suit a person with administrative experience and a basic understanding of finance.

A man of ambition, David Banks wanted a headship. Giving him a first-class reference, I advised him to be choosy and not accept the first offer that came along. Taking note of what I said, he rejected the chance to head a small preparatory school in Hastings with dwindling numbers, claiming what put him off was the cramped accommodation and his son's reluctance to attend another school. Soon after Stephen's shock announcement, David came to me with the news that he had been shortlisted for the headship of Harrington Manor, a co-educational boarding school in Dorset. Over three days he and his wife were intensively grilled at interviews, along with four other candidates. Returning with the triumphant news of success, David informed me he'd been offered the post and would be taking up the position in September. I said he'd done well to beat the other contestants, especially as Harrington Manor was a well-established school with an enviable reputation.

"You deserve this chance," I said. "You're going to be missed here more than you will ever know."

With several new staff to appoint, I was reminded how upset my uncle had been when Duncan Knott and Miss Roberts had handed in their notice. In my mood at the time I thought he was unreasonable. Now I could fully understand his point of view. Knowing the school's success depended heavily on the effectiveness of the people I was losing, my prime concern was to select the highest calibre replacements. To attract maximum interest, and spending a fortune in the process, announcements were placed in several national newspapers.

In all there were five appointments to be made: a deputy head; a master to take charge of the boys' boarding house; a bursar; a mathematics specialist and a secretary for me. Memories of staff problems in the past acted as a warning. Gone were the days when the school depended on a group of teachers unfit for purpose; an octogenarian barely able to walk; a war veteran with shattered nerves; the shoe-wielding Mr Johnson, whose barbarous savagery was a scandal and disgrace. It's little wonder my uncle had cause to complain about some of the people he employed. Since then there had been wide-ranging changes. We now provided a much more friendly environment, having diluted stern traditions in favour of a child-oriented approach. The boys and girls were happy and contented, proud of their school, eager to seize the opportunities on offer. Ours was a bespoke service that treated pupils as individuals, the aim being to single out their strengths, build confidence and develop standards of excellence in all departments. The school's reputation had advanced so strikingly that competition for positions on the staff was fierce. Teachers with high expectations looked upon Oxton House as a shining example of what a prep. school ought to be. Flooded with applications for the various posts on offer, the pressure rested firmly with me to make the right decisions.

Up at five each morning, I was later to be seen having breakfast with the boarders. It was not unusual to still be at work burning the midnight oil as I planned ahead to ensure every eventuality was covered. Believing efficiency stemmed from being content with nothing but the best, the belt-and-braces policy I adopted had become central to my approach. For three months I devoted what spare moments there were to the appointment of new staff, key people whose influence for good or ill would make or break the school. Considering two hundred applications and studying in detail the antecedents of the most likely candidates took an enormous amount of time. Had it not been for the advice and help given by David Banks, the task would have been even more burdensome. Adding the weight of his judgement, he joined a committee made up of parents, staff and a representative from the council. Selection was a democratic process, a minefield nonetheless, so different from the casual wink and nod interview practices of the early post-war years.

The bursar's position was the first to be settled. There were four strong candidates, two of them officers from the forces and two retired bank managers. We finally chose Group Captain Peter Bulkington, who stood quite literally head and shoulders over the other three. At six foot seven inches tall, he would never escape attention in a crowd, but more importantly his credentials were exemplary, confirming he was a first-rate organizer, trustworthy and methodical.

Of the seventy-two applicants for the post of deputy head, seven were called for interview. Keith Marsh, a twenty-nine-year-old Oxford graduate, had for four years taught mathematics at an independent school in Woking. He was by far the most impressive. There were, however, two drawbacks. I was concerned his young age might cause resentment among older colleagues, and a further complication was that he expected the school to provide him with a house large enough to accommodate a family of five. After some initial hesitation, the committee agreed he was the best man for the job. As soon as I had purchased a pretty four-bedroomed cottage close to the school, I realized I was well on the road to achieving my objectives.

Killing two birds with one stone, the housemaster we chose happened to be a classicist, enabling him to fulfil most of the teaching commitments undertaken by David Banks. Recently married, Jonathan Dell was known to set high standards. His previous headmaster was adulatory in his praise, saying he was strong on leadership and pastoral care and inspirational in the classroom. In the previous year alone, two of his pupils had won scholarships at Winchester, having been awarded distinctions for their performances in Latin.

My ability to operate effectively as headmaster depended greatly on the strength of the backing I received behind the scenes. Choice of a suitable secretary was so crucial to my well-being that I left no stone unturned in seeking a woman whose experience and professionalism matched the standards to which I was accustomed. Having made a pledge never again to fall into the trap of being emotionally involved at work, I knew I was safe to select Brenda Bates, a plain and overweight spinster with testimonials that gave prominence to her heart of gold and unsullied reputation. A fresh chapter in the life of the school began with high-octave energy expended, the new staff endeavouring to make their marks. If past experience was anything to go by, I was conscious it would soon be clear whether the good intentions they expressed at interview would satisfy my hopeful expectations.

Competent is the word I would use to describe the newcomers to the staff. There was no obvious deficiency other than a lack of sparkle, which placed them in a different category from their talented predecessors. On the face of it, the school continued to run smoothly. Entry lists remained full, academic results were still above average and the parents were largely contented, some of them generous with their praise. I should have been pleased, but it was the changed atmosphere that unsettled me. The personal emphasis, for years an outstanding feature, had noticeably diminished. With three hundred and seventeen pupils on roll, the impression was of an unwieldy institution that had outgrown itself. What we lacked was the heart and soul that David, Stephen and Polly had contributed to the community through their charismatic efforts, a trademark that was seen to be stagnating. As a human being, I missed their support and friendship; and in Polly's case, her unmitigated love, the lack of which led me to feel abandoned, with a legacy of loneliness impossible to bear.

The departure of my three staunch followers led me to think about the future. I was nearly fifty, divorced and there was nobody to take over from me when I wanted to retire. Having been headmaster from such a young age, I was in danger of burning myself out, lost for imaginative ideas, wearied by the isolation of my office. After tackling the same problems day after day, week after week, year after year, the monotonous repetition was beginning to get to me. I'd wanted a son and heir or a suitable successor to relieve me of the stress and later carry on my work in order to immortalize the achievements of the family. To guarantee continuity, the idea of turning the school into a trust had some appeal, but there were serious disadvantages. The thought of losing control and for major decisions to rest with the likes of Sir Quentin Isaac, Lady Boddington and Evan David was an alarming prospect. I could see no merit in increasing their authority, a situation that would enable them to dictate what I could or could not do. The Elliotts had fought too long and hard for me to relinquish the advantages of independence to a group of dubious outsiders.

I had met a number of owner headmasters who were afraid to retire because by doing so their schools would have to close. Schools that made little in the way of profit were hard to sell, as potential buyers would be unlikely to see a return on their investment. When Uncle Don purchased Oxton House, the value of the goodwill was based on the income from two terms' fees. This formula no longer applied and many proprietors were forced to choose the safer route of selling the land and buildings in preference to giving their businesses away for next to nothing. One head, in particular, ended his days in poverty, having sold out for very little after devoting forty years for the benefit of others. It would have been easy to remain at the helm long past my sell-by date, thinking there was nobody who could continue to drive the school forward in the way that I had done.

Of my many functions, the most important was to maintain numbers at capacity levels by offering parents a value-for-money service. Any financial astuteness I had acquired came from instinct rather than training and I found it extraordinary that many of the teachers were oblivious to the fact their monthly salaries depended on having in place a sound commercial policy. Oxton House was one of the few schools of its kind to be making a significant profit. Despite the strong balance sheet, I knew the transfer or sale of the business would never be straightforward. Few schoolmasters had funds to invest, and entrepreneurs planning to get rich could find better ways of making their money work than in the specialized field of private education.

Had one of the newly appointed masters been blessed with strong leadership qualities, I would have groomed him to take over from me at a later date. I was becoming tired and did not intend to carry on at such a pressurized level for many more years. The burdens of responsibility were massive, and I was aware I was unfit, spending far too long sitting at a desk rather than leading a healthier lifestyle. Since my contretemps with Evan I'd given up playing squash. I was rapidly gaining weight and a short walk up a flight of stairs was enough to make me breathless. Now was the time to plan ahead.

After Keith Marsh and Jonathan Dell had spent a year with me, I was in a better position to evaluate their potential. Keith carried out his duties as my deputy with thoroughness and care. A good disciplinarian, he was strict but fair and as far as I could judge, all the pupils liked him. Everything I asked him to do, he did cheerfully and to the best of his ability. Never moody, he seemed happy at the school. What he lacked was initiative and the ability to make decisions for himself. For this reason, I ruled him out as a possible successor.

Jonathan's wife, Marion, was the power behind the throne. Had he been an unmarried housemaster, he would not have succeeded. Because of Marion's domineering influence, Jonathan, who was no ground-breaker, coped adequately, but his indeterminate actions made him a poor tactician. His results in the classroom were outstanding with gifted children, though he set targets far above the comprehension levels of the least able with whom only a limited impression was made. Marion had pretensions of grandeur and would have run the school on her own given half a chance.

Her husband's modest performance, however, bore little relation to the flattering testimonial supplied by his previous head. I rated his leadership capability as zero.

During my long connection with the school, apart from David and Stephen, and the legendary Duncan Knott, I don't think any of the staff would have had the faintest idea how to steer the ship safely even in calm waters. And when times were tough, a hazard that could occur in any number of disguises, they would have sunk without trace in choppy conditions. To seek a suitable replacement to enable me to plan for my retirement was like looking for a needle in a haystack. Painless transition depended on my ability to make the right appointment. The wrong choice would damage years of work and dedication, putting an end to the passionate radicalism that had played a major part in creating our success. The truth was I was scared beyond belief about the future and what it held in store. Lacking friends in whom I could confide, colleagues I could trust or a close family to show an interest, each day that passed increased my sense of apprehension.

— Forty-One —

WE EMPLOYED TWO qualified nurses, one in each of the boarding houses. Part of a separate management team, they were responsible for the pupils' health and had an important say in the provision of pastoral care. The senior matron, who regularly discussed diet and menus with the catering staff, arranged health checks for every pupil. Such was her influence that many mothers demanded a meeting with matron before deciding whether or not it was safe to board their children.

Good matrons were hard to come by. In spite of the long holidays, rent-free accommodation and other inducements, few state-registered-nurses liked working in a school. Since Miss O'Sullivan's retirement, I must have appointed as many matrons as could be counted on the fingers of one hand. Following an acrimonious discussion with the senior matron at the end of a particularly strenuous summer term, in a fit of pique she submitted her resignation, saying she would not be returning in September.

This was a serious setback. A number of parents had already questioned the boarding house arrangements, condemning the frequent changes of staff. The fact this was a common problem in other boarding schools was not an argument I could use to placate the critics. Something had to be done and soon to prevent disgruntlement from spreading. Educational agents in London confirmed they would be unlikely to find me a matron at such short notice. I met the only two who showed interest. One was more concerned with finding a home for her dog than looking after children. The other talked incessantly about her ailments, warning me her arthritis was so bad she couldn't walk far and under no circumstances could she manage any stairs. Desperate to widen the net, I placed advertisements in *The Lady* magazine and two national newspapers. Offering a list of benefits, including a free place at the school for sons or daughters of the successful candidate, I expected a big response. In the event there were five applications, only one of which was promising.

Mrs Isobel Grundy wrote from an address in Edinburgh, where she was temporarily working as a nanny. Separated from her husband, aged forty-five and a qualified SRN, she provided excellent references, covering seven years as a hospital Sister and four as a school matron. She had an eight-year-old son, who was, she said, her main concern. She ended the letter by stressing she'd set her heart on returning to work in a school. Having made errors of judgement in the past, this time I had to get it right. Prior to meeting Mrs Grundy, I telephoned the headmaster of the prep. school where she'd worked.

"Yes," he said. "I remember her well. A handsome woman, self-assured and totally dependable. A superb nurse, she had no time for the fussy hypochondriac. She was an enormous asset. She was non-resident but lived in on her duty evenings. She left when she was expecting a baby."

"Would you have her back?"

"Most definitely. She never put a foot wrong far as I was concerned."

"How did she mix with the staff? Did she put a foot wrong with any of them?"

"I recall once a master questioning her diagnosis of some childhood illness. She gave him short shrift. She's capable of toughness, doesn't suffer fools gladly. She's one of the best matrons I've had. You'd be lucky to appoint her."

Tall and with the slim figure of a model, Isobel Grundy's most striking feature was her eyes. Her naturally dark hair was tied back severely in a bun, yet her eyes were turquoise blue, the colour of a Grecian sea. Her stern appearance gave the impression she liked to take control. Asking probing questions in the manner of a brief, I knew at once she was not someone with whom I would care to quarrel. Did I find her attractive? In a way I suppose I did, but I have to confess to a feeling of apprehension, a perturbing reticence when in her presence. Was it the Polly effect? The thought did cross my mind that she was studying me as a man, not as an employer, but that moment quickly passed after we'd begun to talk about her son.

"If I'm offered the job, I hope I'm correct in thinking Peter will be eligible to attend the school," she said.

"Subject to his ability to cope academically," I had to say.

"He's mildly dyslexic and for this reason he's hardly academic," she added.

"First we shall have to give him some tests. Catering as we do for a wide range of abilities, unless he's very backward, I'm sure we shall be in a position to offer him a place." Unhappy at the prospect of having to wait for the test results, she went into Harrogate to look at the shops.

Peter's attainment was well below what we would normally regard as the minimum entry standard. His reading age was that of a child of six. He was nonetheless a charming child, well-mannered and polite and I had no doubt, given the right encouragement, he would do his best to cope. Sticking my neck out, if only to secure the appointment of a competent matron, I agreed to take the boy.

"Peter has a lot of catching up to do," I told his mother. "Poor reading is a major obstacle, but with extra help and consistent efforts on his part, there is every chance he'll make the grade."

Her dejected expression changed in an instant to one of supreme delight. For a split second I thought she was going to give me a hug. "Thank you, thank you," she gushed, before promising her absolute loyalty to the school, which she said was the best way to express her gratitude.

With no other contender for the post, I offered Isobel Grundy a generous contract of employment that made provision for the education of her son. Based in the boys' boarding house, the two of them occupied a small flat, which she said more than satisfied their needs. Despite some minor reservations about her manner, I was convinced she had the ability to fortify morale and win the approval of the parents. My instinct proved to be correct. Quickly making a name for herself by setting high standards and expecting no less from others, she knew exactly what she wanted. A perfectionist, she shared much in common with Miss O'Sullivan whose code of conduct had been equally fastidious.

But who knows all? At first I thought my imagination was deceiving me, that her overfamiliar behaviour was merely an attempt to impress. She went out of her way to attract my attention, fixing seductive eyes on mine, staring me out, a discomfiting signal that caused me to look away, embarrassed and perplexed. It was soon obvious she fancied me and was expecting a reaction back. There was something threatening about her actions that warned me of danger, a portent so real it was like seeing a notice with giant red lettering advising me to stay away. As the weeks passed I harboured even greater doubts, by which time she was on friendly terms with the uppity Marion Dell. Her work and the welfare of her son were two topics about which it was natural for us to speak. So whenever I felt uncomfortable, I switched over to the subject of how Peter was progressing.

"Is he really that dim?" she asked, concerned.

My answer was diplomatic. "Dim isn't a word I would use. He appears quick enough to me, but his reading holds him back. We must regard his problems as a challenge."

In the past I'd given extra help to a number of pupils. In two dyslexic cases it was amazing what a difference it made when receiving one-to-one tuition. Scared stiff at the thought of being sucked in by Mrs Grundy's beguiling overtures, I was nevertheless keen to give assistance to her son. Once she got the message, I hoped she would realize that rather than have a distracting relationship to contend with, the responsibilities of school left me time for little else.

Unfailing in his eagerness to please, Peter was much in awe of his mother, who expected far too much. Because of her fanatical desire for him to succeed, she was quick to find fault and it was rare for her to applaud his qualities. Thin-skinned and worryingly introverted, he was getting demoralized and his self-esteem was low.

Soon after I'd started coaching him, I decided to discuss my findings with his mother. I told her he needed more encouragement. She was clearly upset. "Are you saying I'm not supporting him enough?"

"You're a most caring parent, but because you worry constantly about his progress, you are transmitting your anxieties to him."

"It's hard bringing up a boy without a father. If Peter is out of his depth, perhaps it was wrong of me to choose to educate him at a competitive school like this."

Determined not to be defeated, I devised an intensive reading course which meant seeing him in my study on his own for three separate weekly sessions. One of the reasons I singled him out for this special help was to please his mother, knowing she would not want to remain at the school if Peter didn't settle. I'd already made a firm commitment never again to become romantically involved with a member of my staff. By promising to coach the boy, I hoped she would not take this to mean I was yielding to her charms.

To be able to assist Peter was a diversion I relished. Teaching a bright and eager child was not that hard, but to restore the confidence of one who'd been written off as a no-hoper offered a richly rewarding challenge. There were two reasons why I was impatient to achieve results. It was a matter of honour to prove my instinct had been right, that the boy had the character and potential to overcome the barriers that were seen to hold him back. And I wanted to remove some of Mrs Grundy's doubts by making her proud of her son's achievements.

Never a chore, I found it a pleasure to spend time with Peter. Always courteous, not once did he forget a please or thank you, which said something about the standards set at home. I wondered about his father, the man Mrs Grundy referred to as her good-for-nothing husband. Describing him as weak and irresponsible, she constantly ran him down, using a well-practised toxic tongue.

"Not once did he do a thing for Peter. I've always been the breadwinner. Philip's a waster and a drunkard who spends all his money in the pub."

A bitter woman, she could be frighteningly aggressive and had her husband been incapable of standing up to her, I could well understand what made him turn to drink. I once asked Peter about his father and was surprised to discover his account differed greatly from what I'd been led to think.

"Dad loves boats and he taught me to sail," he said, eyes moistening with tears as he remembered happier times. After that, he clammed up, back into his impenetrable shell.

As soon as Peter showed signs of making progress, success spurred him on to further his resolve. Working like a little beaver, he would not let up until every difficulty he faced was overcome. Struggling for hours to beat the problem of the reading, he at last mastered the art of converting the shapes of the letters into sounds. He certainly wasn't stupid and had he not been let down by his early schooling, he would not have needed extensive extra help. I explained to his mother how well he was doing, saying his hard work was an inspiration.

"It's taken time for the penny to drop, but now he knows how to set about it, the signposts to observe, there'll be no stopping him."

"I can't thank you enough," said a delighted Mrs Grundy, who pressed me to drop the formality and call her Isobel in future.

What I'd not expected was for Peter's improvement to reawaken his mother's amorous intentions. Using every opportunity to get me to respond, she must have watched my every movement. Whenever I was seen about the school she would seek me out to discuss some pointless topic. She was brazen, devious and persistent. I knew perfectly well to encourage her would be dangerous.

Becoming bold, determined to pin me down, her next move was to ask me about my taste in music. I fell into her trap. "Of the classical composers, I prefer Beethoven, Elgar and Tchaikovsky, but I'm more into jazz. I used to play tenor sax as a student. No time for it now, I'm afraid."

Her response was enthusiastic. "I've loved jazz for as long as I can remember. Did you know Johnny Dankworth is giving a concert in Harrogate next week?"

Much as this information was of interest, I was aware where her line of questioning was leading. The following day she was waiting for me after morning prayers. "I've bought two tickets for Johnny Dankworth for a week on Friday. I want you to be my guest," she said with calculating slyness.

I had to think quickly. "This is most unfortunate. I'm booked to see some parents. Can you get someone to take my place?"

I could see she distrusted my excuse and made no attempt to disguise her anger. Considering what action I should take, I decided to be blunt. To spell out the truth would leave her in no doubt as to my feelings in the matter. Exercising my most diplomatic form of tact, I told her she was an attractive woman, an invaluable matron and a key member of my staff. It was, I said, a deliberate policy of mine never to become too friendly with employees and that it was necessary to keep the relationship on an entirely professional footing. Despite the pomposity of my words, I was pleased to have made plain my views. She left, muttering under her breath, a thoroughly disgruntled woman, shocked by the potent nature of the snub.

Peter still had much catching up to do before he would be ready to compete on equal terms with the other pupils. I reckoned in twelve months he would be able to fend for himself, without needing individual help from me. He was reading fluently, a breakthrough that gave the impression to have happened all at once.

Next I noticed his writing and spelling were improving, essential skills that enhanced his performance in the English-related subjects. Soon he was beginning to learn some French and it was a privilege to help get him started.

I'm ashamed to admit I favoured this boy above all the others in the school. His sensitivity reminded me of Emma. He was conscientious, affectionate and sweet. He was patently unselfish, displaying a giving nature that placed the needs of others before his own. Had I been blessed with a son, I could have wished for no better than for one who possessed the attributes of Peter. I looked forward to my regular tutorials with him. Reminding me of the cosy chats I used to have as a youngster with Uncle Don, I saw myself as an uncle of a kind, there to guide, sympathise, protect, encourage and inspire. He would never hit the high spots academically, but with continued efforts on his part I hoped one day he would do well enough to pass for a minor public school. With no money of her own, Isobel wouldn't be able to afford the fees. Having earmarked some savings for my retirement, I saw no reason why some of it could not be used to assist with Peter's secondary education, an idea that would have to be treated with the utmost tact.

The school was on a high. Numbers were up, entry lists were full and more scholarships were being won than ever. The only blot on the landscape was the boys' boarding house, which had been the source of a number of complaints. Jonathan Dell's weak leadership had led to the removal of four of the boys, a situation exacerbated by Marion's unwelcome interference. Even though I couldn't abide Isobel as a person, I respected her common sense and professional expertise. An outstanding matron, she spent much of her time ironing out snags and papering over the cracks in a boarding house that was no longer running smoothly. This was a tricky situation bound up with internal political intrigue. Marion and Isobel were thick as thieves and I knew if I removed Jonathan from his post, there would be serious repercussions that would be more unsettling than by simply doing nothing. Just as I was about to face the problem head-on, something happened to change my perspective on everything I knew and cared about.

It was the last day of term and after the Christmas carol service the school would break up for a month. In recent years I'd taken Aunt Olive to a hotel in Brighton for Christmas to give Giles and his family a break. She'd been suffering from dementia and since a rapid worsening of the condition, she was being cared for in a home. Instead of remaining in Harrogate with no company and little in the way of help, I'd decided to take a fortnight's holiday in Madeira. I had an unpleasant task to perform before I could begin to think about relaxing. My eleven o'clock appointment involved confronting Jonathan Dell about his poor performance as housemaster and informing him of my decision to relieve him of the post. My shock was considerable when, having steeled myself for the encounter, Brenda, my secretary, stood at my study door next to a uniformed police officer.

"Can you spare this gentleman a few moments?" she said.

Reeling off a well-practised spiel, the policeman spoke with unsmiling clarity.

"Are you Mr Paul Arthur Elliott, headmaster of this school?"

"Yes, I am."

"It's a delicate matter, sir. There's been a complaint."

"A complaint?"

"Yes, sir, a complaint about your conduct with a pupil."

"There must be a mistake. This is the last day of term, a very busy time. Can't it wait until Monday?"

"No, sir, I'm afraid it can't. An allegation has been made which I need to speak to you about formally and obtain an account on tape."

— Forty-Two —

ENTERING THE POLICE station, bewildered and indignant, I
was herded into a cell-like room, accompanied by two male
officers, the elder of whom viewed me with an expression of
distaste. I told him the chief constable had two boys at the school
and he would clear up any misunderstandings in an instant. The
officer reacted curtly:

"The nature of the allegation is so grave you're going to need a
lot more than friends in high places."

Advised of my right to be represented legally, I asked for Clive
Peters, the partner who'd taken over from Lionel Spriggs.

An hour later he was sitting by my side. A dynamic, quick-think-
ing man in his late thirties, he lacked Lionel's style and experience, but what little work he'd done for me had been competently
handled. All the other solicitors I knew had connections with the
school.

Accused of sexually abusing a pupil, I was so shaken as to be incapable of speech. According to the officer, Peter Grundy complained
to his mother about inappropriate behaviour on my part. Clive came
to my rescue, demanding concrete evidence. "Mr Elliott's been a
distinguished headmaster for over twenty years and not once has
there been anything to suggest he's behaved unprofessionally."

The questioning began.

"How often did you tutor the boy? Over what period of time?
Where did these sessions take place? Why did you choose to teach
him in your study rather than a classroom? Did you ever touch the
person of this child? Why did you single him out over and above
the other pupils? The boy states he was frightened by your behaviour. Can you offer an explanation for this? His mother informs us
he changed in character after coming under your influence and is
less amenable to discipline at home. He is reluctant to be open with
her and blushes every time your name is mentioned. How do you

account for this? Have you ever shown him any affection that could be misconstrued? What are your personal feelings for the boy? Do you have anything to add to what you've said already?"

For three hours the questions continued. Questions piercing me like bullets. Aggressive, bruising questions, A probing that played havoc with my conscience, making me think ill of myself when I'd done nothing wrong. What pleasure could this bullying nobody gain from pulling my life apart, dissecting my every move, insinuating I was evil, a depraved pervert, a child molester, a psychopath totally unfit for the office I held? I wanted to scream back at him, to shake him to get him to see sense. All I could do was cry hidden tears, seized by a suffocating fear, appalled at the severity of my plight.

Taking exception to the manner of the questioning, Clive rounded on the officer. "My client's done as you've asked and considering your tone, he's been exceptionally polite."

"I'm grateful for that," said the officer. "That will be all for today, but I shall want to speak to him again."

"So he's free to go?"

"For the time being, yes."

Back at Oxton House the carol service had taken place and the pupils, apart from three travelling to Hong Kong the following morning, had gone home for the Christmas holidays. The few staff I met eyed me strangely, making it plain they were aware of the problem I was facing. The leak must have come from Isobel as Brenda, my secretary, the epitome of discretion, would have given her life rather than disclose a confidence.

A meeting next day with Clive made me no less anxious. Believing there was further trouble in store, he was convinced the police had more information than they were prepared to divulge. It was up to the Crown Prosecution Service to decide whether there was a case for me to answer. Providing no action was taken during the next few days, he said it could mean there was insufficient evidence for them to challenge me in court. All I could do was forget the holiday in Madeira, sit tight and await developments.

At a second visit to the police station I was formally charged and instructed to appear before the magistrates three days before Christmas. I asked Clive what had caused the rush.

"The CPS lawyers don't waste time when they think they have a case. The magistrates will do nothing other than act on their recommendation and send you to be tried by a judge and jury."

"A Crown Court hearing? God, this is shocking news."

"Don't panic. Let's take it a step at a time. You've said you are innocent. I believe you and most rational-thinking people will view the allegation as the invention of an unbalanced mischief-maker."

"Can we stop the papers from writing about it?"

"I wish we could. The court will be full of journalists thirsting for a story. They'll have to couch the language they use with care, though there's no question of stopping publication. Remember you are innocent until proven guilty. Ours is the fairest justice system in the world."

"What a bloody mess! I had no idea Isobel is such a poisonous bitch."

Three Justices of the Peace watched me solemnly as the charge was read out. Requesting bail, Clive gave a potted version of my career, again labouring the point that I'd enjoyed a blameless reputation throughout my working life. Conferring with his colleagues, the chairman of the bench said bail would be granted on condition I no longer came into contact with the pupils at the school, which was interpreted to mean I would have to move from Oxton House and live elsewhere until the trial was over. I was asked to surrender my passport and report twice weekly to the police station. The case was scheduled to be heard in Leeds at the beginning of April. The entire procedure can have taken no more than five minutes. I left the magistrates' court shamefaced and flustered, eager to get away from the antagonistic crowd that had assembled.

Packing essential items and looking for a temporary place to live, I felt more disjointed, alone and frightened than I thought possible. Brenda offered practical support, saying she didn't mind putting in extra hours and I could call her any time for help. She did her best to boost my morale.

"You're a dedicated schoolmaster, always putting others before yourself. Anyone with a grain of sense knows you'd never harm a child, least of all one as vulnerable as Peter."

She offered to speak for me in court. Intelligent and perceptive, she was capable of straight talking and not one to allow her principles to be altered or opinions swayed under intense interrogation.

But my most powerful witness would have been Polly. She better than any other could vouch for my integrity. She knew I was a man in every sense and would throw out as ludicrous the insinuation I was a danger to my pupils. She was now living in Sussex. As a last resort, I knew she would come to my aid, but if only to show respect for Ronald and keep sacred the years of happiness she'd given me, it was essential to keep her name well out of it. I preferred to go to prison than have it on my conscience I had tampered with her life a second time.

How to arrange the school in my absence was a major dilemma. I dreaded having to approach Sir Quentin Isaac. As chairman of the school council, he would expect me to consult him first.

"Before you go asking for advice, I want to get one thing straight," he said, pointing an accusing finger.

"I know my position looks bad, but I give you my word I have never acted improperly with a pupil. I'm innocent of all the charges and promise I shall fight to clear my name, even if it costs me everything I've ever worked for."

He gave me a sceptical look before making a statement that could not have been more damaging. He said rumours were rife, the whole of Harrogate was talking about the scandal and from what he'd heard several parents had decided to remove their children from the school.

"I'm a businessman, not a mopper up of other people's problems," he said sternly. "I backed you because you ran a tight ship, a respectable prep. school that was a credit to the town, an enterprise with which I was proud to be associated. In my position, I can't afford to back a loser and there's no proof whatsoever you're the person of honour you are at pains to purport to be."

Deeply upset by the shallowness of his reaction, I begged him to reconsider his remarks. Instead of treating my request with the most basic humanity, he turned on me, eyes blazing with a kind of frenzied hatred I never knew existed.

"You were rude to me once. Nobody does that and gets away with it. I resign as your chairman today and you can take it Cyril Snape will shortly follow my example. By the end of the week I doubt you'll have a council."

In these distressing circumstances, my deputy, Keith Marsh, had an impossible mission to fulfil. A thoroughly decent man, he was honest, painstaking, and a sound teacher, but his lack of leadership skills made him a doubtful stand-in choice. The trouble was there was nobody else capable of performing any better. He visited me at the flat I was renting in the centre of Harrogate. I apologized for plunging him in at the deep end and suggested we met regularly until the day of the trial so that I could guide him through some of the problems he would face. I warned him what to expect.

"If numbers drop, and this is bound to happen, the finances of the school are the responsibility of the bursar. Your function is to try to keep things stable. It's going to be hard. Sometimes the difficulties will be overwhelming. I'm on the phone, so you can call me as often as you wish."

Disaster struck in January, soon after the start of term. The bursar, who was another vital link, informed me that, instead of the expected 312 pupils, twenty-four had been withdrawn, with the serious news that their parents were refusing to pay the fees. I said I sympathized with this stance, suggesting there was no point in suing them for unpaid fees until the trial was successfully concluded. Normally optimistic and cool-headed, the bursar, despite an impressive wartime record, was showing signs of a prickly tetchiness he'd not exhibited before.

Stating the obvious that the business would not remain viable with a diminishing income, he reminded me of the dire consequences should numbers continue to drop. Unhappy with the extra burden he was facing, he unleashed an alarming statement.

"Morale amongst the staff is low to the point of desperation. The advisory council has disintegrated, press reports present the picture of a disreputable school in crisis; and if that isn't enough, we have an acting head, who's young and indecisive, unqualified in my view to cope when things are going well, let alone at a disastrous time like this. You must accept I'm not, I repeat *not*, a miracle worker."

He was not the only one to be the bearer of bad news. By half-term numbers had dropped further and Brenda came to tell me there had been several cancelled registrations.

"Prospective parents are giving us a wide berth," she said, not attempting to conceal the fact the future was looking bleak.

Of the thirty-one teachers employed, eleven were applying for jobs and had asked me for a reference. It was only a matter of time before others would follow suit. The school, which in December had been popular and thriving, was on a rapid downward spiral. It had taken years to reach the pinnacle of success and weeks for the foundations to start to crumble, bringing about disarray and chaos. All because I'd been condemned in people's minds before being able to defend myself.

Visualize my frustration, loneliness and sheer terror at having to hide away like a leper, cut loose from the daily tasks I'd for years regarded as a pleasure. Powerless to serve any useful purpose, I paced about the flat, as if practising the routines of a prisoner in a gaol. Having always been an active person, I found the long hours demeaning, wasteful and unutterably sad. Fretful imaginings starved me of what little confidence was left, pinpointing my loss of self-respect and status. On the few times I dared to be seen in public, the paranoia was so intense I was convinced the sneers, the stares, the nudges and the insults were the prelude to a living taste of hell.

Clive was concerned I was spending too much time worrying about the school instead of planning for the trial. He said he'd heard on the grapevine that Harry Spicer QC had been selected as counsel for the prosecution.

"He's as slippery as a snake, devious and ruthless. Once he's torn your arguments to shreds, he'll stop at nothing until he's destroyed your credibility. You couldn't have a nastier opponent."

If he'd been trying to propel me into action by frightening me to death, he had certainly succeeded. It was obvious I needed a top barrister on my side, one capable of competing with the formidable Harry Spicer.

"Who can you recommend?"

"We may have to go to London."

"How much is it likely to cost?"

"Impossible to say. It depends on the hours spent, the length of the trial, the number of witnesses. There are too many uncertainties. It won't come cheap."

"Are we talking about five thousand pounds, ten thousand, twelve? Give me some idea."

"How long is a piece of string? It could be anything up to one hundred thousand pounds. That would be my most pessimistic estimate. I'll eat my hat if the bills exceed that figure."

I sat listening to him, frozen in shock. Up until Christmas I had been financially secure and in terms of personal wealth I was well provided for. Recent events had changed everything. What had recently been a profitable business was now running at a loss. There were huge bank borrowings, involving regular repayments, covered easily in the past from a healthy turnover. Savings for my retirement and a private pension scheme held funds totalling somewhere in the region of forty-five thousand pounds.

The only building over which the bank didn't have a charge was the girls' boarding house. To raise additional funds, the best course was to take out a mortgage or arrange a loan with another bank. My reputation in tatters, the reception I received from lenders was invariably hostile and downright rude at times. Thanks to a helping hand from Clive, after some clever negotiating and smooth talking on his part, I later received a building society cheque in the sum of fifty-three thousand pounds. Enough, I hoped, to cover the costs I would incur.

After carrying out his research, Clive phoned to say he'd arranged for me to meet Geoffrey Seymour-Smith for an initial consultation. He went on to explain he was one of the most eminent criminal law barristers in England. Recently appointed a Queen's Counsel, he was prepared to consider taking on the case, but first wanted to hear my version of events. A date was arranged to meet him in his chambers at Lincoln's Inn.

"What track record of success does he have?" I asked Clive.

"He's a match for Harry Spicer. The two are not dissimilar in character. Both are fighters, both hate losing, and if it's results you're after, Geoffrey Seymour-Smith is marginally the stronger of the two." I wanted to believe it.

After I'd suffered weeks of emotional turmoil, sleepless nights, money worries, friends turning their backs, the shame of being dubbed a villain by the press, the staff, the parents and people who before did not know of my existence, my morale had plummeted to its lowest point.

Geoffrey Seymour-Smith welcomed me warmly, shaking my hand with a vice-like grip. He pointed to a chair. Clive, as the instructing solicitor, sat next to another man. I later discovered it was Geoffrey Seymour-Smith's junior. I had the advantage of knowing a little about Mr Seymour-Smith on account of Clive's investigative work. The younger son of a baronet, he was a product of Eton and Oxford and a scholar of Lincoln's Inn. The man with reputedly no equal in his field, towered over me, his large frame dressed smartly in a dark blue suit that went well with his old school tie. To my surprise, in his buttonhole he sported a red carnation, giving him more the appearance of a city slicker than an advocate of breeding. The deep bass voice spoke with pleasing musicality, a distinctive sound that would be sure to command attention in a courtroom. On stage he would have made a splendid actor. The rosy drinker's cheeks and angry purple nose gave him the appearance of a made-up circus clown, his face flushed in Technicolor brightness. His desk was stacked high with papers, files and books. Some books with pages open, others easily accessible for use. The few surfaces free of clutter were covered with layers of dust, a defect that marred the impression of business-like efficiency in the room. One of the piles reminded me of the leaning tower of Pisa and I couldn't decide whether the vibration of his voice would cause the lot to tumble. Just as I was considering this possibility, he changed from a friend into an intimidating foe.

"Some questions, Mr Elliott," he growled with guttural sharpness.

"Ask me anything you like."

"I want to know what led you to abuse this young fellow, Peter Grundy,"

"I never did! My behaviour has always been professional. All I did was try to help the boy, who was very behind when he started at the school. After intensive tuition, he improved in leaps and bounds."

"Quite so, Mr Elliott, but we all know you are hiding from the truth. All the statements I've read prove that your relationship with this boy went way beyond what would be expected of a teacher towards a pupil. This has gone on over a period of years, three I'm led to believe. Isn't it outrageous that a man in your position should behave so shamefully?"

"I've told you before and I shall repeat myself till I'm blue in the face, I'm innocent of any wrongdoing. Because of malicious, vindictive women, everything I've tried to do for others is being questioned, misinterpreted, and, yes, manipulated into a story that is totally untrue. How can I disprove what's never happened?"

"Your job is to convince the jury. You are *not* convincing me. The prosecuting counsel will make mincemeat of you."

I stood up abruptly, indicating I was not prepared to stay a moment longer. Before making an exit, I fired a parting shot.

"To be accused of outrageous conduct by a person who's supposed to be on my side is unacceptable. I don't want you to defend me. Coming here has been an utter waste of time."

Suddenly he softened, urging me to be calm and listen carefully to what he had to say.

"You think I'm asking you difficult questions? Think what it'll be like when it's the other side asking them! You are clearly not guilty of a crime. Of course I want to fight your case. The battle will be arduous and damaging. I promise to do my utmost, using every measure at my disposal to convince the jury of your innocence."

— Forty-Three —

THE TRIAL WAS fast approaching. My thoughts turned to Peter and the emotions I'd bottled up for months. Of course I'd loved him, not in a physical sense, an affection nevertheless, much more than a schoolmaster's interest in a pupil. A son in all but name, he was trustful, eager and responsive. Searching my conscience, had there ever been a time when I'd behaved immorally? Had I hugged him, held him close, willing him to gain confidence, feel safe and lose his inhibitions? Had my sole purpose been to help overcome his academic hurdles or was there more to it than that? I asked myself whether such fanatical concern had been misguided. Unwise perhaps. Never wrong or sordid? My thinking jumbled and distorted, after suffering stress beyond the limits of endurance, my memory was playing tricks, making it impossible to distinguish fantasy from the truth. Was I innocent? I'd thought I was. I hoped I was. Now I was not so sure. The living nightmare was deepening, a divisive ambivalence that forced me to question the reliability of my judgement.

At the age of eight, I'd encountered a man who'd cheated me with words before satisfying his horrific sexual urges. Had I not run away, he would have done me much more harm. Of that there was no doubt. He was deceitful, cruel, a danger to the young, a wanton paedophile. I shudder to think what would have happened had he imprisoned me in his home, which is what he'd tried to do. My influence over Peter was not like that, nor could it ever be. I'd seen it as my duty to instil into his mind a security he lacked, in an attempt to compensate for his mother's harshness.

In preparation for my defence, I was asked to submit the names of people prepared to vouch for my good character. Friends and supporters willing to speak on my behalf were to be called as witnesses. These individuals required three qualities. A belief in my innocence, the ability to speak fluently and with conviction and it was necessary for them to have pleasing personalities that would earn the jury's trust. As soon as Geoffrey Seymour-Smith knew the case to be presented by the prosecution, he began to plan his strategy. Because Peter was a minor, he had been interviewed initially by a policewoman in the presence of a social worker. In court his questioning would be done by videolink and he would be cross-examined informally by Geoffrey and his team without the use of wigs. The judge, too, would treat the matter with some informality for the sake of the child.

Geoffrey summoned me to a further consultation at Lincoln's Inn. This time his advice was more specific as he had precise details of the crimes I was alleged to have committed. In addition to being accused of abusing Peter Grundy, it was also contended I had behaved improperly with a number of pupils over a period of years. Appalled at this fresh development, I felt a sharp pain in my chest. Breathlessness and panic led me to ask for a glass of water, while Clive, who'd again accompanied me to London, sat there gaping, at a loss to know what to do. Having taken on my case, Geoffrey had become a different person. No longer attempting to tear my character apart, he displayed strengths that showed him to be a skilled tactician, shrewd, unrelenting, thorough and immeasurably kind. Aided by a force that was magnetic, many times in the past he'd successfully demolished opponents by subterfuge and the clever use of arguments. I thanked God he was fighting on my side.

Focusing on the selection of witnesses for the defence, Geoffrey said Harry Spicer's game plan would be to round up my critics to expose any flaws with the purpose of carrying out a character assassination. "Isobel Grundy and Marion Dell I know about. Is your ex-wife trustworthy? And who are Jane Slowe and Horace Bletchford?" he asked.

"Horace Bletchford! How the hell is he involved? I haven't seen him since Cambridge. I've no idea where he lives or what he's doing now."

"That's strange because he's listed as a prosecution witness. Did the two of you not get on?"

"We did have a fallout. It was to do with my being infatuated with a girl during my second year as an undergraduate. Let's say he was an interfering busybody who in part caused the relationship to fail. I refused to speak to him after that."

At first the name Jane Slowe didn't ring a bell. Then it dawned on me she'd been a cleaner in Polly's time. Asked to leave when some school property went missing, she'd turned nasty, threatening to sue. A vindictive woman with a grudge, she would enjoy getting her own back and would think nothing of lying in the witness box.

Geoffrey looked pleased, almost jubilant. "A witness like that is the breath of life to me. Under cross-examination she'll retreat like a wounded sparrow, you mark my words. It's Bletchford I'm worried about. I don't see where he fits in."

"What puzzles me is how the prosecution know so much about my past. We're talking about more than a quarter of a century ago!"

Suddenly serious, Geoffrey warned me not to underestimate Harry Spicer's capabilities, saying he was a master of intrigue and an expert at digging up the dirt.

He gave me a reassuring smile. "The advice I would give would be to listen to each question and then answer it with care. By following this policy, I believe we can get the better of him."

Still on the subject of witnesses, Geoffrey wanted to know if any members of the now defunct school council would be willing to speak on my behalf. At one time I'd trusted Evan David. Since our disagreement, he'd become distant and we had rarely passed the time of day. I contacted him, as instructed, only to be told he was not prepared to offer his support.

"This is serious," said Geoffrey. "We must contact your former PA, Polly Rankin. She will be asked to explain to the court about the Slowe woman's dismissal and what happened after that."

Greatly embarrassed, I came clean about the affair, saying Polly could not be expected to attend because if she did so, her marriage would be wrecked.

"Do you want me to defend you or not?" he snapped.

"Of course I do, but I owe it to Polly to let her get on with her life and for her sick husband to be left in peace."

"You're mad to play the part of the moral gentleman. A fat lot of good it will do you if your defence collapses and you are sent to prison. If Polly won't play ball, she will have to be subpoenaed. Her evidence is crucial. Without her, I'm bound to say you are playing into Harry Spicer's hands."

My stubbornness persisted. I said I would do anything to cooperate, anything at all, on condition Polly was excluded from the trial.

To my surprise, Herbert Bond, who'd already written me a glowing character statement, offered to be questioned under oath about the theft of school property by Slowe. Two musical instruments had disappeared and he'd been the one to see her leaving the music department with a case containing a clarinet. My talented director of music had at one time been rebellious and disruptive. It was ironic that, in my hour of need, he was proving to be more loyal than most of the other staff. Stuart Pennington, now a flamboyant Member of Parliament and my greatest Cambridge friend, promised to do what he could to help. Geoffrey felt his appearance would be beneficial in counterbalancing the opinions of Horace Bletchford.

My defence witnesses consisted of Brenda, Herbert, Stuart Pennington and two parents of the school. Also eager to help were David Banks, my long-standing former deputy, and Nicole Tyler, the Oxton House head of French. My defence team was in possession of twenty-five character references for presentation at the trial. Backed up by the seven reputable men and women prepared to speak on my behalf, Geoffrey said we were in with a chance.

"Without Polly, it's going to be tough. I can't guarantee success. What I *am* able to do is prepare you for the most gruelling battle of your life. Spicer is merciless. He'll make you squirm, he'll taunt you; you will probably want to cry. When he angers you, don't let it show. Appear calm, measured, rational, courteous and professionally beyond reproach. His aim will be to destroy everything you stand for, your reputation, your credibility, the school you love, in an attempt to convince the jury you are rotten to the core. I shall play my part, but when he's firing questions at you, with a large audience watching, thinking the worst and condemning you on sight, you must stand firm, be dignified and strong. I wish you the very best of luck."

— Forty-Four —

ON MONDAY, THE 3rd April, 1989 Clive drove me to Leeds, the date of the start of the trial. He'd been advising me for weeks and finally the results of his labours were to be tested. Inside the Crown Court building, we were met by Geoffrey, who informed us George Miller was sitting as judge. "I'd rather have had Sam Brinton, but George is alright. He's hot on logic and hates nothing more than waffle. It's vital to stick to the facts." After the jury had been sworn in, seven men and five women, the clerk of the court asked how I wished to plead.

"Not guilty," I said.

The preliminaries over, it was Harry Spicer's turn to deliver his opening address. Aged about sixty, he was exceedingly tall, with a long, thin body as narrow as a lamppost. The distinctive features of his cadaverous face were a large patrician nose and protruding eyes that glared at me incessantly. This unnerving habit was enough to intimidate the most shameless criminal. Whilst speaking, he cleverly managed to smile at the jury and between breaths scowled in my direction. To set the scene, be began by talking at length about education, reminding the jury a headmaster was responsible for the welfare of his pupils, the staff and answerable to the parents, who at a private school pay fees, often at great sacrifice to themselves.

"He's a man to be looked up to, trusted and obeyed. His is a position requiring rectitude, dedication and an honesty that can be scrutinized for all to see." He paused for several seconds, long enough to give me a glower of even greater menace.

His speech continued. "The person standing before you wears a mask, a mask hiding a sinister character, one that is so despicable it will be easy for the Crown to prove the case we are presenting. Not only has he abused one of his pupils over a period of years, he carries a long history of lies, hypocrisy and deceit going back as far as 1968."

He went on to tell the jury he would be taking them on a journey. To understand more about the defendant's complex and unnatural nature he said it was necessary first to examine the years he'd spent at Cambridge, a disastrous childless marriage and the countless rumours that had surrounded him ever since. "In cases such as this, because of a reluctance to come forward, children can be put through such extreme misery that they are ashamed to own up to the harm done to them, thinking they are the ones at fault. Our principal witness is an eleven-year-old boy, whose life has been damaged so dramatically he has become a nervous wreck."

The child, he continued, was to be questioned by videolink to protect his identity and to encourage him to be less timid than in the frightening atmosphere of a courtroom. He urged the jury to treat the boy with patience and compassion, accepting the fact it was brave of him to take part in what was going to be a terrifying ordeal. Continuing, he added tersely, "make no mistake, ladies and gentlemen of the jury, once you have listened to the evidence and have heard the overwhelming arguments I shall be asking you to consider, you will be in no doubt of the part you must play and of the obligation placed on you to reach a guilty verdict."

Rather than deal first with Peter Grundy's videolink evidence, Harry Spicer took the unprecedented step of calling Horace Bletchford to the witness stand. My one-time friend had noticeably aged. The thinning sideburns were as white as chalk and apart from a few fluffy wisps at the back of his neck, his hairless head was as smooth as a billiard ball. The last time I'd seen him, he was sullen and unsmiling. In court he was equally glum. Once more it amazed me that the prosecution knew anything about my time at Cambridge. Someone had put in a great deal of homework. Who could this have been? Of what relevance was that distant period in my life? Horace informed the court I'd been an immature student, that I'd drunk too much, had no idea how to treat a woman, and when I'd been ditched by Lorenza my behaviour verged on madness.

"Do you consider this man to be qualified in the emotional sense to run a school?" he was asked.

"No, I do not!"

"Will you please tell the court why you are of that opinion."

"He's unstable. He's always been unstable and what's more we had doubts about his sexuality."

Cross-examined by a persistent Geoffrey, he retreated some-what when questioned about his own success with women. Twice married and now living on his own said it all.

The Crown then sought to call four witnesses about my marriage to Catriona. But Geoffrey had warned me what would happen at this point. He rose and told the judge that "a point of law" had arisen and that members of the jury might "like to stretch their legs" while the court considered it. The judge directed the jury to leave the courtroom and the arguments between the barristers began.

I had read the witness statements long before the trial. What was astonishing was that, apart from two parents of the school, the remaining two witnesses were strangers to me, people I'd never met. The parents said it had been rumoured the marriage ended because I was homosexual. A local shopkeeper and postman confirmed this belief had been so widespread that gossip of a damaging nature had been joked about for years. Harry Spicer drew particular attention to the evidence of one of the parents that it was common practice for boys to be given tuition in private by the headmaster and many complained of tickling and other weird behaviour during these sessions.

Attacking the Crown's case with great thoroughness, Geoffrey insisted that this evidence was irrelevant and prejudicial. Asking a series of rhetorical questions, he demanded to know facts, have detailed proof, not woolly tittle-tattle, speculative rumour and unsubstantiated gossip. He issued a stinging reprimand at counsel for the Crown.

"What can these witnesses tell us other than what they *think* they may have heard? From whom did they glean this information? And when was this exactly? They don't know or can't remember? How very convenient! I'm sorry to say this whole debate is an appalling waste of public money and a misuse of precious time."

Judge Miller, who supported Geoffrey's stance, ruled that the evidence was inadmissible and he called the jury back into court to continue hearing the case.

In view of the interest shown in my marriage, I wondered why the Crown hadn't called on Catriona to be a witness. Geoffrey shrugged his shoulders nonchalantly.

"Obviously she wasn't prepared to give them the answers they wanted," he said.

"That's good, isn't it?"

"Not necessarily. An ex rarely speaks objectively and the jury often take what they say with a pinch of salt. Harry's no fool. You can take it he has a lot more up his sleeve."

The following morning, Jane Slowe took to the witness stand. Her hair dyed matt black, she was got up smartly for the occasion in what was probably her Sunday best.

"Here comes mutton dressed as lamb," whispered a beaming Geoffrey, who was chuckling as Harry Spicer stood up to question her. After establishing the nature of her employment at the school, he asked if she'd ever spoken to the headmaster. With a note of defiance in her voice, she said he was too snooty to bother with domestics, adding that most days she'd seen him walking about the school or talking to pupils.

"In your statement you refer to a number of occasions when you say your employer, the headmaster, was observed by you to be behaving oddly. Can you give me an example?"

"You mean the times he was touching boys' private parts. As soon as I saw it. I told Ivy, one of the other cleaners, and she said that's nothing new, he's always at it."

Geoffrey had been looking forward to his chance to cross-examine. "Mrs Slowe, will you please give me details of these alleged offences. State when and where they took place and I want you to give me the names of the boys involved."

"I don't know their names. The dates I can't remember, but there's no denying what I saw. I've sworn to tell the truth and nothing but the truth."

Geoffrey wanted her to explain to the jury why she'd stopped working at the school. Making the excuse she had been offered a better paid job, she went on to say she'd refused to work any longer for a child molester.

"Was there not some trouble over musical instruments that went missing just before you left?"

"I know nothing about any musical instruments."

"I thought you had sworn to tell the truth, the whole truth and nothing but the truth, Mrs Slowe."

"Now don't you go calling me a liar. You're trying to trick me and I'm not having it, Mr Elliott shouldn't be allowed to have anything to do with kids. Did you know he had a nickname? 'Feeler Elliott'. We all used it. The pupils, the staff, everybody."

The judge, infuriated by the outburst, warned her that any more unsolicited remarks would leave him with no option other than to hold her in contempt. She stepped down from the witness stand, her face blood red with rage.

To corroborate Mrs Slowe's story, two more past parents were called as witnesses for the Crown. Both confirmed my unflattering nickname and said that talk about my conduct with pupils was extensive. One of the witnesses, a portly gentleman with a broad Yorkshire accent, said he'd thought of removing his two sons because of the rumours and had either of them been interfered with, the school would have had a murder on its hands.

Uncertain about the outcome of the trial, I asked Geoffrey how he thought it was going. He told me the judge had expressed concern that the jury was being unduly influenced by the substantial press coverage in what was a high-profile case. The worst outcome, he said, was for there to be a retrial. The thought of starting the process all over again was a ghastly prospect. Having already spent six days in court, the costs had exceeded what I'd set in my mind as a realistic target figure. Geoffrey charged five thousand pounds a day, plus expenses. On top of this, Clive's fees were mounting and I shuddered to think the number of hours he'd worked on my behalf.

News from Oxton House was bad. Numbers were still declining, and staff morale rock bottom. The bursar, frantic with worry by now, was being chased by the bank for the repayment of the loan. After three traumatic months, a school that had been respected throughout the north of England, was unable to pay its bills. Disaster loomed and the ship was sinking. Liquidation of the business was inevitable. The question was, when would the bank decide to pull the plug?

Both barristers were summoned to a meeting in private by Judge Miller. He later discussed with the jury the misleading newspaper articles relating to the case. Satisfied with their reactions, concluding a fair result had not been jeopardized, he informed both counsel he was content to continue with the trial. Relieved to learn of the judge's decision, I again asked Geoffrey if he was satisfied with the progress we were making. He emphasized the danger of complacency. Despite his success in destroying the plausibility of some of the witnesses, he said that the subliminal feeling of negative information about my past was an approach Harry Spicer was an expert at adopting.

"He's a master at sowing the seeds of doubt. By the time you are questioned, his expectation will be for the jury to have already decided on your guilt. It now hinges on the evidence of the boy and whether you can generate a sympathetic reaction from the jury."

Peter's evidence involved the use of videolink transmission. This recently introduced device encouraged minors to speak openly whilst jury members were glad of the greater informality, which made it easier for them to form a rational judgement.

Questioning the boy gently and with sensitivity, Harry Spicer began by asking about his interests. Did he enjoy sport? What did he want to be as an adult? An engine driver? A scientist? An explorer? What kind of music did he like? Where had he been on holiday? Having put him at his ease, he asked him about school. Was he happy there? What didn't he like about it? Who were his favourite teachers?

"Do you like Mr Elliott?"

"Yes sir, I like him."

"Has he helped you with your work?"

"He helped me with my reading."

"Are you a good reader?"

"I'm better than I was."

"How often did Mr Elliott teach you privately?"

"Three times a week. After prep. on Mondays, Wednesdays and Fridays."

"Where did this teaching take place?"

"In his study."

"Was it always there?"

"Yes, sir."

"You say you like Mr Elliott. Have you always liked him?"

"Not always, sir."

"Can you explain what you don't like about him?"

"Sometimes he gets too close."

"What do you mean by that?"

"He touches me, sir. Mum says he shouldn't and I'm afraid to tell him not to."

"Where does he touch you?"

"He touches me near my cock."

"How often has this happened? Once or more often than that?"

"I don't want to talk about it anymore."

281

Sobbing hysterically, he was too upset to utter another word. The judge, looking at his watch, said it was a convenient moment to retire for lunch and that the Crown would be given the opportunity to resume questioning at 2.00pm.

Under closer examination, Peter again burst into tears and after long moments of silence, the judge decided he was in no fit state to be examined further. Geoffrey was worried. How could he mount an adequate defence without questioning the key witness, especially in view of his shocking revelation? After a discussion in the judge's chambers, it was decided to send Peter home on the understanding he would be called again later to be questioned with the utmost caution.

Putting on one of the best acts of his long and successful career, Geoffrey spoke to Peter in the manner of a favourite uncle.

"You must be proud of your achievements at school. Isn't your mother pleased with your progress?"

"Yes, sir. She says I've worked hard and deserve to do well."

"Of all the teachers, who has helped you the most?"

"Mr Elliott, sir."

"Is that because of the extra lessons you were given?"

"Yes, sir." Peter's response was encouraging as he seemed to be more relaxed with Geoffrey than when he was being questioned by Harry Spicer.

"You say you were touched in a private place by Mr Elliott. Did you straight away go and tell your mother?"

"I can't remember, sir. I think I did."

"You say you were upset by what happened, yet you aren't sure whether or not you told your mother. This is very important. Nobody is going to blame you if you aren't absolutely certain about what happened. Are you sure Mr Elliott touched you on or near your cock?"

"He touched me on the shoulder and he used to give me a hug. I think he touched my cock. He put his hand on my knee near my cock. He never hurt me, really he didn't."

"Was your mother glad you were having extra lessons with Mr Elliott?"

"Not after she stopped liking him."

"Why did she no longer like him?"

"She said he was a queer and I wasn't to have any more extra lessons."

"No more questions, your Honour," said Geoffrey.

The two final prosecution witnesses were Peter's mother and Marion Dell. For obvious reasons, Mrs Grundy was restricted to describing how her son's behaviour had changed after coming under the influence of the headmaster. Referred to as the mother of Boy X, she said he'd always lacked self-belief, but that as the weeks went by, she had become increasingly worried about his physical and mental health. He was withdrawn, secretive and moody and returned from his private lessons angry and upset.

Before she was released from the witness stand, Geoffrey had one or two questions for her. "Did you once ask the headmaster out on a date? To a jazz concert, I think it was."

"I may have done, but I can't be certain."

"Didn't you buy two tickets?"

"Yes, I think perhaps I did."

"Weren't you angry when he turned your offer down?"

"Not as I remember. He didn't appear to have any time for women, so I couldn't be bothered after that."

Marion Dell was a much more forceful witness. She rattled away brazenly, embroidering her stories with an imagination gone wild. At one stage, Judge Miller told her to calm down and stick to answering the questions. The gist of her evidence was that she had got to know Boy X very well indeed and that he often confided in her. She, too, had noticed the loss of his confidence and his tension and fear after returning from private lessons with the headmaster.

When she said Boy X once told her he had been abused by Mr Elliott, there were gasps of dismay in the courtroom.

She was cross-examined by Geoffrey. "Mrs Dell, did you report to his mother what Boy X is alleged to have said?"

"No, because he asked me not to."

"Do I take it you act on the instructions of a child in matters a serious as this?"

"I *did* tell his mother somewhat later."

"What was the lapse in time between receiving the information and telling his mother?"

"About a year."

"No more questions, your Honour."

When Geoffrey got up to speak in my defence, he was still beaming confidently, a habit he'd acquired after years of practice at the bar. "Ladies and gentlemen of the jury, you will doubtless remember my learned friend opened the proceedings with an oration lasting one hour and seven minutes. I congratulate you on your patience. It will please you to know my remarks will be short. We were led to understand we were to be taken on a journey. Sadly it's been an uncomfortable ride with an unnecessary number of stops. At these stops you have heard statements that at best were grossly biased and at worst misleading, damaging and false. I am here to prove one thing, and one thing only, the innocence of a distinguished educationist whose entire career has been devoted to the service of the young." He paused for effect. "It is a sorry day for the judicial system of this country that a professional person, who has been belligerently accused, should have to defend himself against what is nothing more than misleading, vengeful gossip. It is my intention, therefore, ladies and gentlemen of the jury, to persuade you to find the defendant not guilty, based on the lack of concrete evidence on the part of the prosecution."

Having waited several days, I took the oath. Geoffrey chose to be brief. He asked me three questions. "Mr Elliott, have you ever been guilty of interfering sexually with a pupil at your school?"

"No, I have not."

"Did you ever touch Boy X on or near his penis?"

"No, never."

"Why did you spend so much time giving extra tuition to Boy X?"

"He was very behind academically and I was glad to be able to help him. He will never be a high-flier, but he's now able to hold his own."

"No more questions, your Honour."

Now I waited to be subjected to sadistic interrogation. Fastening his eyes on mine, using a caustic know-it-all technique, Harry Spicer proceeded to tear my character to pieces. Nothing was left unsaid. Cambridge, my marriage, the rumours, the gossip, the negative opinions and the boy's pluck at telling the truth when he was scared beyond belief.

"Can you sleep at night, Mr Elliott? How does it feel to go to bed knowing you've harmed a defenceless minor? How many more were there? Aren't you ashamed to have used your position to take advantage of a young person in your care?"

On and on came the questions, harsher, more outrageous, callous questions that hit below the belt, until the injustice of it stung so potently that it was as much as I could do not to scream back at him. He was goading me to lose my temper and had nearly succeeded. I thanked God I'd stuck to my guns and had managed to appear calm, dignified and strong.

The first defence witness was Stuart Pennington MP, who described me as kind, sensitive, honourable and a little naive with women. "Many of us suffered initial shyness during the process of growing up. I was no different. We all had our relationship problems. I believe it was Paul Elliott's extreme sensitivity that caused him to take longer and suffer more than the rest of us."

"You have a family, don't you?"

"Yes. two sons and a daughter."

"Would you trust the defendant to look after your children?"

"Indeed I would. Had we lived nearer to Harrogate, I would have had no hesitation in sending them to his school."

"Do you think of him as a danger to children?"

"He's one of the most normal men I know. To suggest otherwise is absurd."

A present parent of the school was next questioned about the rumours, with particular reference to the nickname I'd been given. His response was that all schoolmasters had nicknames and it was nothing more than a bit of fun nobody treated seriously.

Herbert Bond proved to be a useful ally. Not only did he describe with great clarity the part played by Mrs Slowe over the missing musical instruments, he gave me a complimentary reference. "Mr Elliott's a thoughtful employer, fair-minded and supportive. I consider myself fortunate to have worked for someone I admire and respect."

"Have you any reason to suspect Mr Elliott of moral impropriety?" asked Geoffrey.

"I've been involved in education for approaching thirty years. I know what's right and what isn't. I know when an adult's straight and when he isn't. Mr Elliott's as straight as they come and I don't mind saying so in public."

An entire afternoon was taken up with the appearance of three defence witnesses: my former deputy, the current head of French and a parent from Polly's time. All spoke with sincerity and affection, describing me as the perfect headmaster, morally sound, conscientious and resourceful, with other eulogistic words thrown in. There was, they said, no blemish or defect, no chinks in my armour or skeletons hiding in my cupboard.

Given the chance to cross-examine, Harry declined. "I don't see any point, your Honour, I'm sure there's nothing to add to the glowing praise we've heard already."

"A clever ploy," commented Geoffrey, who responded privately it took only one false move or a hurried indiscretion to cancel out the good in a person's reputation.

Brenda, my secretary, was the last defence witness. Her detailed knowledge of the school's internal politics led Geoffrey to think her evidence would add considerable weight to his final arguments. Asked about the mother of Boy X, she said she was a capable matron, but that she was a conniving woman, impossible to please. She added the possessiveness of her son was unhealthy and she gave examples when he was seen to be manipulated by her. Jealousy was another of her traits and Brenda cited three occasions when she'd seen her attempting to flirt with the headmaster.

"Of course he likes women, but the school comes first, always has. He doesn't believe in fraternizing too closely with members of his staff."

On the subject of Marion Dell, she was even more scathing. Describing her as dangerous, she said she was a stirrer, untrustworthy and egotistical.

"Did Mrs Dell have any reason to dislike the headmaster?"

"It all boils down to her husband, Jonathan. As housemaster of the boys' boarding house, he simply wasn't coping. Everyone knew it, the parents, the staff and the boys themselves."

"What's that got to do with her dislike of the headmaster?"

"Her husband had already been given a written warning and she knew he was in danger of losing his job."

"Did you ever hear her speak ill of the headmaster?"

"Yes. often. She's spiteful and disloyal. She seemed to get pleasure from criticizing him and blackening his name."

"No more questions, your Honour."

In his closing speech, Harry Spicer said Mr Elliott was a Jekyll and Hyde character. He warned members of the jury not to be taken in by some of the glowing references they had heard.

"The defendant is clearly guilty of one of the most serious crimes on record, the abuse of a child. There can be no forgiveness, no leniency. The evidence is irrefutable. Once you have searched your consciences, ladies and gentlemen of the jury, you will, I know, be quick to reach a guilty verdict."

Geoffrey had a nasty cough, complaining he was suffering from the flu. Despite the croaky voice, he refused to allow a minor setback to mar the delivery of his closing arguments. I felt for him, though, and implored God to give him strength during the all-important moments.

"Ladies and gentlemen of the jury, you are here to deliver justice, to see fair play and an honourable ending to what has been a long and gruelling trial. You have heard a number of unsatisfactory witnesses do their best to destroy in your minds the character of the defendant. An acquaintance from university whom he hadn't seen in over twenty-five years, a man who, incidentally, is no role model when it comes to marriage and relationships. Then there was the dishonest cleaner, the one seen stealing a musical instrument. Can you believe her testimony? Of course you can't. She was sacked and bears a grudge. The mother of Boy X tried flirting with the defendant to no avail. In retaliation she sowed the seeds of doubt concerning the morality of her employer, so much so that her son was manipulated into thinking things that never happened. His tears were not of suffering from abuse, but tears of fear and distress at being forced to tell a lie. The housemaster's wife also bears a grudge. She was too involved herself to be fair-minded, too friendly with the mother of Boy X to be unbiased; and having stirred up a hornets' nest by her actions was too frightened to retreat and say that she was wrong. I invite you to find the defendant is a decent man. He's built up a magnificent school from almost nothing, is dedicated, hardworking, scrupulously honest, a fair employer – his attributes are endless. On the evidence presented you cannot, ladies and gentlemen of the jury, find a single piece of evidence that signifies anything more than hearsay, rumour and fiction-making filth. Stabbed in the back by those who owed him their loyalty and support is treachery at its worst. Now is the time to free this selfless person from the burdens he now carries by finding him not guilty, the only just conclusion to this case."

Reading his formal instructions to the jury with scholarly precision, Judge Miller urged them to consider carefully all the arguments. He thanked them for their patience and said fourteen days in court had imposed on them a strain of which he was well aware.

Whilst clarifying certain legal points, he offered guidance with the interpretation of the evidence. Stressing the importance of thoroughness and clarity in their deliberations, he reminded them that, for the defendant to be found guilty, it was necessary for the Crown to prove the case beyond all reasonable doubt.

When the jury withdrew to consider their verdict, my brain was in turmoil, wild thoughts racing through my head, thoughts of incarceration, ending the day in prison, the ultimate degradation and disgrace. As the hour-long minutes passed, my heart thumped with a banging so loud that I imagined it was deafening the spectators in the courtroom.

— Forty-Five —

S ITTING IN MY hotel room alone, still shaken, nursing a refilled glass of steadying alcohol, I could still only wonder and barely believe the unlooked-for event that ended the court process so dramatically, my trial as an accused paedophile.

I sat barely noticing the room darkening as evening advanced. There were things to do. It was several hours since a sudden flurry of activity in the courtroom surprised all present, including the judge. Both counsel were ordered to report to the judge's chambers, while everyone else, myself more than any, sat mystified by the added tension, already highly charged by awaiting the jury's decision. When the judge returned with the defence and prosecution counsel, the members of the jury resumed sitting and were invited formally to enter a verdict of not guilty. This bombshell shocked the whole court into silence for a long eerie moment before an excited babble broke out to be stopped by the judge demanding quiet.

Bewildered by the sudden turn of events when I had psyched myself up to accept the worst, I was too much out of it to be aware of Geoffrey grabbing my hand to shake it, congratulating me on being completely exonerated, without a stain on my previously unblemished character. Bemused, I could take in only that my trial was somehow unbelievably over. It had ended and I was guiltless.

Only after pulling myself together could I take in the facts of the collapse of the case against me. It was explained that during that fatal hour, following a vicious summing up branding me the most evil of evil men, behind the scenes young Peter Grundy had suffered a complete change of heart regarding his given evidence and provided a truthful account of the hours spent alone with his headmaster, who was never anything but kind and helpful during the extra tuition sessions. Nothing wrong had ever happened. All this was poured out by the boy in a torrent of sobbing in the presence of my legal team, the court medical officer and other officials.

Peter begged that his father be brought to take him away to live with him. He had been so mixed-up with all the talk fed to him by his mother that when the time came to give evidence it had proved too much. All he could find to answer to the questioning was what he had been told and re-told as his mother's version of what was the truth, backed by others who had reason to harbour a grudge against me. Thankfully Peter had found the strength to realize the evidence he'd given was very wrong. After investigation, so it was that the case was dismissed and my life could resume.

I was brought out of my reverie by a knock on the door of my hotel room. It was Geoffrey and Clive, who informed me a little celebration awaited me downstairs. A group of people who had stood up for me in court were waiting in a private room to congratulate me. I was clapped on the back, shaken by the hand, told my innocence was never in question, which is more than I'd thought, and offered a glass of champagne. It was then, in my brief moment as hero of the hour, I saw Polly standing in the background looking as lovely and desirable as ever I remembered her.

Across a crowded room, as the song says, I was drawn to her, greeted with a loving smile. Words not being necessary, we made for each other's arms and kissed lingeringly. I was dimly aware of my supporters clapping hands and cheering, applauding us.

"You're here, you came," was what I said in delight and gratitude as our lips parted. "You came!"

"All through the trial," Polly answered. "Came to give evidence on your behalf, but was told you said I was not required. I was ready and willing."

"I had no desire to harm your reputation. You're a married woman. How could I drag you into what was a sordid enough trial?"

"Because I was willing and what we meant to each other. I've been widowed for two years. I thought you knew that."

As soon as I could, curbing my impatience and still in a haze of wonder and joy, I guided Polly to my room to have her to myself. Again we kissed, said how much we had missed each other. Polly reminded me of our last night of heightened passion together, joking that recalling the occasion in evidence in the court would surely have settled the question of my sexuality. I in turn remarked that whatever the outcome of the trial, there being no smoke without fire it would mean my headmaster's days were over, if indeed the school itself survived.

"What will you do?" Polly asked. "I know how you loved to teach."

"I don't have the stamina to unravel the problems at the school. I've had enough of trying to keep everyone happy and failing to succeed."

"The trouble is you're a perfectionist. Always have been."

Did I really feel able to allow the school I loved so much to disintegrate before my eyes? Before making rash decisions, there were practical matters to consider. In four months, pupil numbers had halved, registrations were non-existent, there were colossal debts and the employees who remained in their posts were angry and disillusioned. Regardless of my acquittal, many people remained convinced of my guilt and made mean-spirited remarks about my suitability to be in charge of children. Incensed by these cruel assertions, I made a resolution. I decided to sell up and move to Avignon in Provence, a place I'd always loved, with Polly as my wife.

When a property developer offered me four and a half million pounds for the school site, I was speechless with delight. A sum of this magnitude would cover the cost of redundancies, the bank loan, my legal costs and all tax liabilities. After making some charitable donations, I would be left with a comfortable income.

Eager for a swift conclusion, I signed the contract, which committed me to the disposal of all the Oxton House land and buildings. After receiving the ten per cent deposit, other payments were to be made in stages and I would have to wait more than a year for the final settlement. I was nonetheless elated with the outcome.

Not once had Giles written, phoned or visited during the period of the trial. His lack of support had not worried me unduly, as we'd never been close, even after our reconciliation. His lack of concern, though, had provoked a feeling of foreboding. A letter saying he wanted us to talk urgently made me much more anxious.

He demanded a meeting on what he described as neutral ground and stated that he had no intention of seeing me at the school. Two days later we met in a private room at the Majestic Hotel. He had aged markedly. His thick hair was greying, he'd put on weight and his tanned face and hands indicated he had recently been on holiday. His venomous expression and cold eyes reminded me of how he looked on the occasions he had bullied me as a child. He was sitting stiffly at a table clutching a file and made no attempt to offer any form of greeting.

He wasted no time in telling me what he wanted. On hearing the school was about to be sold, he said he expected to take part in the negotiations in view of his entitlement to a share.

"You don't have a share. The business, land and buildings are all mine," I said calmly.

"You may think that, but my solicitor takes a different view. He says he can prove that as the legitimate son and heir I'm entitled to at least half the sale proceeds if Oxton House no longer remains a business."

"That's not how it is and you know it. Your parents made everything over to me and when questioned about it at the time you said you didn't object. An agreement was drawn up and there are documents to prove it."

"I see no reason why you should end up a millionaire as a reward for abusing one of your pupils. Father would turn in his grave if he could see what you're doing."

"You haven't changed a bit. Sly, nasty, greedy and still an utter shit. After that remark you've lost any chance of an ex gratia payment from me, so you can argue and threaten as much as you like. In any case, I've already sold the school."

"You've what?" Lost for words, Giles sat opposite me, mouth open wide, sweat dripping from his brow, possessed with a rage of hysterical ferocity. It took him some while before he could regain his equilibrium.

I was flabbergasted by what he said next. The cheek of the man! Not only had he carried out a survey of the school site, he said he was about to put in a planning application for a change of use. The old buildings would be converted into luxury flats, whereas the field provided space for forty new-build properties.

"Once planning permission is granted," he said, "We know of several builders who'd give their eye teeth to develop the site. Philippa's father is in property. With planning permission, he reckons we can expect offers in excess of seven million."

"There's no 'we' about it! You don't have a say in what I do. A deal's been struck already. I'm satisfied with what I'm getting. The decision has nothing to do with you."

Giles was now puce in the face. I thought he was going to explode. He began shouting. "You fucking idiot! Don't you realize you've been had? Anyone with a grain of sense would know not to sell an asset such as this without planning permission in place. You are depriving me of my birthright. My solicitor, a top man, not one of your provincial twits, will be issuing a writ tomorrow. The blue-eyed boy thinks he's won, but believe you me, you haven't!"

To hell with it, I thought. Money did not and had never ruled my life. Giles' thirst for more wealth at the expense of family loyalty, decency and respect hardened my heart. It didn't bother me that I'd been tricked into accepting a modest offer for the site. Giles had done nothing to assist his parents in their sterling efforts to preserve the school, nor had he given me credit for my part in the expansion. He'd forfeited his right to a lawful claim, now or in the future.

His solicitor sent me a vituperative letter. Clive Peters, who was aware of the impending challenge, was suitably prepared. "Giles knows he hasn't a leg to stand on," he said. "It's no more than fantasy and bluster."

"Are you sure he doesn't have a case?"

"Quite sure. I expect we shall receive more letters, but there can't be any substance. The trial was a close-run thing. Nobody can harm you now, not even the mercenary Giles. I suggest you get on with deciding how to spend the proceeds of the sale."

This was easy. After paying the debts, Aunt Olive had to be the first priority. She had been a mother to me and supported Uncle Don in providing me with an opportunity that was unique. The least I could do was to pay her nursing home fees and visit her as often as I could. The balance left over would enable a house to be purchased in France, and would provide Polly and me with a more than ample income. The surplus, calculated to be in the region of a million pounds, would be donated to an educational foundation.

We decided to take our time searching for a place to live in France. On a two-month vacation, we must have viewed more than a hundred properties. At last we found the perfect sanctuary, a taste-fully renovated six-hundred-year-old villa in Villeneuve-Les-Av-ignon, a medieval village steeped in history and within walking distance of Avignon itself. After a considerable delay, due to the notary's inactivity, the house was rightfully ours.

Twelve months after the end of the trial, Polly and I were married in the registry office in Harrogate, with a dozen friends as witnesses. I couldn't believe my good fortune.

"You don't have to worry," said Polly. "I know we're going to be happy till death us do part."

"The end of a dream it all seemed a year ago," I whispered in her ear. My eyes welled up with tears as I held her tight. "Now I think it's really a beginning."